0453402 −○

Plant Histochemistry and Cytochemistry

AN INTRODUCTION

EXPERIMENTAL BOTANY

An International Series of Monographs

CONSULTING EDITORS

J. F. Sutcliffe†

School of Biological Sciences
University of Sussex
Falmer, Brighton, UK

and

J. Cronshaw

Department of Biological Sciences
University of California
Santa Barbara, California, USA

A complete list of titles in this series is given at the end of the book.

Plant Histochemistry and Cytochemistry
AN INTRODUCTION

Peter B. Gahan

*Biology Department
Queen Elizabeth College
London, UK*

*Physiologie Végétale
Université de Genève
Geneva, Switzerland*

1984

ACADEMIC PRESS
(Harcourt Brace Jovanovich, Publishers)
London   Orlando   San Diego   New York
Toronto   Montreal   Sydney   Tokyo

ACADEMIC PRESS, INC. (LONDON) LTD.
24-28 Oval Road,
London NW1 7DX

United States Edition published by
ACADEMIC PRESS, INC.
Orlando, Florida 32887

British Library Cataloguing in Publication Data

Gahan, P. B.
    Plant histochemistry and cytochemistry.

    Bibliography: p.
    Includes index.
    1/ Plant histochemistry--Technique. I. Title.
QK725.G17   1984   581.8'212   84-11063
ISBN 0-12-273270-7 (alk. paper)

PRINTED IN THE UNITED STATES OF AMERICA

84 85 86 87   9 8 7 6 5 4 3 2 1

Preface

The literature abounds with papers and monographs on histochemistry, yet some-one trying to apply histochemistry to plant material for the first time will find little specific help from a single text more recent than that of Jensen (1962). Consequently, this book is primarily intended to give an up-to-date introduction to modern histochemical methods for advanced undergraduate and graduate students in plant sciences. It is hoped that the fully fledged research worker may also find this text useful.

The first part of the book is devoted to those aspects of tissue preparation which impinge directly upon histochemical methodology and contains a sample of the methods available for the histochemical analysis of a particular tissue. It should be stressed that many methods of plant histology have been omitted when they cannot be positively employed as tools of histochemistry. It is not intended to offer a comprehensive compendium of histochemical techniques since these are already available in other volumes, but to present a minimal set of methods which will allow an elementary analysis of plant cells and also show the basic principles behind the procedures, both qualitative and quantitative, to be adopted. Subsequently, it should be possible to adapt additional methods for a given tissue. An elementary description of various applications of microscopy in histochemical analysis is also included. The applications of such analyses to the cellular studies of physiological significance as well as those of a more chemical nature are given at relevant places throughout the text. Some of the references are recent and some are not so new. This is deliberate, and the intention in offering examples is to demonstrate the development of a series of studies with time as well as illustrating both key and carefully performed experiments.

The practical methods included as a guide to some of the many techniques available are those which the author has found to work satisfactorily upon specific plant tissues, and which also have been performed successfully in classwork by students.

The idea of presenting the analytical approach to plant cytochemistry in the form of a ''group analysis'' situation familiar from inorganic chemistry has been exploited by Chayen et al. (1973). This approach was discussed with Professor J. Chayen some years ago whilst I was working in his laboratory, during which period he whetted my appetite for plant cytology in its broad connotation. The

v

approach seems to fit well with the methods available for plant studies, though this is only a start, and as new and more reliable methods become available, so it should be possible to modify the scheme presented.

There are no colour photographs—a deliberate choice which has been made in order to keep the price of this volume to a minimum. Black and white photographs can be of use in cytochemistry, and as such they have been included.

Any book of this type must represent a personal approach to the subject, and hence any shortcomings are my responsibility. I would be pleased to hear of any errors or misrepresentations that occur.

I hope that this book will serve as a useful introduction to the application of histochemistry and cytochemistry to the study of plant biology.

Finally, I must acknowledge my debt of gratitude to Professor J. F. Sutcliffe, who over a period of years gave constant support and encouragement to the application of cytochemical analysis in the resolution of botanical problems.

London, 1984   P.B.G.

To M.F.G.

Acknowledgements

Many people have been involved in stimulating the preparation of this book, especially the undergraduate and post-graduate students who have used the various methods cited during practical sessions—and made them work! Suggestions as to the content of the book have come from a number of people, but in particular I am very grateful to Professor Peter Bell, Dr. Peter Hurst, Dr. Alan Dawson, Dr. Olga Bayliss-High and Mrs. June Rickard for having critically read various sections of the book. Special thanks also must go to Dr. David Adams for having read the complete manuscript and for offering many valuable comments. I thank also Margaret Meadows and Gwen Turner for their valiant efforts in translating my handwriting into a legible final text, John Pacey for help with the illustrations, and Elisabeth Scheurer, Dr. Brian Gardiner, and Afzul Rana for their excellent help with the Bibliography.

Finally I am indebted to the late Professor James Sutcliffe for his constructive remarks and to Academic Press for their long-lasting patience during an exaggerated gestation period.

I wish to acknowledge the kind permission and cooperation of the following in allowing the inclusion of their illustrations: Mr. B. Bright (Fig. 2a), Professor R. B. Knox (Fig. 10), Dr. C. Cave (Figs. 18 and 39a), Mrs. J. Rickard (Fig. 20), Vickers Instruments Ltd. (Figs. 24 and 25), Dr. J. M. Chapman (Fig. 38) and E. Leitz (Instruments) Ltd. (Figs. 32 and 33).

Contents

1. Introduction to Histochemistry

I. INTRODUCTION

In order to obtain a more fundamental understanding of the general metabolism and functioning of plants, it was realized at an early stage in the development of botany that investigations at the gross morphological and anatomical level were insufficient. Following the advent of the light microscope and its subsequent development, it was concluded that the cell is the fundamental, complete unit of most living organisms. Thus, the consideration became one of a study of the cell as a basic unit that might in turn allow an understanding of the workings of an organ and hence of an organism.

Despite the recent concentration of attention on the structure and function of the cell through the efforts of many biologists, it is important to remember that such studies were started more than a century ago. Historically, they segregate conveniently into those performed pre- and post-1940. This arbitrary division is one based on the availability of essential techniques for the development of the subject now known as cell biology. The break in the main development of this study during the 1930s was due to the lack of techniques rather than a lack of ideas, for the cell biologists of the pre-1940 era were asking basically the same questions as the workers of today.

II. THE PATH TO HISTOCHEMISTRY

The importance of the early work on the chemistry and physiology of the cell can be readily seen by listing some of the landmarks (reviewed by Baker, 1948, 1949, 1952). Thus, following on from the early work of Hooke, Malpighi and Grew, and the pronouncement of the cell theory by Schleiden (1838) and Schwann (1838a,b) came the identification of the protoplasm by von Mohl. The observation by Meyen, von Mohl and Nageli that cells multiplied by division culminated in the description of mitosis in 1880. The cellular contents were identified at an early stage, chloroplasts by Meyen, the nucleus in orchid epidermal cells (Brown, 1833), the nucleolus by Fontana (1781), dictyosome-like bodies by Golgi (1898), and plant mitochondria by Meves (1904). Having established a fairly detailed picture of the structure and content of plant cells, biological chemists endeavoured to determine the physiological behaviour of the cell. Thus, in the early part of this century, Haas was making efforts to measure cellular pH, and in a long series of detailed studies, Heilbronn (1928) attempted to study the viscosity of the cytoplasm during an assessment of the physical nature of the protoplasm. The later papers of Zirkle (1928a, b) are good examples of how cytologists were attempting to interpret their results in terms of the chemistry of biological compounds, although biological chemistry as a subject barely existed at that time. The position is emphasized perhaps, when one realizes that although Meischer described the nucleic acids as long ago as 1897, little was known of basic nucleic acid biochemistry prior to 1940, and the perplexity of Brachet in 1932 over the possible presence of a phytonucleic acid (ribose nucleic acid) in animal cells illustrates this point. It was not until the early 1940s that both RNA and DNA were shown to be present in the same cell, it being thought until then that RNA was present only in plant cells and DNA only in animal cells.

However, it is not to the discredit of the earlier workers that, having attempted to visualize their problems in terms of cellular chemistry, they were unable to answer the questions they posed because of the lack of biochemical and biophysical tools and information. Having achieved all that was possible with the techniques available in terms of cell structure and chemistry (e.g., Seifriz, 1936; Guilliermond, 1941) cytologists turned instead to the rapidly developing subject of cytogenetics. In consequence, Darlington's (1938) "Recent Advances in Cytology" contains scant reference to the cytoplasm, and it was Baker (1933), Brachet (1957) and Caspersson (1940) who virtually laid the basis of modern cytology.

The post-1940 period owes its tremendous impetus to the breakthrough in the techniques of biochemistry and biophysics. A few examples of these advances are enough to show just how recent is the knowledge and apparatus required for modern cytological studies. The technique of homogenization of tissues followed by fractionation of the sub-cellular organelles owes its evolution to the rapid post-war development of refrigerated ultra-centrifuges and zonal centrifuges capable of yielding the high centrifugal forces necessary for the separation of the subcellular components. The application of X-ray diffraction to components of biological tissues also resulted in the development of a powerful biological tool. Up to 1930, microscopists had available bright field, fluorescence, polarized light and dark ground microscopes that enabled a number of studies to be performed, generally on preserved tissues, but which would not allow a resolution of more than 0.25 μm. Although Zernicke had attempted to interest people in phase-contrast microscopy as early as 1934–1935, he had met with little success in London due to the attitude of some British microscopists of that period, and it was not until after 1942 that this valuable apparatus became commercially avail-

able (Zeiss, 1941; Zernicke, 1942, 1946). Interference microscopy was adapted
for possible biological use by Dyson (1949, 1950, 1953; Barer, 1952), but it was
first shown to be capable of use in biology to weigh cell components by Davies *et
al.* (1954). Increased resolution became available with the advent of the ultra-
violet light microscope, but it remained the tool of the specialist until the development of reflecting objectives (Wilkins, 1953). Electron and X-ray microscopy
also were not known outside specialized laboratories until well after the World
War II, though with their great increase in resolving power over the light microscope, they were to provide a remarkable impetus to the study of cellular ultra-
structure and function.

The measurement of the amount of dye in cellular structures including nuclei
and chromosomes was totally inaccurate until the production of the methods and
instruments of Patau and Swift (1953) and of Deeley and his co-workers (1955,
1957), which enabled the amount of nuclear DNA in a cell to be measured
precisely by the Feulgen reaction (1924). More reactions have been quantified in
a similar way so that it is now possible to measure levels of DNA, RNA, proteins
and certain enzymes with reasonable accuracy.

Perhaps the technique primarily responsible for the advancement of the dynamic approach to cell biology has been the application of autoradiography to
cell studies (Bélanger and Leblond, 1946; Pelc, 1947), a bonus from the development of fine-grained photographic emulsions during World War II.

The application of biochemical techniques to the study of plant cells has
yielded much information concerning the composition of the various subcellular
components, the constitution of the multi-enzyme pathways, the various chemical compounds present and the biosynthetic and degradation pathways of many
compounds. However, this knowledge has been obtained by methods that initially require the destruction of not only the particular organ, but of the cells
themselves. In consequence, it has been necessary to piece together the information obtained to demonstrate a particular pathway that ultimately may have been
determined under biochemically ideal conditions. Such optimal conditions may
not exist in cells at all times if ever, and hence, it may be questioned whether
such a complete reaction or pathway operates as such within all intact cells in an
intact organism. In order to test the applicability of the biochemical findings to
all living cells, it has become necessary to perform the biochemical measurements within the confines of the living cell so as to disturb its dynamic state as
little as possible. Such an approach has been developed through histochemistry,
which concerns the study of the chemistry of tissues and, as such, includes
cytochemistry, which is the study of the chemistry of cells.

The concept of histochemistry is not new, and the earliest known publications
appear to be those of the French political philosopher and botanist, Raspail,
whose early works (1825,a,b, 1830, 1833) included the use of frozen, unfixed
sections, and of iodine during his studies on fertilization in the Gramineae; he

applied the xanthoproteic reaction for proteins and the furfural test for carbohydrate to tissue sections. However, only during the past 25 years has the subject
really made an impact in the study of cell and tissue chemistry. Histochemistry
has had to overcome the additional difficulty of mis-application by a number of
past and present workers who, in general, despite their extensive knowledge of
histology, have been poor chemists, and in consequence have not studied tissue
chemistry, but have merely applied themselves to the extension of histology.

III. WHY HISTOCHEMISTRY?

It has been common practice to utilise a biochemical approach for the determination of the chemical composition of subcellular compounds and ions. This has
necessitated homogenizing the tissue and separating the components, usually by
differential centrifugation, into the fractions of cell walls, nuclei, plastids, mitochondria, ribosomes, vacuoles and supernatant. These fractions have been analysed for their enzyme content or for various chemical constituents. Whilst not
underestimating his work, it is important to realize the limitations involved in
attempting to relate the data to the intact cell or tissue.

Any plant organ consists of an heterogeneous population of cell types. In
consequence, the application of a purely biochemical approach to studies of roots
or shoots or leaves results in, for example, a nuclear fraction containing nuclei
from a variety of cell types at various stages of the cell cycle or of cellular
differentiation. Thus, the mean DNA content of this fraction will not necessarily
show the true DNA content of any particular nucleus. Attempts to obtain more
accurate information have yielded alternative methods of analysis that relate to
the cell or tissue level. Linderstrøm-Lang and his colleagues developed the
approach of using alternate sections for morphological and biochemical analyses
(Linderstrøm-Lang and Engel, 1938; Linderstrøm-Lang and Holter, 1932; Bottelier et al., 1943; Linderstrøm-Lang, 1952). In this way the first section would
be taken for morphological analysis (e.g., cell area, number of cells per unit
area, consideration of cell contents), the next serial section for enzyme assay and
the next for total protein nitrogen determination, the whole requiring nine serial
sections to allow the assays to be performed in triplicate. This method, however,
does not allow consideration of either the stage of differentiation or the different
physiological states of morphologically similar cells. Thus, expressing data on a
per section basis does not indicate if a fall in enzyme activity is due, for example,
to a genuine decrease in activity per cell or to a mere "dilution" resulting from
the presence of many cells with little or no activity. An example of this may be
seen in the case of the response of roots of *Vicia faba* to the substrate naphthol
AS-D acetate in which the stele and the epidermis react very strongly, but the
cortex offers a nil to very weak response. A more commonly used method for

histochemical studies on roots was developed by Brown and Rickless (1949) in which total cell numbers were determined by counting cells from a known volume of suspension with the aid of a haemocytometer after having macerated the tissue in either chromic acid or pectinase. It is possible also to calculate the average cell volume by relating the volume of the organ or tissue mass to the cell number (Brown and Broadbent, 1950). These authors determined cell numbers on successive 0.2 mm sections of the root of *Pisum sativum* covering the terminal 9 mm. Average cell volume was calculated as the volume of the tissue section divided by the number of cells, and so measurements of protein, respiration and dry weight were calculated similarly on a per cell basis. Whilst such a study permitted a mean value to be determined for these parameters, it did not allow for the physiological variation between cell types from tissues such as epidermis, cortex, xylem and phloem. Thus, the results are indicative of a hypothetical "average" cell. Furthermore, the use of average cell volume can also yield misleading results since if biochemical measurements are related to this standard, it will not take into account the physiological state of the individual cells where cells of similar volume and morphology may respond differently to an enzyme substrate. This may be seen in the response of root cortical cells of *V. faba* to sodium β-glycerophosphate when employing the reaction for acid phosphatase activity (Gahan and Maple, 1966). It is clear from such studies that adjacent cells may be sufficiently different, both morphologically and physiologically, to suggest that the graphs of parameter versus "per cell or segment" represent a mean value with large standard deviations, and thus cannot be used as an adequate approach for the determination of cellular changes during development and differentiation.

An alternative approach to tissue volume measurement was developed by Jensen (1955a) in which a 10 μm section was cut from the mid-region of the root segment (100–200 μm) to be examined. The section was drawn or photographed and the area of the various tissues determined by planimetry, the volume being calculated by multiplying tissue area by segment length. The transverse section area of the cells can be determined by dividing the tissue area by the number of cells per tissue area. Cell length can be found from longitudinal sections, and hence the cell volume per tissue can be calculated. Thus, cell volume divided into tissue volume will yield the number of cells per tissue. This has formed the basis of a number of studies by Jensen (e.g., 1955b, 1956a, 1958, 1960), but it still does not overcome the difficulty that adjacent cells within the same tissue may be markedly different with respect to features such as enzyme activity (Avers, 1958; Gahan and Maple, 1966; McLean, 1969).

The application of direct quantitative histochemistry to histological sections (Kalina and Gahan, 1965) is limited also in that it can be applied satisfactorily only to tissues in which there is a single cell type, and all cells are physiologically identical.

At present, the development of accurate quantification at the cell level seems to depend upon cytospectrophotometry measurements (see Chapter 9), auto-radiographic measurements (see Chapter 9), or the micro-dissection approach of Lowry (1953). In the last method, frozen sections are transferred directly from the microtome knife to a specially prepared container cooled to the temperature of the cryostat cabinet, and kept covered to prevent drying and shrinkage. When full, the container is moved to a drying tube and the whole placed in a refriger-ated container at $-30°$ to $-40°C$. When the drying tube and its contents have reached a temperature equilibrium, the tube is evacuated to 0.1 mm Hg or less. After 1–6 h the tube is allowed to warm to room temperature and the vacuum released. After removal of the sections from the container, the required groups of cells are dissected from the frozen and dried sections, weighed on a quartz-fibre balance and assayed biochemically for the component required. This approach has been little used with plant tissues, in part because of the problems of micro-dissection of some tissues (Jones *et al.*, 1977).

IV. APPROACHING HISTOCHEMISTRY

In order to apply histochemical methods successfully, two basic criteria must be considered. Firstly, it is imperative that there is a full understanding of the chemistry of the reaction to be performed upon the cells. Secondly, the reactions should be performed upon cells that are retained in a state that is as close as possible to that of the living cells. Any treatment of the cells as part of a tissue preparation programme must be closely monitered, and the impact of the prepa-ration on the availability and localization of the substances or reactions to be studied must be carefully assessed.

Given an adequate control over these conditions, it is possible to derive a number of tests that enable a qualitative assessment of activity and subcellular localization to be obtained. Furthermore, in many instances, these tests have been developed into fully quantitative methods. Thus, it is possible to adapt biochemistry to a study at the intact cell and tissue level, one that retains the dynamic approach and allows accurate measurement as an immediate goal of microscopic histochemistry.

Of the two basic criteria, the first, an understanding of the chemistry of a reaction, is the more readily attained. Tissue preparation, however, has provided a major obstacle to the progress of histochemistry since owing to the nature of the methods, whole organs cannot be readily examined as such, and it is necessary to make tissue sections or single cell preparations. The latter may be obtained by special methods whereby the cells of a particular organ are grown in culture, or they can be prepared by teasing or squashing the organ. Sections for light microscopy must be of 0.5–10 μm in thickness, and it is here that the question of tissue preservation is initially important. To obtain such sections, the tissue must be supported, and wax has proved to be a popular support medium, although epoxy resins are employed both in electron microscopy and for the production of semi-thin sections for optical microscopy. However, in order to protect the tissue from distortion during infiltration with the wax, it is necessary to preserve chemically, or "fix", the tissue. Many fixatives have been tried, but although each fixative possesses merits for certain uses (Baker, 1960; Jensen, 1962) an ideal chemical fixative has yet to be produced. The alternative method of freeze-drying was tried as long ago as 1889 by Altmann, but though reasonable success was achieved with animal tissues, plant tissues did not lend themselves readily to such procedures, and until recently this did not prove a very adequate method. Thus, it is not surprising that such a critical worker as Danielli (1953) should have been cautious about developing histochemistry when even the best pre-paratory procedures such as freeze-drying did not preserve all cellular compo-nents. Recent work has produced more acceptable methods of freeze-drying plant tissues (Jensen, 1962; Thaine and Bullas, 1965), and also of cutting un-fixed frozen sections (Gahan et al., 1967) so allowing an opportunity of studying cells preserved in a life-like condition.

A moderately satisfactory resolution of these two basic criteria of histo- and cytochemistry has permitted the examination of a range of problems concerning cell and tissue chemistry and physiology.

When examining a chemical system, a complete analysis comprises both a qualitative and a quantitative assessment. This comment is applicable to chem-ical systems whether they be in a test tube or in a cell or tissue. To analyse a substance or a cell qualitatively, a series of reactions is required to show which components, molecules or atoms are present and in histochemistry, to localize these components at the sub-cellular and tissue levels. Normally, qualitative analysis precedes a quantitative analysis, and sufficient methods are now avail-able for qualitative analyses of cells to be described in terms similar to those used for inorganic or organic chemistry (see Practical Appendix). Quantitative analy-ses are considered more fully in Chapter 9.

2. Tissue Preparation

I. INTRODUCTION

Ideally, histochemical and cytochemical studies should be made upon intact living tissue, but this presents difficulties in isolation of individual cells and achieving the penetration of the reaction components into the cells. The immediate alternative is the use of razor-cut sections of fresh material (razor-cut sections), but this has a number of drawbacks including the problems of (a) producing many serial sections of 10 μm or less thick; (b) sectioning a number of organs, such as small apices; (c) the penetration of the sections by dyes and reaction components; and (d) the reduced retention and good localization of water-soluble compounds.

Many methods have been devised to assist this exercise, including various forms of fixation and embedding, and the various modifications of freezing. Since the latter methods have proved of greater use in facilitating the production of tissue sections in a close to life-like condition, they will be considered before the other methods employing fixation and embedding.

II. FREEZING

Most plant tissues have a high water content and, consequently, on cooling to below 0°C, the water freezes with the formation of ice crystals. The amount of cell damage caused by the production of ice crystals has provoked various studies to determine the conditions of freezing in which ice damage can be reduced to a minimum. If the tissue is frozen slowly, then large, extra-cellular ice crystals are formed (Asahina, 1956). Conversely, if the tissue is frozen rapidly, the cytoplasm appears as a micro-crystalline solid in which the ice crystals are very small and tend to be below the resolution of the light microscope (Bell, 1952). Rapid freezing may be achieved by plunging small pieces (1–2 mm thick) of tissue directly into liquid nitrogen (−170°C) or into either isopentane (−165°C) or propane (−185°C) cooled with liquid nitrogen. Liquid nitrogen is the least satisfactory because the latent heat of the tissue is enough to cause a gaseous layer around the piece of tissue so decreasing the rate of heat loss and resulting in the

8

production of larger ice crystals. Isopentane is most widely used, being liquid at room temperature and not as inflammable as propane. These advantages are offset by the fact that isopentane is difficult to use near its freezing point which is higher than that of propane. The latter is gaseous and has to be liquidified prior to use—not a very convenient process. There does not appear to be a great deal of difference between these two quenching media with respect to tissue preservation.

More rapid cooling of the tissues has been achieved by use of liquid helium II that has super-heat conductivity which, combined with its low temperature, results in very rapid freezing of the tissue (Fernandez-Moran, 1960). However, this method can only be used with very small pieces of tissue and is expensive!

The previous methods of freezing depended upon reducing the size of the ice crystals formed. However, it has been established that plant cells may be cooled to below 0°C and yet essentially remain in a super-cooled state (Asahina, 1956). Based upon these findings of Asahina who used such methods to preserve the viability of sperm and other cell types, Chayen et al. (1960a,b) suggested less severe temperatures for the freezing of plant tissues. More recent studies (Gahan et al., 1967) have supported the initial contention of Chayen et al. (1960a,b) that freezing plant tissues at temperatures between −55° and −65°C seems to preserve cells in a condition similar to that of the cells in unfixed, razor sections of living tissues. Measurements of the rate of freezing of the tissue, by recording the rate of cooling of a copper–constantan thermo-couple placed in its centre, have shown that at freezing temperatures of between 0° and −40°C there is evidence of ice crystal formation. This is confirmed by the damaged cytoplasm of the cells from tissues frozen in this temperature range. On freezing between −55° and −65°C, there is no obvious sign of ice crystal formation either by direct measurement of the cooling curves or by observation of cells from tissues frozen in this manner in either the optical or electron microscope (Fig. 1). It was considered that since the thermocouple was primarily in contact with and measuring intra-cellular material, it was possible that little or no ice crystal formation occurred within the cells.

Chayen et al. suggested that similar good preservation of the cells may be explained in that upon cooling at an optimal rate, the extra-cellular water freezes first and desiccates the intra-cellular protoplasm. For this to happen, the cell membrane must remain intact and act as a barrier to the extra-cellular ice crystals. The lack of intra-cellular ice crystal artefacts suggests either that at those particular temperatures the protoplasm never freezes, remaining super-cooled, or that at these low temperatures it may freeze, but has too low a water content to cause much damage.

In the studies of Chayen et al. (1960a,b) and Gahan et al. (1967), polyvinyl alcohol (PVA) was used as a tissue stabilizer prior to freezing; this treatment appears to assist in the preservation of cell organelles on freezing. Gahan et al.

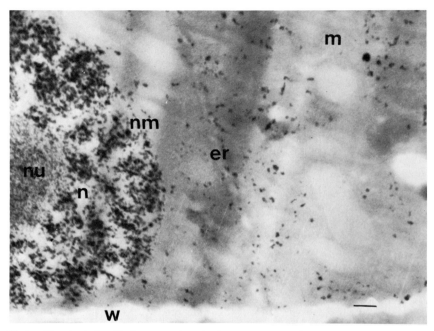

FIG. 1.   Unstained ultrathin frozen section of apical meristem cell from root of *Vicia faba* reacted for acid β-glycerophosphatase activity for 30 min at 37°C. Deliberately over-reacted to introduce lead into this section. n, nucleus; nu, nucleolus; nm, nuclear membrane; er, endoplasmic reticulum; m, mitochondrion; w, primary cell wall. Scale, 200 nm.

(1967) suggested that the PVA may assist in maintaining the cells in a super-cooled state. Kistler (1935) found that ice crystals forming in aqueous solutions rich in hydrophilic colloids were apt to become covered with a sheath of dehydrated colloid and so fail to seed the entire solution. Thus, if a cell were covered with such a solution, the layer of the condensed solution formed at the moment of freezing may not only retard the propagation of freezing, but effectively seal the surface of the growing ice front, so that ice crystals can hardly be in direct contact with the cell surface (Asahina, 1958). It is possible that the PVA present in the treated tissues may prevent the extra-cellular ice crystals, if formed, from seeding any intra-cellular water, the cytoplasm remaining in a super-cooled state.

Whilst the present author has not found it necessary to employ specific anti-freeze agents, other than PVA, this approach has provided satisfactory results, especially with tissues containing highly vacuolated cells (Knox, 1970). Thus, tissues can be treated with 10% dimethyl sulphoxide (DMSO) at 2°C for one to several hours. In some anatomical or developmental studies, DMSO has been replaced by 10% glycerol or ethandiol for 18–24 h either at room temperature or at 37°C. If cryo-protectants are used, attention should be given to the effects upon enzyme reactions that can be enhanced by this treatment (Reiss, 1971). This may be due to an increased membrane permeability of cell and/or organelle membranes (Hayat, 1973). Hanker *et al.* (1970) also suggested a facilitated transfer of electrons from the thiol groups of dehydrogenases to the tetrazolium acceptors.

The technique of freezing forms the basis of other types of tissue preparation, namely, freeze-substitution, freeze-drying and freeze-sectioning, all of which have been of enormous importance.

A. Freeze-Substitution

Freeze-substitution has been relatively little used in botany since its inception. The method involves pieces of tissue or individual cells that are frozen rapidly, the ice so formed being subsequently removed with cold methanol. The procedure is relatively simple since after quenching in, e.g. isopentane or liquid propane, the tissue is rapidly transferred to methanol cooled to about −30°C. The speed necessary for the success of the method is governed by the temperature at which freezing occurs and by the amount of ice formed. Thus, the lower the temperature, the less ice will be dissolved by the alcohol, although if the tissue is placed in absolute ethanol at about −35°C, the ice will be removed during a period of about 2 days. Two or three alcohol changes are recommended during the drying period. Individual cells can then be reacted after rehydrating, or tissues can be transferred to toluene and brought to room temperature prior to wax embedding. Since proteins and nucleoproteins are not noticeably denatured by freezing or treatment with alcohols at low temperatures, and since toluene is not a protein precipitant, the tissue appears to be relatively unfixed (Jensen, 1962). Thus, the type of fixation achieved will depend upon the nature of the first solution which makes contact with the frozen-substituted tissues. The main objections to the use of frozen-substituted tissues seem to be (a) damage by rapid freezing, (b) the use of lipid solvents that will remove some lipid components, (c) the need to treat the tissue with solvents, possibly causing a redistribution of materials within the cells and tissues; and (d) the need to de-wax sections prior to performing many reactions. Tissues prepared by this method appear to be suitable for studies of nucleic acids and proteins but not lipids, enzymes and ions (Jensen, 1962). In a study of frozen-substituted *Neurospora*, Zalokar (1960a) found that cytochrome oxidase and succinic dehydrogenase were completely destroyed, β-galactosidase partially inactivated, and acid and alkaline phosphatases unaffected. Fixation has been effected with animal tissues during the substitution phase (Feder and Sidman, 1958; Bell, 1959), but this possibility does not seem to have been tested on plant tissues. An extension of this method to the freeze-substitution of frozen sections has been employed with animal tissues and may be of help in some types of investigation such as enzymology (Chang, 1969).

B. Freeze-Drying

Whilst frozen sections were used initially by Raspail as long ago as 1825, freeze-drying was not considered to be a useful scientific tool until 1889 (Altmann). Gersh (1932) really stimulated a wider interest in the possibilities of this method, and since these early studies, many types of apparatus have been developed for freeze-drying and have been fully discussed by Jensen (1962), one of the main workers in the field. Essentially, the method involves the freezing of plant tissues followed by drying out at $-30°C$ in high or partial vacuum with a moving stream of gas, the latter improving the rate and completeness of the drying process. On completion of drying, the tissue temperature is raised and the tissue infiltrated with molten wax or water-soluble resin. The embedding medium is hardened and the tissues sectioned in the normal way. Whilst the technique has worked well with animal tissues (Gersh, 1932; Gersh and Stephenson, 1954; Glick and Malstrom, 1952; Glick and Bloom, 1956; Stowell, 1951; Bell, 1952) many difficulties were encountered initially when working with plant tissues. Thus, Goodspeed and Über (1934) found that plant tissues took a long time to dry and were difficult to infiltrate with wax, problems encountered by later workers (Bell, 1952). The occasional pieces of tissue that were successfully processed showed good cellular preservation, but the method was by no means routine. A series of studies by Jensen (1954a,b) and by Jensen and Branton (1962) resulted in the production of a much improved system of freeze-drying that reduced the drying time and overcame the difficulties of wax infiltration through the dried plant cell walls. Since these difficulties now seem mainly to have been overcome (Jensen, 1962; Thaine, 1962; Thaine and Bullas, 1965) the method should prove to be more widely useful in plant histochemistry.

Despite the advantages of using un-fixed frozen-dried material, the method is still open to criticism in that (a) some freezing damage still occurs due to the rapid quenching utilized; (b) it is only applicable to small pieces (1–5 mm thick) of tissue; (c) there is still a need to infiltrate with an embedding medium; (d) sections must be dewaxed by floating them on either xylene or water; (e) the first solution with which the section makes contact essentially becomes the fixative; and (f) the process can be time consuming, and prolonged exposure of the tissues to low temperatures during the drying period can result in the splitting of lipid–protein linkages. Advantages include the production of serial, relatively un-fixed sections for both optical and electron microscopy, and the better preservation of cytological detail and enzyme activities than achieved with chemical fixation.

C. Freeze-Sectioning

The early method of cutting frozen sections involved the use of a microtome on which the block-holder, tissue and sometimes the knife were cooled by jets of compressed CO_2. This form of tissue section preparation has not been very successful since the tissue and knife can only be kept at a little below 0°C so that the tissue cannot be kept completely frozen, thawing during and immediately after cutting. This form of sectioning is not useful in plant cyto- and histochemistry though it may be of value in plant histology (Johansen, 1958) and some aspects of electron microscope cytochemistry.

The development of the cryostat by Linderstrøm-Lang and his collaborators (1938) enabled the microtome to be used in a refrigerated cabinet, and through various refinements (Pearse, 1968; Pearse and Bancroft, 1966) has given a valuable means of producing serial, frozen sections of animal tissues with excellent preservation. Application to plant tissues has been relatively recent, but it has emerged as a potentially valuable tool in the preparation of serial, unfixed sections of many plant tissues for cytochemical study (Chayen et al., 1960a,b; Gahan et al., 1967). Essentially, the apparatus consists of a microtome enclosed in a refrigerated container (Fig. 2). Thus, the temperature of the environment in

FIG. 2.   Brights' cryostat. (A) Freestanding model. (B) Interior of cabinet showing microtome equipped with anti-roll plate (a), knife (b), and specimen (c)

which the sections are being cut can be fully controlled, as can the temperature of
the knife. Initially, cooling of the knife below the temperature of the refrigerated
cabinet was achieved by placing solid CO_2 about the knife handle, but attach-
ments are now available to achieve a more fully controlled cooling. Investigations of the cutting conditions have shown that for non-woody tissues, good
sections may be obtained (a) if the knife is sharp and without a shoulder behind
the knife-edge resulting from sharpening; (b) if the cabinet temperature is between $-23°$ and $-28°C$; (c) if the cabinet is regularly defrosted; (d) if the knife is
at the correct angle to the block (approximately 30° from the perpendicular); (e)
if the anti-roll plate is at the correct position to the knife edge; and (f) if the knife
is at the correct temperature that will vary slightly from tissue to tissue (Gahan *et
al.*, 1967). If the cabinet temperature is lower than $-28°C$ the sections tend to
crumble as they are cut, but if the temperature is higher than $-23°C$ there is a
tendency for the friction heat generated by the knife cutting through the block to
cause the sections to thaw. They re-freeze on a colder part of the knife, but
become crumpled and useless for study. Cooling of the knife below the cabinet
temperature appears to be necessary for tissues with a high sugar content, e.g.
leaves. A fuller consideration of the thawing of sections on cutting has been
given by Thornburg and Mengers (1957) and by Pearse (1968, 1980). The
application of this method to obtaining frozen sections of woody tissues has been
considered by Weaver and Layne (1965), and has been found to be applicable to
twigs of up to 4 years of age, especially if sections are cut longitudinally (Fig. 3).
Further modifications have improved the application of this method to a wide
variety of tissues and include the use of 1.5% Reten to encapsulate the piece of
frozen material to aid in cutting (Williamson *et al.*, 1976). Reten provides a final
texture which is much harder than gelatin and permits sections to be obtained
from woody tissues. However, it has been observed that entry of the Reten into
cells causes cytological damage. Furthermore, it should be added after freezing
the tissue when soft tissues are employed since, if frozen directly into the Reten,
the tissue will be crushed as the Reten freezes (P. B. Gahan, unpublished data).

In using the cryostat, it is necessary to attach the material to the block-holder
of the microtome. This can be achieved by placing a drop of water on to the
block-holder, which is cooled by a mixture of absolute ethanol and solid CO_2
(Fig. 4). Just as the last drop of water is about to freeze, the specimen is rapidly
transferred to the block-holder such that only a minimal portion of the base of the
tissue is caught in the drop of water as it freezes. This is essentially the method
for freezing plant tissues recommended by Gahan *et al.* (1967) and enables the
tissue to be frozen and mounted in one operation.

If it is necessary to mount pre-frozen material, then it should be kept ready,
for example, on crushed, solid CO_2 and be rapidly transferred to the block-holder
with forceps pre-cooled to $-60°C$ (Fig. 5). In this procedure, no supporting
medium is required to ensure that sections will be cut, and whilst some workers

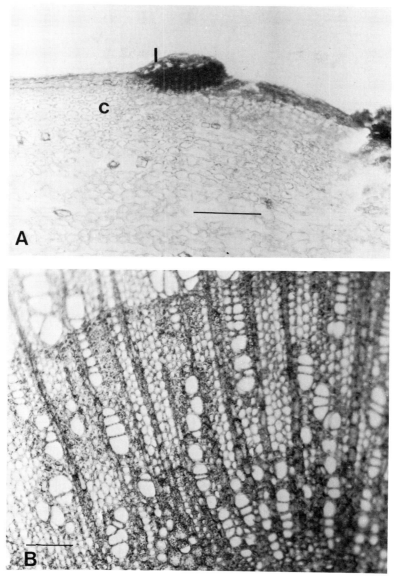

FIG. 3.   Unfixed, transverse section of twig from *Acer pseudoplatanus*. (A) Cortex (c) and lenticel (L). (B) Woody tissue. Scale, 0.1 mm.

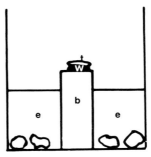

FIG. 4.   Diagram of freezing tissue. Just as the last drop of water is about to freeze on the block-holder (W), the tissue (t) is placed into that water so that only the smallest part of the tissue is in the ice. b, block-holder; e, ethanol–CO_2 freezing mixture.

embed in gelatin (Knox, 1970) or rat liver and brain (Laüchli, 1966) or in Reten (Williamson *et al.*, 1976), prior to freezing, this has been found to be necessary only for certain types of tissue.

The freezing–sectioning method has been extended to the production of ultra-thin frozen sections. Drawing upon experience from animal tissues (Christian-son, 1969; Appleton, 1977), a number of approaches have been devised for preparing plant tissues. An earlier method merely extended the approach used for cryostat sections by pretreating the tissues with PVA followed by freezing blocks of tissue (base size 0.5 mm^2 and trimmed to a pyramid) directly onto the spec-imen-holder at $-65°C$ in order to preserve cytological structure. Lower tem-peratures for cutting could then be exploited. Further improvement was achieved on replacing PVA with gum-sucrose as the cryoprotectant (Gahan *et al.*, 1970).

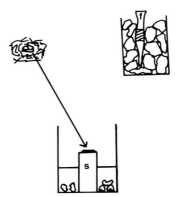

FIG. 5.   Prefrozen, tissue is mounted in a similar way to that described in Fig. 4, except that care must be taken not to let the tissue thaw during the handling procedure. Tissue (t) surrounded by solid CO_2 prior to transfer with chilled forceps (f) to chilled specimen holder (s).

Subsequent methods have employed glycerol or DMSO as cryoprotectants, and the tissue frozen at liquid nitrogen temperature (Roland, 1978a; Roland *et al.*, 1975). As when using the cryostat, ultra-cryotomy does not require embedding media and can be applied to fixed or unfixed material. Indeed, it is here that its virtue lies.

Once frozen and mounted for sectioning, the problems encountered are somewhat similar to those experienced in cryotomy. Most modern ultra-cryotomes permit the independent controlling of both knife and specimen temperatures (Fig. 6). Glass knives may be used, although diamond knives tend to yield better sections with a variety of tissues. The method is very much in its developmental phase, and a number of different cutting temperatures have been employed ranging from $-140°$ to $-145°C$ for the specimen (yeast) and $-100°C$ for the knife (Roomans and Seveus, 1976; Osumi and Sato, 1978) to as high as $-60°C$ to $-80°C$ for the specimen (tissues of *Vicia faba*) and $-30°$ to $-40°C$ for the knife (Gahan *et al.*, 1970). Clearly, the main problem is one of avoiding section thawing by the heat of friction generated as the knife passes through the specimen, and the lower temperatures may be significant in this respect. Once cut, the sections may be floated onto a liquid bath containing an anti-freeze agent such as DMSO, e.g. 50% DMSO in 10% aqueous ethanol (Gahan *et al.*, 1970), or may be picked up directly from the dry knife (Appleton, 1977). Such sections have little electron opacity. This is advantageous for the identification of the

FIG. 6.   View from above of cutting chamber of a Reichard OMU3 ultra-cryotome showing the knife (k) and specimen holder (s) which are independently chilled by controlled flow of liquid nitrogen gas. The chamber and specimen holder are fitted to the conventional ultra-microtome.

electron-opaque products of subsequent cytochemical reactions (Fig. 1), though difficulty may be encountered in identifying the subcellular organelles involved. Negative staining in which the background is stained, but not the specimen, is achieved by floating the mounted sections for 30 s on 0.2–1% silicotungstate or phosphotungstate at pH 7–7.2 (Roland, 1978a). This seems more reliable than positive staining with uranyl acetate or lead citrate when particular components of tissue macromolecules stain by combining with the heavy metal atoms. This may be due, in part, to the lack of binding sites for the heavy metals in unfixed, frozen, ultrathin sections where there is less disruption of membranes than normally encountered in standard electron microscopic preparations.

III. FIXATION

For a fully detailed analysis of the various fixatives available the reader is referred to the excellent monographs of Baker (1958, 1960), Jensen (1962), Hayat (1970), and Glauert (1975). It will suffice to consider briefly the types of fixatives available and to examine their value in histochemistry rather than their general use in histology. Many fixatives are prepared from more than one component, and the general effects of the commonly used components upon cell contents will now be considered.

A. Ethanol

Ethanol, usually as a 50% or 70% aqueous solution, has been used frequently as a fixative since it penetrates plant tissues fairly rapidly, appearing to preserve by coagulating many of the proteins by hardening. It is not a successful cytochemical fixative because (a) coagulation of proteins results in inactivation of a number of enzymes; (b) some lipids are solubilized; (c) it effects a splitting of lipid from protein to cause an ''unmasking'' of lipid; and (d) it does not stabilize nucleoprotein, which may be dissolved out.

B. Formaldehyde

Four percent formaldehyde ($\equiv$ 10% formalin) has a pH of about 4 and is normally used either after buffering to about pH 7 or on standing over marble chips to keep the pH near to 7. It has been used extensively in animal and plant cytochemistry for both optical and electron microscopy. It does not coagulate proteins and nucloproteins or precipitate DNA from solution. The retention of the activity of some enzymes occurs. Most lipids appear to be well preserved, although some lipid–protein complexes are dissolved out of tissues. However, phospholipids remaining in the tissue tend to be insoluble in lipid solvents, and so not lost on further processing.

C. Glutaraldehyde

Glutaraldehyde, generally used as a 2.5% solution in phosphate or cacodylate buffer has become the fixative of choice for many cytochemical studies with the electron microscope. Little information is available concerning its reactivity with the various cell constituents, but it probably behaves in a similar manner to formaldehyde (Pearse, 1980) and is of particular value in enzyme cytochemistry when the activities of acid hydrolases are reasonably well preserved (Sabatini *et al.*, 1963).

D. Chromium Trioxide

One percent chromium trioxide, which is often used in conjunction with formal-dehyde (e.g. 1 : 1, 1% chromium trioxide and 4% formaldehyde; Lewitsky, 1931) is much the strongest oxidising agent of all the fixatives, penetrating slowly, shrinking tissues and hardening them moderately. The affinity of pro-teins for basic dyes is rather low, which suggests a blocking of the —COOH groups of the acidic amino acids (Baker, 1958) and that acidic proteins are dissolved out of the tissue. After short fixation times, lipids are still soluble in lipid solvents, but become insoluble with prolonged treatment. Polysaccharides appear to be oxidized to aldehydes (see Chapter 7, Section A), although glycogen does not appear to be fixed. Enzyme activity is lost after this fixation, but chromosome morphology is quite well preserved, DNA being precipitated in an insoluble form.

E. Osmic Acid

Osmic acid, although relatively little used in optical microscope histochemistry is much employed in electron microscopic studies, mainly as a post-fixative after performing a particular reaction. It should be handled with great caution since it sublimes and emits a vapour that is damaging to the epithelium of the eyes, nose and mouth. It penetrates tissues rather slowly without hardening them, and does not coagulate proteins or nucleoproteins, but blackens unsaturated lipids without affecting saturated ones.

F. Potassium Dichromate

Potassium dichromate in aqueous solution is a strong oxidising agent that softens tissue. It does not coagulate protein or nucleoprotein, does not fix carbohydrate, but does dissolve out DNA and renders fats insoluble in lipid solvents. It causes much shrinkage of the cytoplasm generally, and swelling of mitochondria.

G. Acetic Acid

Acetic acid can be used as an aqueous solution of various concentrations, e.g. at 45% as a fixative in chromosome studies, although it is frequently employed in combination with absolute ethanol (Clarke, 1851). Alone it does not coagulate proteins, but extracts histones and lipid–proteins, although DNA is precipitated from solution. Acetic acid neither fixes nor removes carbohydrates. Penetration is rapid, causing marked swelling of protein gels and hardening of tissues. Whilst metaphase or anaphase chromosomes appear relatively well-preserved, the cytoplasm is very poorly preserved.

IV. DEHYDRATION AND EMBEDDING

Since many waxes and resins are immiscible with water, dehydration of plant tissue is essential after treatment in an aqueous fixative. This may be achieved by freeze-drying as already discussed or by passing the tissue through a graded series of concentrations of aqueous ethanol from 30% to absolute. Since most waxes are not very soluble in ethanol, the tissue is then passed through a further series of solutions such as mixtures of *n*-butanol and chloroform to absolute chloroform in which the wax is soluble and so can infiltrate the tissue easily. In dehydrating, ethanol can be replaced by acetone in which tropical ester wax is soluble (Chayen and Gahan, 1958). For general details of these procedures, the reader is recommended to consult Gray (1954) and Johansen (1958) although some procedures are given in the Practical Appendix. The choice of wax is important, since waxes are of various melting points and hardnesses. Ideally, embedding should be performed in a wax of the lowest possible melting point to avoid overheating the tissues, but those with a very low melting point may not always provide adequate hardness. The choice of wax is ultimately determined by the type of tissue and the conditions in which the work is being performed.

An alternative way to avoid dehydrating the tissue is by the use of water-soluble waxes such as Aquax and Carbowax. Many workers have been satisfied with this form of embedding, although shrinkage of some tissues has been noted. Embedding in gelatin has also been widely used, but whilst avoiding shrinkage and retaining oil droplets it is normally difficult to obtain sections of 5 μm or less without recourse to a freezing microtome; furthermore, it is difficult to obtain a ribbon of sections, and the gelatin cannot be removed after section cutting.

In preparing tissues for cutting ultra-thin sections required in electron micro-scope cytochemistry, it is necessary to embed the tissue in material harder than wax. Methacrylate was used originally for this purpose, but because of its instability in the electron beam, it has tended to be replaced by araldite or epon. An alternative approach to minimize tissue distortion due to prolonged preparation procedures and the adverse effects of dehydration on the end-products of various cytochemical reactions includes the use of water-soluble embedding media. One such method that has been successfully employed in cytochemistry makes use of water-soluble glycol methacrylate (Ashford *et al.*, 1972). However, this is a time-consuming procedure since the final infiltration step can take as long as 2 weeks in the case of root apices of *Zea mays.*

Alternative methods have been developed to obtain ultra-thin sections, and include treating the tissue blocks for a particular cytochemical reaction, infiltrating them with gelatin and then freezing-sectioning them in an ultra-microtome housed in a refrigerated cabinet (Bernard, 1965; Bernhard and Nancy, 1964). Another method developed by Tranzer (1965) is to cut a section about 20 μm thick and pick it up on the end of an epon block. The section is then reacted for the histochemical test and air dried. The block is attached to the ultra-microtome and ultra-thin sections cut. Each of these methods allows the production of ultra-thin sections without the normal hazards imposed by dehydration and embedding, though perhaps the better approach involves the direct preparation of ultra-thin frozen sections (Gahan *et al.*, 1970; Barton, 1976; Roland, 1978a).

3. Group I: Nucleic Acids

I. INTRODUCTION

Whilst there have been extensive biochemical and biophysical studies of nucleic acids, it was cytochemistry that was responsible for the early information concerning the localization and function of nucleic acids in cells, and especially in plant cells. Before discussing the chemistry of the reactions employed in the cytochemical methods for nucleic acids, it is of interest to consider how they have been applied to the localization and function of these molecules, since the results have been fundamental in initiating the direction of the development of cytochemistry as a whole, and illustrate many of the points that are relevant to other methods and their applications. In particular, the results indicate the way in which cytochemistry can be used as a tool of cell biology.

A. Deoxyribonucleic Acid

The early studies of Brachet (1945) and Caspersson (1950) using ultra-violet light absorption microscopy established that both RNA and DNA were present in the same cell. An extension of this method by Walker and Yates (1952) further showed that there was a variation in the DNA content of interphase nuclei within a population of dividing cells. The development of the early form of the integrating microdensitometer (e.g., Deeley *et al.*, 1957) for measuring Feulgen staining in nuclei indicated a similar pattern of events, the distribution of the DNA content per nucleus being as shown in Fig. 7.

The amount of Feulgen stain is directly proportional to the amount of DNA so that a plot of the amount of stain per nucleus against numbers of nuclei will give the populations of nuclei with different DNA contents. The value c is given to the amount of DNA per haploid set of chromosomes per species. Thus, newly formed (G_1) diploid interphase nuclei plus anaphase and telophase sets of chromosomes will be $2c$. Metaphase and prophase chromosomes will be $4c$, as will be a diploid interphase nucleus that has synthesized new DNA (G_2) in preparation for division. An analysis of the DNA content of interphase nuclei showed three distinct populations, namely, those containing (a) the same amount of DNA as an anaphase or telophase set of chromosomes ($2c$); (b) the same amount as a

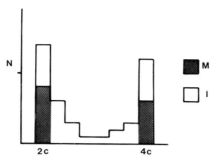

FIG. 7.   Histogram of number of nuclei (N) measured versus DNA content per nucleus. Diploid cells (2c) have the same DNA content as anaphase and telophase sets of chromosomes. Tetraploid nuclei (4c) have the same DNA content as prophase and metaphase figures. M, mitotic figures; I, interphase nuclei.

prophase or metaphase set of chromosomes (4c); and (c) amounts intermediate between 2c and 4c values. It was concluded that there was a synthesis of DNA during interphase, though it is not possible by this method to identify the precise timing of this event.

The now classic autoradiographic approach employed by Howard and Pelc (1951, 1953) established the method that allowed the introduction of a temporal element into the studies. They followed the course of DNA synthesis throughout the cell cycle by the incorporation of $^{32}PO_4$ into the DNA of chromosomes. The later introduction of tritium as a radioactive marker of compounds, and in particular the availability of [^{3}H]thymidine in 1957 has led to a refinement of the original autoradiographic approach so that a relatively standard method is available for the determination of (a) the actual length of the cycle, and (b) the specific lengths of the various phases of the cycle (Cleaver, 1967).

In making such measurements *in vivo*, it is frequently the case that a mixed population of cells is studied, which are of variable ages and of different physiological states and which are usually dividing asyncronously. If such a population of cells is exposed briefly (10–20 min) to the labelled precursor, then only those cells actually synthesizing DNA or about to start synthesizing DNA will become labelled. In order to ensure that the exposure to the label is sufficiently short, the labelled pool is usually chased from the cells with unlabelled precursor. Samples of cells are taken at intervals after labelling, and autoradiographs are made. The percentage of labelled mitoses in each preparation is noted, and a graph of the percentage of labelled mitotic figures against time after labelling is drawn (Fig. 8).

From the early studies of Howard and Pelc (1951, 1953), there appeared to be four main phases to the cell cycle, i.e. (a) mitosis (M); (b) a gap or rest period (G_1); (c) a DNA synthesis period (S); and (d) a further gap (G_2), the cycle recommencing with another mitosis. In an ideal situation, the wave of labelled mitoses corresponds to successive divisions of that part of the population that was synthesizing DNA during the availability of the labelled precursor. Therefore, the fraction of labelled mitoses is zero until the end of the first period on the graph termed G_2, when it rises rapidly to 100% during a period of mitoses. The labelled fraction then remains at 100%, equal to the duration of synthesis (S) less the time taken for mitosis (M), i.e. $S-M$, and eventually falls to zero. The second wave of labelled mitoses appears after a further time lag equal to the period of time notated $G_1 + G_2$ (Fig. 8). Usually the rate at which an individual cell completes the cycle reduces the definition of successive waves of mitotic figures, and normally it is possible to obtain only two and rarely three curves. If all of the mitoses are scored, regardless of the stage of mitosis, then the time from the mid-point of the labelling pulse to that at which 50% of the mitoses are labelled is equal to $G_2 + I/2M$, i.e. t_2 and hence M can be calculated. Thus, it is possible to determine G_1, G_2, M and S by difference from the cell cycle time. It is also possible to calculate the length of duration of the various phases of mitosis if each of them is graphed separately (Odartchenko *et al.*, 1964). Other methods are available for determining the length of the various phases of the cell cycle and for this purpose the reader is referred to Cleaver (1967). The lengths of these various phases vary according to the species considered, and to a certain extent, to the manner in which the experiment is conducted (for a full discussion, see Schultze, 1969). Table 1 shows data obtained for a variety of plant species.

It should be stressed that studies on the time of synthesis of DNA have added further parameters to the study of the cell cycle as a whole. By reference to the cytochemical studies of DNA during interphase, it is possible to define six major time parameters against which to measure other cellular activities. These parameters are the start and finish of each of G_1, S and G_2. If we add the phases of mitosis, then there are ten measurable parameters against which to time other cellular events, and which are demonstrable cytochemically.

It is clear from the results presented in Table 1 that similar figures are not obtained for the same species, on occasion, which appears to throw doubt upon the efficacy of the method. However, perhaps an important point concerns the

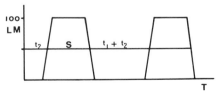

FIG. 8.   Diagram to show the calculation of the length of the cell cycle by plotting the percentage of labelled mitoses (LM) against time (*T*) after completion of a very short pulse label (identified by autoradiography). $t_2 = G_2 + \frac{1}{2}M$: $t_1 = G_1 + \frac{1}{2}M$; S, DNA synthesis period.

TABLE 1. Cell Cycle Times in Root Meristems for a Variety of Plant Species

Species	Cell cycle time (h)				
	G_1	S	G_2	M	T
Tradescantia sp.	1.0	10.5	2.5	3.0	17.0
Tradescantia sp.	6.7	10.5	3.0	—	20.2
T. paludosa	4.0	10.8	2.7	2.5	20.0
Allium cepa	10.0	7.0	3.0	5.0	25.0
Allium cepa	4.5	2.25	3.5	1.25	12.0
Pisum sativum	6–10	6.0	3.0	—	15–19
Vicia faba	12.0	6.0	8.0	4.0	28.0
Vicia faba	4.9	7.5	4.9	2.0	19.3
Vicia faba	4.0	9.0	3.5	1.9	18.0
Vicia faba	1.9	5.4	4.4	3.3	15.0

fact that the meristems studied are comprised of many cells that include "stem" cells for different tissues, the cell cycles of these different groups of cells varying widely (Barlow, 1971). Thus, the results presented for a population of meristematic cells must be a mean value for a number of sub-populations.

It is also clear that the way in which the experiment is performed will affect the results of such studies. Thus, Evans and Savage showed an exponential increase in the mitotic time with a decrease in temperature, a point also shown by the studies of Wimber (1966) in which the duration of the nuclear cycle of *Tradescantia paludosa* root meristems was evaluated at 13°, 21° and 30°C. The main differences observed were (a) the shortening of G_1 between 21° and 30°C; and (b) G_2 and S at 13°C were 3 and 2 times as long, respectively, as at 21°C.

Further temperature effects were shown by the cytochemical studies of La Cour *et al.* (1956) who found that lowering the temperature of the plant gave a decrease of 20% in the DNA content of nuclei from root tips of six different plant species. If the plants were grown at the low temperatures (0° to −6°C) for 3–5 d and then returned to 19°C for 2 d, the DNA content returned to normal. This was confirmed by the autoradiographic studies of Ashraful (1963). Alone, these data may seem inadequate to allow the development of the concept of low temperature causing a reduction of DNA levels, but if they are taken in conjunction with the data from studies on animal tissues (reviewed in Roels, 1967; Pelc, 1972), then it is clear that low temperature conditions can affect the amount of DNA in a nucleus.

The original work on the constancy of the amount of DNA per haploid set of chromosomes using Feulgen photometry (Swift, 1950) has been supported by many other workers. However, there is an increasing number of reports concerning changes in the amount of DNA per haploid set of chromosomes through the loss of DNA, as in the cold treatment of plants. In addition, there is evidence demonstrating the incorporation of [³H]thymidine into cells that are neither synthesizing DNA for cell replication nor for the formation of polyploid nuclei (Pelc and La Cour, 1959; Sampson and Davies, 1963; Hurst and Gahan, 1975; Gahan, 1976). The integration of these findings with those from studies on animal cells again illustrates an apparent metabolic activity of at least some of the DNA, and which cannot be easily explained in terms of DNA repair. Such changes have been readily detected cytochemically, but have been less obvious with a biochemical approach in which changes in some cells have been lost in the analysis of a mass of cells.

Cytochemical methods have also been applied to determine at which points on the chromosome and in which sequence new DNA is produced. More studies of this type have been made on animal than on plant cells, but the latter were used by Wimber (1961), for example, who found that generally, after administration of [³H]thymidine, the terminal portions of the chromosomes were found to contain duplication near the end of S, whilst the other parts of the chromosome had ceased to synthesize DNA. Using high resolution autoradiography, Bernier and Jensen (1966) found that there were three types of labelled nuclei, i.e. those with labelling in (a) both the dispersed and condensed chromatin; (b) only the dispersed chromatin; and (c) only the condensed chromatin. Further evidence concerning the ordering of the replication of DNA on chromosomes has come from the classic studies of Taylor (1957), which showed that on feeding roots of *Crepis capillaris* with [³H]thymidine, the first chromosomes to label were regularly labelled around the centromere (i.e. those labelled late in S), whereas those labelled shortly afterwards often showed a labelling gradient from the ends of the arms towards the centromeres, indicating that the centromeric region was the last to synthesize DNA. In contrast, studies on chromosomes from *Bellavalia* and *Vicia* indicated that replication does not necessarily start from one end of the chromosome, but that there are many potential starting points for synthesis, a concept that has been fully considered more recently (Lewin, 1974).

Cytochemical evidence has also been produced by Taylor (1963) that the DNA is replicated on plant chromosomes in a semi-conservative fashion. This was contested by a La Cour and Pelc (1958, 1959), who considered that whilst some autoradiographs were compatible with the data of Taylor, a number of labelling patterns of chromosomes appeared which did not fit the theory.

If cytochemistry has been instrumental in helping to establish the behaviour and synthesis times of chromosomal DNA, then it has been also of paramount importance in indicating the occurrence of non-nuclear DNA localization in plant cells. Initially, a biochemical assay in which DNA was found to be present in the cytoplasmic fraction of an homogenate was dismissed as a biochemical artefact. However, the early observations made with ultra-violet light absorption micros-copy by Chayen (1949) and Chayen and Norris (1953) indicated the presence of a

DNA-like component in the cytoplasm of cells from roots of *Vicia faba*. These findings were confirmed by Chayen and Denby (1960). Unfortunately, it was not possible to demonstrate these low concentrations of DNA by either the Feulgen reaction or the use of methyl green, and it was not until the method of preparing frozen sections of plant tissues was employed in conjunction with autoradiography that cytoplasmic DNA was demonstrable by another method. In the latter case DNA was demonstrated by its ability to incorporate [^{3}H]thymidine, its resistance fo extraction with weak acid or digestion by ribonuclease, and its sensitivity to deoxyribonuclease (Gahan and Silcox, 1961; Gahan *et al.*, 1962). There then followed a series of studies of a range of plant tissues in which it was demonstrated that the DNA was present in the mitochondria and plastids (e.g., Bell and Mühletehler, 1964; Stone and Miller, 1965; Sagan *et al.*, 1964; Kisley *et al.*, 1965; Bisulpatra and Bisulpatra, 1967).

Attempts to relate the S period for cytoplasmic DNA with that of the nuclear DNA have yielded somewhat variable results. Thus, in *Saccharomyces cerevisiae*, mitochondrial DNA appeared to be synthesized at all times in the cell cycle (Williamson and Moustacchi, 1971) whilst in *Physarum polycephalum*, it appeared that non-nuclear DNA was synthesized during the nuclear G_2 phase and represented about 5% of the total cell DNA. On the other hand, Bernie and Jensen (1966) found a synchronization of nuclear, proplastid and mitochondrial DNA synthesis. An extensive study of *Chlamydomonas reinhardtii* indicated that during the vegatative cycle, the chloroplast DNA is replicated in a semi-conservative fashion, but that the replication of the chromosomal DNA is independent and separable from that of the cytoplasmic DNA. It seems from these few examples that many more studies are needed of a broader range of species before any significant pattern of nuclear/cytoplasmic DNA replication can be obtained.

Cellular differentiation involves a series of changes in a cell that may be of a structural nature or merely of a physiological form. In both cases, there is a cessation of cell division, and the cell takes on a different and more permanent specialization. Thus, during differentiation, it is possible that there will be changes in the DNA that can be referred to standard parameters derived from the cell cycle studies. For example, polyploidy has been an observed feature of a number of differentiating cell types in higher plants. Using Feulgen photometry, Swift (1950), List (1963) and Lai and Srivastava (1976) demonstrated that most of the differentiated cells in the roots of *Zea mays* have 4–8 times the diploid amount of DNA, though xylem vessel elements may be as high as 32c. Similarly, Deeley *et al.* (1957) examined cells from squash preparations of micro-dissected tissues (meristem, cortex and stele) from specific root segments of *Vicia faba* using an improved method of Feulgen photometry. An increase in the DNA content of cortical cell nuclei was observed from 2c to 4c, 8c, and 16c, though this increase was not accompanied by mitosis. Confirmation of these data was achieved by McLeish and Sunderland (1961) on roots from *Vicia faba, Pisum sativum, Lupinus albus, Lactuca sativa, Tradescantia ohionensis, Scilla campanulata, Allium cepa, Lilium longiflorum, Zea mays* and *Secale cereale,* whereby the further back from the tip of the root were the cells, the higher was the DNA content.

The classic histochemical studies of Jensen (1958) on the DNA content of roots from *Vicia faba,* in which the DNA content of 200 μm segments of root were assayed biochemically, have revealed that there is an increase in the mean DNA content commencing some 800 μm behind the root apex and continuing to a distance of some 3 mm behind the tip. The increase represents a two- to fourfold increment in the DNA that appears to occur from 600 to 1100 μm behind the tip. A similar increase in the DNA content of nuclei from root tips of *Pisum sativum* has also been reported by Bucknall and Sutcliffe (1965) when assessed by determining the amount of fluorescence per nucleus after staining with acridine orange at pH 2.6 and controlling the reaction with deoxyribonuclease and ribonuclease digestion.

Since the amounts of DNA found in the nuclei of differentiated cells are normally multiples of the amount found in the diploid meristematic cells, and since polyploidy has been shown to occur in mature cells, the general concept is that the increase in DNA content of the nuclei of differentiating cells reflects an increase in the ploidy of the cells. However, autoradiographic studies (Pelc and La Cour, 1959) on roots of *Vicia faba* indicated that some caution is necessary in the interpretation of these results, since they found [³H]thymidine incorporation into the nuclei of cells which were at the 4c level and in which increments of DNA were not expected. They suggested that a metabolic exchange occurred, as a possible explanation of these results. This concept was later supported by the biochemical findings of Samson and Davies (1963) in which they demonstrated two DNA fractions, one of which was comparatively labile and had a rapid turnover of its thymidine content. More recently, these results have been interpreted as identifying DNA repair mechanisms, but the studies of Hurst *et al.* (1973) also revealed a turnover of the thymidine component of nuclear DNA in collenchyma cells from stems of *Lycopersicon esculentum,* and which could not be readily accounted for by DNA repair or synthesis for either cell division or a shift to higher ploidy (Fig. 9).

Studies on the cytoplasmic DNA in differentiating cells have also yielded interesting results. Thus, whilst cytoplasmic sites in root meristematic cells and stem cambial cells readily incorporate [³H]thymidine, there is a rapid decrease in the facility to incorporate by similar sites in cells of differentiating and differentiated cells, being almost nil in cells such as collenchyma and very low in cortical parenchymal cells of *Vicia faba, Allium cepa, Zea mays,* and *Lycopersicon esculentum.* A similar loss of ability to be labeled also occurs in ageing meristem cell populations of *Zea mays* (Gahan and Hurst, 1976).

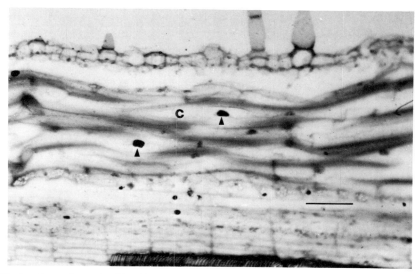

FIG. 9. Autoradiograph of longitudinal section of stem from *Lycopersicon esculentum* fixed in acetic acid–ethanol (1 : 3) after feeding for 24 h with [³H]thymidine. Arrows indicate heavily labelled nuclei in collenchyma (c) Scale, 0.1 mm.

B. Ribosenucleic Acid

Confirmation of the early observations that RNA was present in the nucleoli, interphase nucleus and cytoplasm has been obtained through the application of a range of cytochemical methods, including the use of pyronin (with methyl green) to indicate sites of RNA (Brachet, 1940a,b, 1941), acridine orange (reviewed in Kasten, 1967) and azure B bromide (Flax and Hines, 1952). Autoradiography has also made its contribution to the study of RNA both with respect to its localization in the cell (Woods and Taylor, 1959; Woodward *et al.,* 1961; La Cour, 1963) and to its metabolic involvement.

It is abundantly clear from numerous biochemical and cytochemical studies that RNA is synthesized in the nucleus of eukaryotic cells. However, the analysis of the processes involved have been complicated by the fact that at least four forms of RNA can be distinguished, i.e. (a) messenger RNA; (b) transfer RNA; (c) hn-RNA; and (d) ribosomal RNA. Thus, cytochemical studies of RNA metabolism have been somewhat complex to analyse. In the early investigations concerning the sites of synthesis of RNA, the classic study of Goldstein and Plaut (1955) on *Amoeba* were paralleled by the elegant experiments of Zalokar (1959) on *Neurospora crassa*. This experiment depended upon centrifugation of the hyphae of *Neurospora crassa* to cause the hyphal contents to become stratified.

[³H]Uridine was fed to the intact mycelium for various lengths of time during the active growth phase, centrifuged and then fixed. The hyphae were extracted with 5% tricholoracetic acid to remove unincorporated label and were then washed prior to the preparation of autoradiographs. After feeding for 1 min with [³H]uridine, only the nuclear region showed labelling. When the feeding time was lengthened, the labelling appeared progressively in the mitochondrial band and in the ergastoplasm.

If the hyphae were fed for 1 min with [³H]uridine followed by unlabelled uridine for 1 h, then the labelling was heavy over the ergastoplasm and light over the nuclei and mitochondrial band. Labelling of the ergastoplasm increased with increasing "chase" times, and there was a corresponding decrease in the nuclear label. The labelled material was confirmed to be RNA since it was resistant to extraction with cold 5% trichloroacetic acid, and was lost on digestion with ribonuclease.

A similar type of experiment was performed by Woods (1962) on *Vicia faba* in which [³H]cytidine was used as the labelled precursor since it was found to be more readily incorporated into RNA than was uridine. Autoradiographic studies revealed that on continuous feeding, there was an initial incorporation into the nucleoli and chromosomes with a steady state of labelling being reached in 14 min for chromatin and 90 min for nucleoli. The cytoplasm did not appear to become labeled until 90 min, after which time the concentration of label rose continuously until the end of the experiment after feeding for 8 h. In a second series of experiments, the roots were fed for the period of time required to label the nucleoli but not the cytoplasm, after which the plants were transferred to an unlabelled solution. The nucleolar labelling was found to decrease and the cytoplasmic labelling increased. From these types of experiments, it was shown that very little RNA synthesis occurred in the cytoplasm, and there was an indication that it was more likely to be synthesized in the nucleoli and passed to the cytoplasm.

One of the problems concerning the study of RNA during the cell cycle relates to the behaviour of the nucleolus that "disappears" at the end of the prophase and is "reformed" at telophase. A number of investigators have attempted to determine the fate of the nucleolar material at the time during mitosis. Thus Kaufman *et al.* (1948) found that chromosomes of *Allium cepa* acquired an RNA-like material at prophase in that it stained as RNA and was lost after treatment with ribonuclease. This RNA was lost from the chromosomes at telophase, and so it was inferred that there was a relationship between the chromosomal material and the nucleolus. Similar studies and results came from Jacobson and Webb (1952) with animal cells in culture. An RNA–protein material was present in the nucleoli during interphase, but from the end of prophase when the nucleoli are lost, an RNA–protein appeared on the chromosomes, remaining there until anaphase when it appeared to be shed from the chromosomes and into the area between the two groups of chromosomes.

These cytochemical observations link with the electron microscope studies of Lafontaine (1958) who identified the "pre-nucleolar" substance in root tips of *V. faba* and *A. cepa* as small dense bodies containing a class of particles 14 nm in diameter, and which are characteristically nucleolar.

In contrast, Belyaeva and Volkova (1964) found that in root tips of *V. faba*, *A. cepa* and *Pisum sativum,* an RNA–protein appeared on the surface of the chromosomes in early telophase. During mid- and late telophase the material condensed in the region of the nucleolar organizer to form the nucleolus. The RNA–protein first appeared on the chromosomes at the commencement of despiralization, and if anaphase chromosomes were induced to despiralize by treatment with cobalt, then the pro-nucleolar material was found on the chromosomes at anaphase.

A carefully controlled autoradiographic study by La Cour (1963) indicated that RNA passed from the nucleoli from root tips of *V. faba* and *Trillium cernum* to the chromosomes in mitosis, and that this material appeared on the chromosomes in the vicinity of the nucleolar organizer. It was suggested that the metaphase chromosomes were possibly the carriers of the dispersed nucleolar material from prophase to telophase.

Very few studies are available that attempt to relate RNA synthesis to the DNA cycle in the cell. Van't Hof (1963) assessed the rate of incorporation of [^{3}H]cytidine into RNA of primary roots of *P. sativum*. After pulsing for 30 min with the labelled precursor, the plants were transferred to a non-radioactive solution and the roots sampled at intervals for 12 h. This was run in parallel to experiments on the incorporation of [^{3}H]thymidine into DNA. Whilst there was a clear-cut S period of 4.5 h, a G_1 of 2.5 h, a G_2 of 2.5 h and a calculated M of 2.5 h, there was no such pattern for RNA, which appeared to be synthesized throughout the cycle except during metaphase and anaphase. This was apparently related in some way to the period of time in which dissolution of the nucleolus occured and implicated the nucleolus in the synthesis of RNA. The incorporation of the labelled precursor into highly polymerized RNA was not immediate but took a little more than 3 h. After this period of time the situation remained stable, indicating either a stable situation or a steady state with respect to the transfer and turnover of labelled RNA.

Although most studies have been involved with the establishment of the relationship between chromosomal, nuclear and nucleolar RNA, some attempts have been made to ascertain the behaviour of both mitochondrial and chloroplast RNA, for example, studies of the rates of incorporation of [^{3}H]uridine into the RNA of mitochondria and chloroplasts as opposed to the RNA of the rest of the cytoplasm in *Ochromonas danica*. High resolution autoradiography showed that there was no lag in the incorporation of the precursor into mitochondrial or chloroplast RNA with feeding times of 0.5 or 2 h, but that a distinct lag occurred in the labelling of other cytoplasmic RNA, allowing the interpretation that most, if not all, of the chloroplast and mitochondrial RNAs were synthesized *in situ.*

The apparent discrepancy between the results of the early workers and those obtained more recently are in part due to the improved cytochemical methods now available, and the increased specific activity of the labelled precursors. The development of high resolution autoradiography, has increased the ability to detect small amounts of a compound.

Histochemical studies on RNA in differentiating plant tissues are not very common. Jensen (1956a) found that in root sections of *V. faba,* in the region of the quiescent centre, there was a minimal amount of RNA per cell that was slightly higher in cells of the root cap. Two millimeters from the tip of the root there was a threefold increase, though in a later study (1958) there appeared to be a fivefold increase. Similar results were obtained by Heyes and Brown (1956) in which a threefold increase in RNA per cell was noted for roots of *P. sativum* between 1 and 9 mm from the tip.

At the cytochemical level, Bucknall and Sutcliffe (1965) endeavoured to ascertain the changes in nuclear RNA content of the cortex, outer and inner stele, meristem and root cap by means of microfluorimetry after staining with acridine orange. Studies on the cortex showed an increase in RNA of 3.7 times between 0.8 and 2.5 mm. There was a rise of 2.4 times at 4 mm recorded for the outer stele, and for the inner stele a rapid fourfold increase between 0.5 and 3.2 mm from the tip, and with a fivefold increase in the root cap. Thus, in general, the micro-fluorimetric results are compatible with the biochemical data and further indicate that the increases are closely related to cell size, though in the outer stele, the increase was due partly to a rise in the content of cytoplasmic RNA.

Studies on the RNA content of shoot apices were initiated by Lance (1957) using a fully controlled methyl green–pyronin reaction. These early studies on shoot apices of *Chrysanthemum segetum* showed that certain groups of cells had low RNA contents as indicated by pyroninophilia, e.g. the axial zone of the apex, whilst others had high RNA content, e.g. cells of the initium and leaf buttress regions. Similar zonation of high and low RNA contents per cell has been reported for many angiosperms and gymnosperms (reviewed in Nougarède, 1967). Studies of RNA have been extended through the application of auto-radiography. Thus, for example, during the transformation from a vegetative to a flowering apex, there is an active incorporation of labelled precursors into RNA in cells on the flanks of the meristems in *Lolium temulentum.* These are the regions that will give rise to the spikelets, and the change occurs 1 d after the trigger to flower has been applied, a time interval that is calculated to allow the stimulus to arrive at the apex (Knox and Evans, 1968).

II. CYTOCHEMICAL INVESTIGATION OF THE NUCLEIC ACIDS

The biochemical determination of nucleic acid depends upon an assay of one or more of its pentose sugar, phosphate, purine or pyrimidine components (Dische, 1955; Jensen, 1956a; Kupilagi *et al.,* 1961; Markham, 1955; Ogur and Rosen, 1950). Similarly in histochemistry, the identification of RNA and DNA depends upon the presence of phosphate groups (methyl green–pyronin reaction, acridine orange, autoradiography), nitrogen bases (ultra-violet light absorption microscopy, autoradiography) and pentose molecules (Feulgen reaction). In no case is there a totally specific reaction for DNA or RNA, and in all cases the reactions must be accompanied by a series of control reactions as will be detailed below.

A. Physical Methods

A general indication of the presence of RNA and DNA can be obtained by means of ultra-violet light absorption microscopy, such absorption being dependent upon the double bonds present in purines and pyrimidines. Although nucleic acids have an absorption peak in the region of 260 nm, many other compounds have overlapping spectra. Consequently, absorption at this wavelength indicates the total nucleic acid together with any interfering substances that may be present. This may be corrected by remeasuring after the removal of DNA or RNA, or both, through digestion with ribonuclease or deoxyribonuclease, or by extraction with hydrochloric acid. A second method of detecting the presence of purines or pyrimidines is by autoradiography of material from organisms fed with [14]C- or ^{3}H-labelled nucleosides or nucleotides. Since DNA usually contains thymine and not uracil, and the converse for RNA, it is possible to distinguish between the locations of DNA and RNA by means of feeding ^{3}H]thymidine or ^{3}H]uracil, respectively. Such studies must be carefully controlled, for the addition of a methyl group to uracil will convert it to thymine, and so whilst the organism may have been fed with ^{3}H]uridine, conversion to ^{3}H]thymidine could occur, resulting in the labelling of DNA. Similarly, it is possible for thymidine to be demethylated and become incorporated into RNA, although a specific precursor of DNA (Reichard and Estborn, 1951) has been given to the organism. Erroneous autoradiographs may be minimized by the use of thymidine labelled in the methyl position only, when demethylation will result in the loss of label from the uridine so formed. Thus incorporation into RNA will not result in labelling, unless breakdown of the thymidine has occurred through prolonged storage when both RNA and protein may label (Maurer, 1981).

B. Phosphate Groups

The presence of phosphate groups in the nucleic acids endows the molecules with the ability to bind basic dyes at an acid pH, and hence allows their localization with either methyl green–pyronin or acridine orange. When reacted under specific conditions, DNA is coloured green and RNA pink by the methyl green and pyronin, respectively. Kurnick (1955) suggested that only highly polymerized DNA reacted strongly with the methyl green, the degree of staining being proportional to the degree of polymerization of the DNA. The actual binding of the dye appears to be due to the similarity of spacing of the phosphate groups of the DNA and the cationic groups of the methyl green, but which are differently spaced on the pyronin molecule and available to bind to RNA. However, there is no clear-cut explanation, and Scott (1967) found that polynucleotides bound methyl green and pyronin more strongly than would be indicated by an electrostatic bonding. Furthermore, pyronin was shown to react best with nucleic acid molecules in which purines and pyrimidines were freely accessible as in single-stranded molecules, e.g. RNA and DNA. In contrast, methyl green was shown to favour the intact double helix of DNA. Similarly with the binding of

$$(CH_3)_3 \overset{+}{N} - \bigcirc - C \underset{=\overset{+}{N}(CH_3)_2 (Cl^-)}{\overset{-N(CH_3)_2}{<}}$$

Methyl green

$$(CH_3)_2 N \diagdown \underset{\underset{H}{C}}{\bigcirc O \bigcirc} \diagup \overset{+}{N}(CH_3)_2 (Cl^-)$$

Pyronin Y

acridines, there would seem to be a relationship between the acridine dye and the phosphate groups of the DNA. When examined by fluorescence microscopy (Chapter 9), DNA fluoresces green-yellow and RNA fluoresces red on reacting with acridinge orange. The mechanism of acridine orange staining is well discussed by Pearse (1972) and would seem to depend upon whether the dye is in the orthochromatic (monomeric) form which fluoresces green, or the metachromatic (dimer) form when it will fluoresce red. Thus, when binding to the double-stranded helix of DNA, the dimethylamino groups of the dye molecule are in contact with the phosphate groups, and the acridine ring is in contact with the purine and pyrimidine rings of the upper and lower bases of a pair, resulting in a stable complex (Rigler, 1966). As a result of this form of binding, dye molecules will be sufficiently spaced that they remain as monomers (i.e. no dye interaction can occur) and will fluoresce green. In contrast, if acridine orange binds to a single-stranded random coil, it can bind to almost every nucleotide unit via the phosphate group. The mobility of the random coil allows the dye molecules to approach sufficiently closely to each other so that dye–dye interaction can occur leading to polymer formation and hence the red fluorescence, as in the case of RNA. This interpretation was further confirmed when it was shown that heat denaturation of the rigid double helix of DNA resulted in a random coil configuration that permitted the dye molecules to interact and so lead to red fluorescence on staining with acridine orange.

Acridine orange

   Autoradiographic analysis of sections and cells from organisms fed with $^{32}PO_4$ will also assist in the localization of nucleic acids into which the $^{32}PO_4$ is incorporated, although care is needed to distinguish between the labelling of nucleic acids and other phosphorus-containing compounds such as lipids by control autoradiographs from which RNA and DNA have been removed by enzyme digestion.

C. Feulgen Reaction

One of the most frequently used methods for DNA is that of Feulgen and Rossenbeck (1924). The tissue is treated by hydrolysis in HCl in order to split the purine–deoxyribose linkages. The aldehyde groups so formed react with Schiff's reagent (decolourized para-rosanilin) to yield a deep magenta colour at the sites of DNA. Later studies by Scott and Harbinson (1971) have indicated that the amount of colour produced on reacting Schiff reagent with simple mono-aldehydes is proportional to the square of the aldehyde concentration. This implies that a pair of aldehydes must combine with each molecule of Schiff reagent. When the reagent was reacted with polyaldehydes, the colour developed was linearly proportional to the polyaldehyde concentration, as would be expected since both aldehyde groups are present on the same molecule. However, reaction of simple dialdehydes such as glutaraldehyde gave the same response as the monaldehydes presumably because the aldehyde groups were not correctly spaced on each molecule so as to behave like the polyaldehydes.

   It has been concluded that the stoichiometry of Schiff's reagent in solution depends upon the distance separating the aldehyde groups and, further, that the

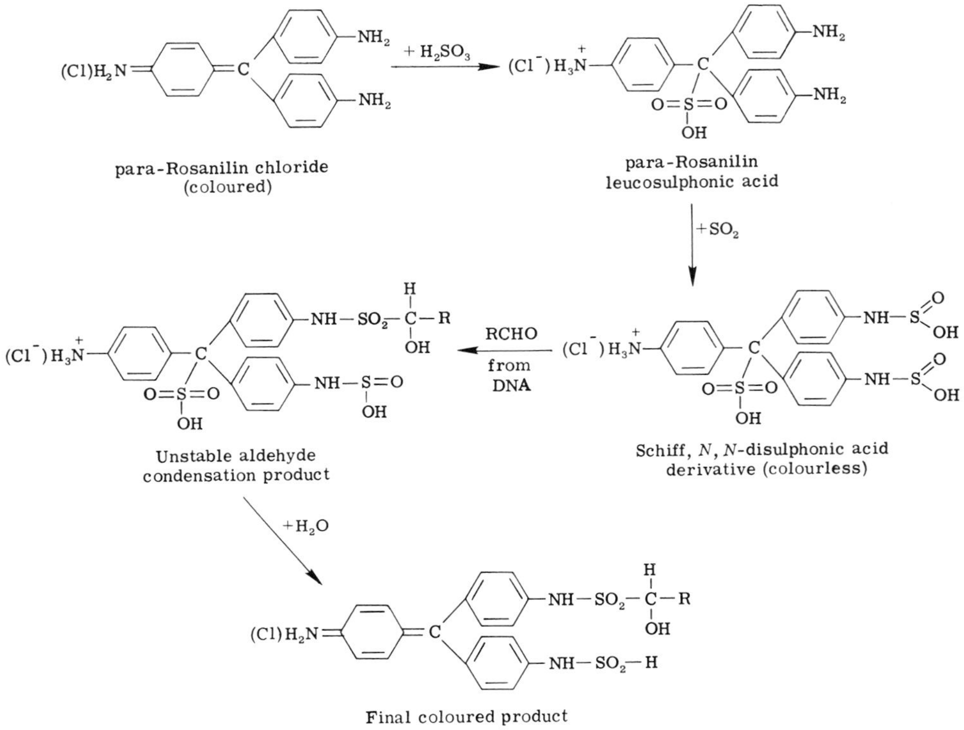

para-Rosanilin chloride
(coloured)

$+ H_2SO_3$

para-Rosanilin
leucosulphonic acid

$+ SO_2$

Unstable aldehyde
condensation product

RCHO
from
DNA

Schiff, N,N-disulphonic acid
derivative (colourless)

$+ H_2O$

Final coloured product

reaction is identifying pairs of suitably spaced aldehyde groups on the same or adjacent molecules.

Recent developments in analytical cytology, especially in relation to clinical studies, have led to the increased use of fluorescence reactions. As will be discussed in Chapter 9, this has important implications for quantification and for the possibility of measuring simultaneously more than one reaction upon the same cell.

para-Rosaniline, the basic ingredient of Schiff's reagent, is not itself fluorescent at any pH from 1 to 7, but after performing the Feulgen test for DNA or linking Schiff's reagent to aldehyde groups in the presence of SO_2, the bound para-rosaniline is fluorescent, emitting a red light when excited with green light (Böhm and Sprenger, 1968). Thus, the Feulgen reaction itself may be used for fluorescence studies. However, the method has been extended to include the use of a variety of fluorescent dyes, a great many of which were screened by Ornstein et al. (1957) and by Kasten (1958, 1959). The more suitable dyes included acriflavine, proflavine, cresyl violet, bis(aminophenyl)oxidiazole (BAO) and Hoechst 33258. Acriflavine–Schiff was recommended for both DNA and periodic acid–reducing solution–Schiff (PARS) reactions (Ornstein *et al.*, 1957) and for DNA (Culling and Vasser, 1961). More recently, cresyl violet and Hoechst 33258 have shown useful qualities when used as nucleic acid cytochemical reagents in quantitative studies including the stability of the fluorescence (Fukuda *et al.*, 1979).

For DNA studies, the material is hydrolysed as for the Feulgen reaction and then stained with the fluorochrome instead of Schiff's reagent. Acriflavine and proflavine have been used at concentrations of $4 \times 10^{-4} M$ in a solution of $2.2 \times 10^{-2} M$ $K_2S_2O_5$ in 0.05 N HCl. The presence of SO_2 is necessary for the success of most of the reactions that seem to involve it in the dye-binding process (Stoward, 1967), though it does not seem important in the case of acriflavine (Gill and Jotz, 1974).

Ethidium bromide has also been employed as a DNA fluorochrome and would appear to act by intercalating into the DNA molecule. It may be excited with blue and green light when it fluoresces red (Le Pecq, 1973). For further reading the following reviews are suggested: Kasten (1959, 1961), Stoward (1967) and Prenna (1969).

As with the preceding methods, the Feulgen test must be strictly controlled since any free aldehydes in the tissue will react with the Schiff reagent and yield a positive colour. Interference with the reaction can occur through the presence of tannins (Ishida, 1961; Milovidov, 1949) and some proteins (Ishida, 1961). Lignin will also give a false-positive reaction (Jensen, 1962). Thus, in addition to controlling the reaction by the extraction of DNA from the sections, it is also important to control the hydrolysis by comparing with sections that have been hydrolysed at room temperature in 1 N HCl. The Feulgen reaction has the advantage of being specific under controlled conditions, and, moreover, the colour produced is directly proportional to the amount of DNA present that is thus measurable with the integrating microdensitometer. Whilst initially the hydrolysis was performed in 1 N HCl at 60°C, for quantitative studies, hydrolysis is performed in 5 N HCl at 20°C for longer periods of time. This results in a broader period of maximum hydrolysis and reduces the loss of DNA through overhydrolysis.

D. Tissue Preparation

Most studies on nucleic acids have been performed on tissues chemically fixed and embedded in wax. Frozen-dried and frozen-substituted tissues have been used as well as frozen sections and razor sections of plant tissues. The accuracy of the localization of the nucleic acids is dependent upon the accuracy of preservation of the cytological detail. One important effect that has been observed on the Feulgen reaction is that the length of hydrolysis required to yield a maximal colour depends upon the fixative employed (Appendix 3, p. 198).

E. Problems in Demonstrating Nucleic Acids

Recent studies have indicated that not all DNA sites can be demonstrated color-imetrically. Some algae such as *Oscillatoria* and *Spirogyra,* some ferns such as *Pteridium aquilinum,* and some bryophytes such as *Marchantia polymorpha* and *Mnium hornum* show very weak or no nuclear reaction with the Feulgen test. Nuclei from cotyledons of a number of species of higher plants will not react completely and consistently by the Feulgen reaction for DNA. Such nuclei will not react completely with other tests for DNA (D. G. Smith, personal communication). This may be due to the small amount of DNA present in the nuclei (Hillary, 1939; Bell, 1963), to the susceptibility of the DNA to extraction during the acid hydrolysis (Ishida, 1961; Gahan, unpublished), to the chromatin being too compacted to permit either complete hydrolysis, or to the molecules of Schiff's reagent orienting themselves so as to bind to available aldehyde groups (Duijndam and Van Duijn, 1975a,b). Further difficulties have been encountered with the use of conventional tissue preparation techniques and conventional colorimetric cytochemical tests for the demonstration of cytoplasmic DNA in somatic cells (Gahan and Chayen, 1965). Cytoplasmic DNA appears to be present in smaller concentrations than nuclear DNA and also to be more labile than the latter (Chayen, 1959; Gahan *et al.,* 1962; Suyama and Bonner, 1965), so that this DNA can be readily lost from the cytoplasm when tissues are subjected to routine preparative procedures. Less drastic methods such as the use of pectinase squash preparations (Chayen and Denby, 1960) or frozen sections (Gahan *et al.,* 1962) seem useful alternatives. The most sensitive methods of demonstrating the small concentrations of nucleic acid appear to be either ultra-violet absorption microscopy (Chayen and Denby, 1960; Bell, 1963) or autoradiography (Gahan *et al.,* 1962).

F. Metachromasia

Although not a specific method for nucleic acids, it is perhaps pertinent to comment on metachromasia in view of its possible aid to the identification of the components reacting with the methyl green–pyronin method in the absence of nucleic acids (Chapter 1). When a dye reacts with a tissue element to produce a colour that is similar to that of the dye, it is known as an orthochromatic stain. If, however, on staining with an acidic or basic dye, the wavelength of the transmitted light is shifted away from that of the dye, often towards the red end of the spectrum, this is known as metachromasia. It probably signifies the presence of free electron-negative surface charges of a certain minimum density (Sylvén, 1954; Michaelis, 1950; Walton and Ricketts, 1954). In the case of toluidine blue, binding to the acidic groups of a molecule results in the shift of the transmission spectrum peak from blue to red. Thus, metachromasia will result in the demonstration of sulphated polysaccharides and polyphosphates. Examples of metachromasia can be seen with the ''volutin'' granules from yeast and polyphosphate in *Aspergillus niger* and cell walls of red algae.

4. Group II: Structural Proteins

I. Introduction

There have been few cytochemical studies of cellular structural proteins due in part to the fact that interest has shifted in recent years to enzyme proteins (Chapter 5). Nevertheless, cytochemical considerations of structural proteins were of importance during the period when the DNA–gene equation was being enunciated. Thus, whilst biochemical studies had shown a close relationship between DNA and histone in nucleoprotein, it was by means of quantitative cytochemical studies that histone, as well as DNA, was found to be constant in amount per haploid set of chromosomes. This was observed in 1953 by Alfert and Geschwind who firstly demonstrated the specificity for basic proteins by the fast green reaction, and then used this method to quantify the amount present. They were further able to show that histone was being replicated at the same time as was DNA (i.e. during the S period) through the doubling of the amount of histone in the interphase nuclei (Alfert, 1954; Block and Goodman, 1955).

Biochemical examination of nucleohistones showed that (a) the amino acid, arginine, is present in large amounts (Serra, 1946); (b) in many different species with different DNA contents, the ratio of DNA phosphorus to arginine remains constant (Vendreley and Vendreley, 1953; Vendreley et al., 1956); and (c) arginine is apparently associated with the acidic groups of the DNA (Wilkins, 1956). The development of the Sakaguchi reaction for quantitative cytochemical estimations of arginine (McLeish et al., 1957; McLeish and Sherratt, 1958) enabled McLeish (1959) to make a comparative study of the amount of DNA and arginine present in plant nuclei from roots of *Scilla campanulata;* diploid, triploid and tetraploid plants of *Ranunculus ficaria;* and diploid and tetraploid plants of *Tradescantia ohioensis* from which anthers were also obtained. He also studied the arginine and DNA contents of the same nuclei from roots of *Vicia faba, Allium cepa* and *Scilla campanulata* by making measurements of the stain from the Feulgen reaction for DNA on nuclei that were then decolorized by treatment in 5% trichlorocetic acid at 90°C for 30–40 s followed by reaction for arginine with the Sakaguchi test. It was found that in *R. ficaria* and *T. ohioensis* DNA and arginine values gave ratios that agreed closely with the number of chromatids known to be present, and suggested that the nuclear arginine content was not only relatively constant but paralleled that of DNA. The amount of nuclear arginine was found to double during interphase as happened with the DNA, and it was shown that this synthesis, if not simultaneous with that of DNA, occurred at least in the same relatively short period, thus confirming the earlier reports by Alfert (1954).

Later observations in which the general nuclear protein content has been examined quantitatively, employing the dinitrofluorobenzene reaction (Mitchell, 1967), were similar to those of McLeish. An analysis of the whole cells rather than just the nuclei of cultured callus cells from Jerusalem artichoke (Mitchell, 1968) indicated that the dividing cells of the cultures had an S period of 14 h for DNA synthesis and that there is a rapid increase in the mean protein content per cell shortly after the beginning of S, with a subsequent falling off in the rate of accumulation, and a final active accumulation near the end of S. On completion of S, it was shown that there had been an approximate doubling of the protein content of the cells, this value being equivalent to the mean protein content of the cells actually undergoing mitosis.

There have been few autoradiographic studies of protein synthesis during the cell cycle in plants due probably to the difficulty in interpreting the results. Thus, even if the incorporation of the labelled precursor can be taken to be a measure of synthesis of the protein when controlled by suitable inhibitor studies, lack of labelling may not mean lack of synthesis, but merely that owing to differences in pool sizes, there has not been an adequate incorporation of the labelled precursor. Nevertheless, such studies were made by De (1961) who followed the incorporation of [^{3}H]amino acids simultaneously with that of [^{3}H]thymidine into the root tips of *A. cepa*. Autoradiographs were made from sections of frozen-substituted material and sections from which the nucleic acids had been removed for the evaluation of total protein labelling only. This total protein was further characterized into histone and non-histone proteins by extraction of the sections with 0.01 N HCl at 25°C after removal of the nucleic acids, when the histone fraction was removed. The results indicated that the DNA and histone were synthesized concurrently during interphase, in agreement with the results obtained by earlier colorimetric methods. Histones were also found to accumulate in the nucleolus during this period. If the onion roots were exposed to [^{3}H]amino acids for 1 h prior to transfer to a non-radioactive medium, both labelled histone and non-histone proteins were lost from the nucleoli. These losses were paralleled by an increased labelling of the chromatin–histone and of both chromatin and cytoplasmic non-histone proteins.

Confirmation by autoradiography of the synthesis of proteins in nucleoli of plant cells came from the work of e.g., Woodward *et al.,* (1961). A number of distinct regions in the nucleolus have been described due to their staining properties and ultra-structural characteristics (Lafontaine and Chouinard, 1963), i.e. (a) fibrillar regions; (b) granular regions; (c) lacunar regions; and (d) vacuolar regions that are not always present. Chouinard and Leblond (1967) attempted to determine which of these regions were involved with protein synthesis by means of high resolution autoradiography of the incorporation of [³H]arginine into nucleoli of root meristem cells of *A. cepa*. After feeding the roots for 5 min with [³H]arginine, the fibrillar and granular regions of the nucleoli of interphase cells were well labelled. Occasional silver grains were associated with the lacunar regions, but never with the vacuolar regions. A feeding period of 5 min followed by a chase period of 15 min did not change this pattern of labelling, and it was concluded that the three labelled regions were all sites of protein synthesis.

Studies during differentiation initially concerned the biochemical analysis of segments of root apices, the gross measurement being expressed either as protein per 100 μm from the root apex or as a mean amount per cell per segment at specific distances from the root apex of *A. cepa, V. faba, P. sativum* and *Z. mays* (Brown and Broadbent, 1950; Erickson and Goddard, 1951; Robinson and Brown, 1952; Jensen, 1955a, 1957, 1958; Heyes and Brown, 1956). In general the results all pointed to a low protein content in cells of the meristem of the root, the protein content increasing with distance, i.e. with age or with differentiation, from the tip, to reach a constant value. This varied from twofold in *Z. mays* and *A. cepa* to threefold or elevenfold in *P. sativum*. These increases in protein per unit volume or per unit surface area of the cell are falsely high since the increase in cell volumes were very much greater than the increase in protein so yielding an actual decrease in protein content per cell with differentiation (Clowes, 1961).

The rate of protein synthesis as measured by the rate of incorporation of labelled amino acids increases with differentiation. An autoradiographic study of this problem allowed the analysis to be made at cellular level. Clowes (1958) found that the incorporation of radioactive leucine into the roots of *Z. mays*, on a per cell basis, was low for meristematic cells, rising as cells differentiated on either side of the meristem. The most conspicuous rise was in the central stele, but a lower rate was found in cells of the quiescent centre as compared to cells of the adjacent meristem. If the information was presented on a unit volume basis, then the meristem cells, especially those bordering onto the quiescent centre, had the highest rate of incorporation. As the meristematic activity ceased, the rate of incorporation fell, rising slightly again on both the proximal and distal sides of the quiescent centre. The rate of incorporation in the quiescent centre, on a unit volume basis, was found to be intermediate between the meristematic cells and the differentiating cells (with the lowest rate). Similar results were obtained by Jensen (1957) with respect to the incorporation of phenylalanine into roots of *A. cepa*. However, since there is no information as to pool sizes in the cells under investigation, it is not clear if the labelling data reported represent a true picture of events.

If we accept these data for the present, the rate of incorporation of amino acids appears to be very much higher than the increase in total protein per cell. Thus, in Z. *mays* the rate of incorporation of leucine per cell is 15 times higher in the epidermis, 25 times higher in the inner cortex and 50 times higher in the central stele at 3 mm from the tip of the meristem (Clowes, 1961), implying a higher turnover of protein in these regions.

II. CYTOCHEMICAL INVESTIGATION OF STRUCTURAL PROTEIN

A. Chemical Interaction

Protein can be demonstrated generally by staining at a controlled pH, which is important because the reaction will depend upon the isoelectric point of the protein. Due to the presence of free (basic) amino and (acid) carboxyl groups, proteins in solution appear as amphoteric electrolytes. The basis of the method for the detection of the protein is that the dyes used will dissociate in solution to form negatively or positively charged ions depending on whether they are acid or basic dyes, respectively. Below the isoelectric point of a protein, acid dyes will combine with positively charged proteins, but above the isoelectric point basic dyes will combine with negatively charged proteins. Hence a tissue component will be stained by a basic dye with the pH above its isoelectric point, and by an acidic dye with the pH below this point. From the literature reviewed by Pearse (1968), it does not seem possible to determine the true isoelectric points since the staining intensity of a protein in a buffered dye solution has been shown to be dependent upon the interaction of the dye–protein, dye–buffer and buffer–protein systems. As the types of dye or buffer, or concentrations of dye or buffer are varied, so too is the isoelectric point (Levine, 1940). Many difficulties were overcome by using dilute ($2 \times 10^{-3}\,M$) dye solutions in dilute ($10^{-1}\,M$) buffers and by staining until an equilibrium was reached (24 h).

The results of the above method, and indeed of all staining methods for proteins, will be affected by the tissue preparation procedure employed. Fixatives will alter the types and number of available reactive groups in protein molecules to varying degrees, and so razor-cut or frozen sections should be used. However, the possibility of the loss of material from unfixed sections must be considered when interpreting results. In general, it is of interest to apply a number of tissue preparation procedures and to compare the results after assessment of the limitations of the individual methods used.

Proteins can be further characterized by simple solubility tests that must be performed on razor-cut or frozen sections since the use of fixatives alters the solubility of the proteins. This will allow the characterization of albumins, globulins and histones. Solvents employed include water, 1 N sodium chloride, half and fully saturated ammonium sulphate solutions, and various buffers.

Whilst this approach has been used effectively in animal studies (Gersh, 1949) it seems to have been little used in plant studies (De, 1961).

Another method employs 2,4-dinitrofluorobenzene (DNFB), which reacts with the α-amino groups of the N-terminal amino acid, although it can also interact with the ε-amino group of lysine side chains, phenolic hydroxide group of tyrosine residues, the sulphydryl group of cysteine and the imidazole ring of histidine (Sanger, 1945). The resultant product is either yellow or colourless, and therefore is of little value microscopically.

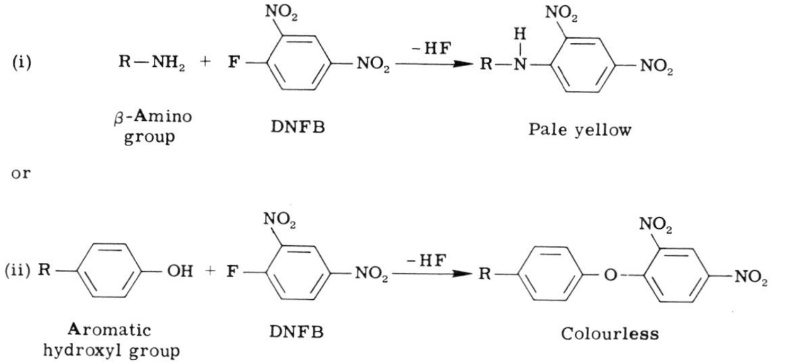

(i)   R—NH₂ + F—[NO₂ ring]—NO₂ —HF→ R—N(H)—[NO₂ ring]—NO₂

β-Amino group   DNFB   Pale yellow

or

(ii) R—[ring]—OH + F—[NO₂ ring]—NO₂ —HF→ R—[ring]—O—[NO₂ ring]—NO₂

Aromatic hydroxyl group   DNFB   Colourless

However, readily observable colour may be achieved by reducing the nitro groups in the DNFB to amino groups, which are diazotized and linked to H or K acid to yield a reddish colour. Although devised for studies on animal tissues by

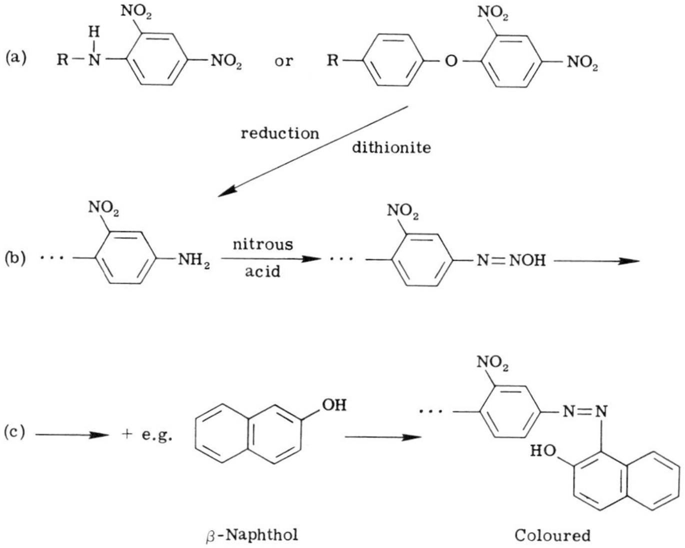

(a)   R—N(H)—[NO₂ ring]—NO₂   or   R—[ring]—O—[NO₂ ring]—NO₂

reduction / dithionite

(b) ⋯—[NO₂ ring]—NH₂   nitrous acid→   ⋯—[NO₂ ring]—N=NOH →

(c) → + e.g. [β-Naphthol with OH]   →   ⋯—[NO₂ ring]—N=N—[naphthol HO]

β-Naphthol   Coloured

Danielli (1953), the method has been applied successfully to plant tissues by Surrey (1957, 1958), Maddy (1961a,b), and in the author's laboratory. The method may be used specifically for the identification of the individual reactive groups by the use of careful blocking procedures as outlined by Danielli (1953).

Similarly, a general protein reaction may be achieved by treating tissues with tetra-azotized o-dianisidine, which reacts with histidine, tryptophan and phenols to yield a red product on the linked tetra-azotized o-dianisidine with H or K acid.

Coloured product

More recently Coomassie brilliant blue 250 has been proposed as a reliable quantitative stain for total protein in plant cells based on the fact that it yields a stoichiometric reaction with all proteins examined by acrilamide gel electrophoresis. Studies on gel model systems and anthers from *Lilium* sp. showed the reaction to work well (Cawood *et al.*, 1978) and to be lost from material that had been treated with protease.

Histones have a high content of basic amino acids and have iso-electric points that are more acid than other proteins. Generally, when a tissue is at pH 8.0 most proteins are near to, or above their isoelectric points except the histones, which will be below their isoelectric point. Alfert and Geschwind (1953) produced a method in which fast green FCF was applied at pH 8.0 when, in the absence of nucleic acids, only histones will possess groups capable of binding the dye. This method was shown to be specific for basic proteins, and the colour developed was directly proportional to the amount of histone and could be assessed spectrophotometrically.

Alternative reactions involve the identification of individual amino acids. Perhaps the oldest of these is the Millon reaction (1849), which depends upon the complex between tyrosine and tryptophan, mercury and nitrate. Most phenolic compounds will react if they are not doubly substituted in the ortho and meta positions. The phenol appears to form first an unstable complex with the mercury, which is then made relatively stable by the addition of nitrite. Rasch and Swift (1960) in a careful study found that the Millon reaction may be applied as a quantitive method in the study of nucleo-protein complexes of cells, but only when certain variables have been corrected.

Arginine may be demonstrated by modification of the method of Sakaguchi (1925) by combination with α-naphthol, 2,4-dichloro-α-naphthol or 8-hydroxy-quinoline and sodium hypochlorite at an alkaline pH. The studies of McLeish *et al.*, (1957) and of McLeish and Sherratt (1958) yielded a much improved reaction in which the final colour was stable for longer periods, being usable in quantitative studies. A further method for detecting arginine, and hence basic proteins, is that of Deitch (1955) employing naphthol yellow S. This is the sodium salt of flavianic acid used originally as a precipitant of arginine from protein hydrolysates. The reaction is stoichiometric and hence is quantifiable (Deitch, 1955, 1966; Tas *et al.*, 1974).

Tryptophan can be demonstrated readily by the method of Bruemmer *et al.* (1957) in which it appears that the reaction between nitrous acid and protein produces an *N*-nitroso compound involving the nitrogen of the indole ring. Coupling then appears to link the nitrogen of the nitroso group to the nitrogen of the free amino group in *N*-(1-naphthyl)ethylenediamine. Indol-3-yl acetic acid (IAA) will react by this method, and so whilst most of the IAA will have been lost from the tissues after fixation and embedding, it may prove troublesome in frozen or fresh sections.

A rapid method of detecting —SH groups is that of Chévremont and Frédéric (1943) in which the sections are reacted in a freshly prepared solution of potassium ferricyanide and ferric sulphate. This has been used in a study of developing conidiophores of *Aspergillus nidulans* (Oliver, 1974), but the disadvantage of this method is that other reducing substances react similarly and so the procedure must be carefully controlled by, for example, blocking the —SH groups with mercury so that they will no longer react.

A more reliable and better studied quantitative method is the mercury orange reaction of Bennett and Watts (1958) in which —SH groups react with mercuric compounds to form coloured mercaptides. Care must be taken in studies on

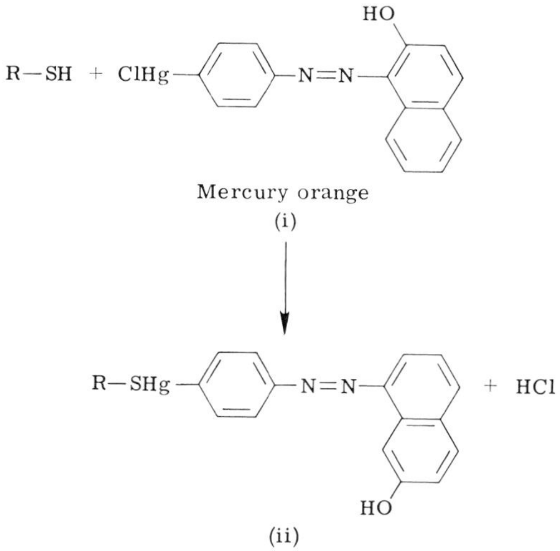

Mercury orange
(i)

(ii)

—SH amino acids since these groups are readily oxidized. The reactions above do not demonstrate disulphide bonds, and if they are to be found, they must first be reduced to —SH:

$$R—S—S—X \xrightarrow[\text{at 40°C for 15 min}]{\text{20\% sodium dithionite}} R—SH \; HS—X$$

Thus, —SH determinations on sections before and after treatment to reduce disulphide bonds may be used to identify the two forms of sulphur. A number of compounds, such as sodium dithionite, may be used as the reducing agent.

B. Autoradiographic Analysis

Protein sites may also be demonstrated by autoradiography after the incorporation of ^{35}S-, ^{3}H-, or ^{14}C-labelled amino acids. This approach will only demon-

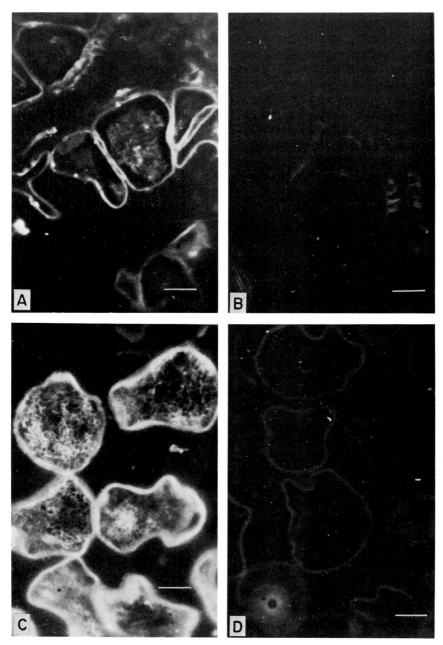

FIG. 10.   Immunofluoresence localization of rye-grass pollen antigen A. Direct method (A) showing binding of fluorescein–isothiocyanate-labelled antibodies to sites of antigen A in frozen dried

strate the metabolically active proteins and represents essentially the localization of the amino acid rather than the protein molecule. Moreover, it is difficult to distinguish between incorporation into a newly formed protein and amino acid exchange processes, except by the use of specific protein synthesis inhibitors, such as chloramphenicol and cycloheximide (Hall *et al.,* 1974).

C. Immunological Assays

The structure of proteins is such that either the complete protein molecule or the individual amino acids may be localized by immunochemical procedures in which a particular protein can be detected by its reaction with a specific antibody, which may be tagged with a fluorescent molecule (Coons, 1958; Nairn, 1962), with a radio-active marker, or with an enzyme molecule (Nakane, 1973; Avrameus, 1969). The last two methods have the advantage of yielding a high resolution method in addition to their use with the optical microscope. Labelling the antibody with ferritin provides an additional high resolution method.

Whatever the method of labelling the antibody, there are a number of fundamental ways of performing the reaction. The original method depended upon the attachment of the labelled antibody to the antigen in the section. The protein to be detected is at first isolated and purified. It is then injected into a suitable animal such as a rabbit for the production of antibodies to the protein (antigen). These antibodies are removed from the animal and purified and labelled by a variety of procedures. The labelled antibody is then applied to a section containing the specific protein to be identified (antigen), and the labelled antibody will link to the antigen, thus allowing its demonstration through the attached marker molecule. This approach had the disadvantage that even if all technical difficulties were overcome, only a one-to-one linking of antibody to antigen was possible, so giving a low concentration of marker molecule.

An alternative "sandwich" method was then derived. There are many modifications of this approach, but in essence they are based upon the idea that the antibody of the direct method can itself act as an antigen to γ-globulin antibody. Thus, if the marker molecule is attached to the γ-globulin instead of the original antibody, a reaction can be achieved:

Antigen   +   Antibody   → Antigen–Antibody
(protein to be detected)   (unlabelled)   (complex)

Complex + (γ-Globulin–Marker)x → Antigen–Antibody–(γ-Globulin–Marker)x

where x is more than one. The importance is that whilst the original reaction allowed only one linkage of antigen and antibody, more than one γ-globulin

pollen. Control (B) made with pre-immune serum giving a much reduced fluorescence. Localization of the pollen antigen A using the indirect method (C) showing enhanced fluorescence when compared to (A). (D) is the pre-immune serum control by the indirect method showing little fluorescence. Scale, 10 μm.

molecule can link to the original antibody so increasing the number of marker molecules associated with the original protein molecule being localized, and making visualization more easy to achieve.

There has been only a limited attempt to apply this approach in plant studies, although there is no obvious reason why it should not be as successful as it has been in cytochemical studies of animal tissues, as studies on phytochrome (Pratt and Coleman, 1976) and pollen have indicated (Knox *et al.*, 1980) (Fig. 10).

This is probably due in part to the difficulties encountered by botanists in having access to animals for raising antibodies to the pure protein extract. In addition, there is a general autofluorescence of plant tissues when excited by the wavelengths of light used with many fluorescent dyes, and this can make the visualization of the labelled antibody somewhat difficult. This second point is now less of a problem since it has been found that the autofluorescence of plant tissues can be avoided when working with fluorescein isothiocyanate (FITC) by use of longer wavelengths of excitation light, i.e. shifting from 400 to 490 nm (Ploem, 1980). Moreover, rhodamine has proved to be a useful marker dye for antibodies since its fluorescence colour is strikingly different from that of the plant autofluorescence and hence is readily distinguished (Hapner and Hapner, 1978). The approaches available for immunofluorescence studies have been well reviewed by Knox *et al.* (1980).

5. Group III: Enzymic Proteins

I. INTRODUCTION

Although enzyme cytochemistry is one of the more recent aspects of the general field of cytochemistry, it has developed with great speed and is now being applied to many diverse areas of plant biology. Unfortunately, in spite of rapid developments, reliable methods are available for less than a hundred of the more than 900 enzymes listed in the *I.U.B.* "Commission of Enzymes Report" (1961). This does not seem to have been such a handicap in some areas of study as might have been predicted, and work on some groups of enzymes has gone ahead with a rush. An early enzyme cytochemical test that was applied to plant tissues was the use of the tetrazolium reaction to the study of seed viability (Mattson *et al.*, 1947; Jensen *et al.*, 1951). Due to the presence of the electron transport pathway, triphenyltetrazolium chloride is reduced to a formazan by the live embryo, and so is acting as an indicator of dehydrogenase activity. Curiously, the application of this method to the study of dehydrogenases has produced little new basic information about plant cells, although the introduction of a more quantitative approach may lead to a better understanding of, e.g. cell differentiation (Vithanage and Knox, 1976; Gahan *et al.*, 1979).

Genuine progress has been made by the application of cytochemical methods to the study of acid hydrolases in which the early use of the methods for acid phosphatase enabled their particulate sites of localization in plant cells to be identified (Jensen, 1956b; Beneš *et al.*, 1961; Avers, 1958, 1961; Walek-Czernecka 1962, 1963, 1965; Gorska-Brylass, 1965; Sorokin and Sorokin, 1966). These were shown to have lysosome-like properties (Gahan, 1965a) and were identified as various sub-cellular organelles containing acid phosphatase activity (Poux, 1963; Gahan and McLean, 1969; Coulomb and Coulon, 1972). Finally, this led to the concept of a plant lysosomal system (reviewed by Gahan, 1968; Pitt, 1975; Matile, 1975), together with the presence of a Golgi–endoplasmic reticulum–lysosome (GERL) system in plant cells (Coulomb and Coulon, 1972). This has further given rise to studies of the roles of hydrolases during a variety of processes, such as secretion (Heslop-Harrison, 1975), cell development (Avers and Grimm, 1959; van Fleet, 1959; de Jong, 1967; Sutcliffe and Sexton 1968;

Berjak, 1968, 1972; Ashford and Jacobsen, 1974) and cell senescence and death (Gahan and Maple, 1966; Berjak, 1968; Berjak and Lawton, 1973; Matile, 1975). In addition, such work has formed the basis for extending the study of acid hydrolases into plant pathology (Pitt, 1975). These few examples for one group of enzymes indicate the range of possibilities available with enzyme cytochemistry. It can be argued that some of these studies do not really resolve the situation, as in the case of adenyl cyclase and its possible presence in plant cells. Nevertheless, the diligent application of existing methods in attempts to answer specific questions can be invaluable and can often complement a bio-chemical study in providing information on, for example, mixed cell populations that may be present as a variety of cell types in a normal tissue or as a fungal infection in a higher plant. Not that this has always produced much useful information, for in some instances all that one can deduce from the published data is that the enzyme reaction works! One is increasingly aware of the rela-tively unquestioning way in which enzyme cytochemistry is being applied. For example, the method for acid β-glycerophosphatase may be applied to a patho-logical lesion in a plant (a) because somebody has said that this enzyme is a lysosomal marker and so should be indicative of cellular change in response to infection; (b) in a thoughtless manner which will not answer any specific ques-tions; (c) with no thought to technical details such as the permeability to the reactants of whole cells as opposed to sections; (d) with no valid controls; and (e) with no ideas as to what the reaction means in terms of the enzymes under study. This illustrates some pitfalls for the unwary in the application of an enzyme cytochemical method to an interesting situation.

The absence of assay methods for many of the enzymes has already been mentioned, and much more developmental work is needed to remedy the situa-tion. Of those available, the following are examples of reactions that will work satisfactorily with some plant tissues. A guide to additional methods is indicated, though much fuller accounts are available elsewhere (Pearse, 1968, 1972). How-ever, in this chapter, it is proposed to give only a few basic methods from which it is possible to build up a further range. For instance, only selected examples of dehydrogenase methods are given, but a little thought and reading will provide a series of additional methods to increase the variety available for the study of these enzymes.

Enzyme histochemistry emphasizes many of the basic problems inherent in the subject of histochemistry. During the enzyme reaction, one must obtain an accurate, sub-cellular localization of both the enzyme and its end product as it is produced, yet without inhibiting the enzyme activity or changing the preserva-tion of the sub-cellular organelles and hence the localization of the enzyme. Before discussing the methods in detail, there are some general points worth making.

A. Choice of Enzyme

When studying a metabolic event there are many possible enzyme reactions from which to choose, and it is important to try to select the reaction for an enzyme that will best yield information concerning the system under investigation, rather than just an aesthetically acceptable image. Thus, in the case of the tricarboxlic acid pathway, succinic dehydrogenase yields an enzyme reaction that is reliably and simply measured. In consequence, in the past, this has been used in many (especially animal and human) studies as a marker for the activity of the metabolic pathway. A new approach to the understanding of metabolic regulation implies that succinic dehydrogenase cannot in fact give such an indication, since it is involved in a near-equilibrium reaction in which the *in vitro* maximum activity will be much higher than in the *in vivo* flux through the pathway. It becomes important to choose enzymes involved in non-equilibrium reactions. Two flux-generating steps have been identified for the citric acid cycle, namely, acetyl coenzyme A to α-ketoglutarate and α-ketoglutarate to oxaloacetate (Newsholme and Crabtree, 1979, 1980), and so α-ketoglutarate dehydrogenase would be the choice of an enzyme involved in a non-equilibrium reaction and which also appears to be involved in a flux-generating step. However, there is as yet no satisfactory method for this enzyme.

Pette and Hofer (1980) have further suggested the concept of ''constant proportion'' groups of enzymes, in which, for muscle, they have been able to show that the enzymes of co-ordinated function in some pathways display approximately constant ratios of activities independent of their varying absolute activities. In consequence, when metabolic functions are changed, these constant proportion groups of enzymes also change as a whole. Thus, identification of such groups in plant tissues could provide valuable information from which decisions can be taken as to which enzymes to measure in experiments dealing with changes in metabolic pathways.

B. Effects of Fixation

Inactivation of enzymes can occur readily during tissue preparation procedures as discussed by Pearse (1968, 1972), Burstone (1962) and Hayat (1973). Ideally, enzyme cytochemistry should be performed on unfixed cells as obtained by razor sections of fresh tissues (van Fleet, 1952) or by the use of unicellular or hyphal organisms (Zalokar, 1960a; Williamson, 1973), pollen tubes (Gorska-Brylass, 1965), staminal hairs or onion scale epidermis material (Sorokin, 1955). Unfortunately not all tissues lend themselves to this treatment. Further, there are some more fundamental difficulties, namely, (a) razor sections can lead to a loss of organelles and soluble enzymes from the cut cell surfaces (Gahan and Kalina,

1965; Hall and Sexton, 1972); (b) there are penetration problems in that the reactants do not always readily enter into the cells (Maggi, 1965; Gahan *et al.*, 1978; Washitani and Sato, 1976); (c) the penetration of the incubation medium into the unfixed cells may result in diffusion of the enzyme, either through damage to the organelles with which the enzyme is associated or simply by diffusion of soluble enzymes together with the infiltrating liquid front.

These problems cannot be ignored when examining other tissues for although ways are open for the production of serial thin or ultra-thin frozen sections of plant tissues for both optical microscopy (Gahan *et al.*, 1967) and electron microscopy (Gahan *et al.*, 1970; Barton, 1976), clearly workers face the same problems with thin sections as with razor sections, although possibly to a lesser degree.

Under certain circumstances, unfixed, frozen sections can be used at the optical microscope level (see later), but by far the most frequently used electron microscope cytochemistry methods require the tissues to be fixed (Hall *et al.*, 1977). The moment fixatives are employed, the cytochemist is faced with a situation of compromise between the best cytological preservation possible, and the maximum activity of the enzyme under study. Frequently, the fixatives yielding the best cytological preservation will destroy almost totally the enzyme activity, and vice versa. Specific fixatives for each group of enzymes will be treated separately (see later), but an example may be given of the effects of fixatives on acid phosphatase activity studied in the classic paper of Sabatini *et al.* (1963) in which, as far as rat liver was concerned, glutaraldehyde gave the best compromise between enzyme activity preserved and cytological ultrastructure. The effects of fixation for any given fixative, will vary to some degree, according to the enzyme and tissue under study. In trying to assess the effects of a fixative on a given enzyme in a given tissue, a number of points should be borne in mind:

1. The speed of penetration of the fixative will influence the length of time of fixation and possibly dictate the temperature at which fixation should be performed.

2. The amount of time needed to wash-out excess fixative after fixation (post-fixation wash).

3. The mode of action of the fixative (see Chapter 2) and its likely effect upon the enzyme under study.

4. The pH at which the fixative should be employed.

5. The molarity and possible effects of the buffer components upon the enzyme and the reaction (e.g. phosphate buffers should be avoided if phosphatase activity or lead salt methods are to be employed) and some buffer components inhibit some enzymes (e.g. aryl sulphatase activity by citrate and phosphate ions) (P. C. J. Brunet. personal communication).

6. If partial inhibition of the enzyme has occurred, then in the case of an enzyme with known isoenzymes, it may be worth checking if all isoenzymes are equally affected or if there is a differential inhibition, and if inhibition occurs at specific enzyme sites in a cell rather than at others.

7. Fixation will affect membrane structures and can render them more permeable to the reagents employed, which in turn will lead to a faster speed of reaction during the enzyme incubation (e.g., Gahan, 1965a). This is one way of overcoming membrane permeability barriers to the reaction mixture often encountered when using whole cells (Maggi, 1965; Washitani and Sato. 1976).

8. As the fixative penetrates the tissue it must cause at least a minimal diffusion of some of the cell components and hence some of the soluble enzymes. Thus, there may be a modified localization of enzymes when studied at the electron microscopic level, though this should prove less of a problem when studied with the optical microscope.

C. Effects of Enzyme Reagents

Accurate localization is a fundamental factor in any cytochemical study, and whilst organelle cytology is important, the reaction employed is of equal importance. Normally, the enzyme site can only be resolved through the deposition of the end-product of an enzyme reaction. For optical microscopy, the product will need to be coloured for ease of viewing, and in electron microscopy the product will need to be electron dense for easy detection. Often, a study at these two levels of resolution will require two different methods, since not all coloured products are electron dense and vice versa, though newer methods are attempting to exploit the same reaction for both forms of microscopy, e.g. acid and alkaline phosphatases.

The enzyme can be demonstrated by its ability to act upon a soluble compound, which is rendered immediately insoluble [Reaction (1)]. Alternatively, the radicle may be cleaved from the soluble compound and be rendered insoluble by further reaction with a second compound or trapping agent [Reaction (2)].

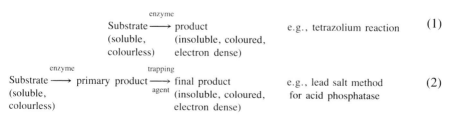

In Reaction (2), not only is the speed of cleavage of the substrate important, but obviously the rate of the reaction will also be dependent upon the speed of coupling to the trapping agent. Any delay in the second step could allow the primary product to diffuse from the enzyme site, and also will slow down the speed of appearance of the end product.

It is imperative to remember that the principles involved in enzyme bio-chemistry (Dixon and Webb, 1958; Webb, 1963) are equally applicable to enzyme cytochemistry. Thus, the reaction will be affected by temperature, pH and concentrations of substrate and trapping agents. The reactants are able to affect the pH of a solution in which they are present, hence the need to buffer the solution in order to perform the reaction at an optimal pH. Incidentially, the biochemical optimal pH for the isolated purified enzyme may not be identical to that for the cytochemical reaction for a variety of reasons, e.g. the two-step enzyme reaction such as NAD-linked dehydrogenases may be governed by the second step, which will have a pH optimum different from that of the enzyme under study. Checks must also be made on the molarity of the buffer (e.g. see acid phosphatases) and on the possible inhibitory capacity of the buffer components (see Section I,B). Inhibition may also occur through a component of the reaction medium or by the reaction medium or by the reaction product. For example, in the Burstone (1958) acid phosphatase reaction, the substrate naphthol AS-BI phosphate appears to inhibit enzyme activity in bean root tissues at concentrations higher than $0.5\ M$ (J. McLean and P. B. Gahan, unpublished).

The speed of reaction is of some importance, since the longer the incubation period, the greater the possibility of the diffusion of the end-product. Whilst ideally the reaction could occur at room temperature, elevation of the temperature to 27°C or even 37°C may aid the process. Conversely, if the cells react too heavily at room temperature in a very short incubation period, the reaction can be slowed by lowering the temperature to as little as 4°C.

The problem of the mobility of the end-product is a real one, and it is important to know if the product is substantive, i.e. will bind to protein and so stay at its site of origin, or is water- or lipid-soluble. If water-soluble, e.g. the formazan of 2-(p-iodophenyl)-3-(p-nitrophenyl)-5-phenyl tetrazolium chloride (INT), then the end-product will be soluble in the incubation medium, if lipid-soluble, e.g. the formazan of neotetrazolium or diazonium salt complexes, then they may become preferentially adsorbed by neighbouring lipid sites during incubation.

The size or amount of end-product deposited at a particular site will be of importance. There is a minimal amount of deposit required for its visualization at each level of resolution, though electron microscopy will require less than optical microscopy. More or less product will depend initially upon the length of incubation; though there must come a moment when the product encapsulates the enzyme site, no more substrate reaches the enzyme and the reaction stops. This is not strictly inhibition for if the product is removed, the enzyme activity may start again (Barter *et al.*, 1955). The visualization of the end-product is also dependent on the size of the particles of end-product, as is the resolution. For example, the formazan of INT is in the form of large long crystals, readily seen but yielding poor sub-cellular localization, whilst that of tetra nitro blue tetrazolium (TNBT) is in the form of less readily observed, fine, small, crystals giving very good localization at the sub-mitochondrial level.

D. Controls

If the cytological preservation is good, the reaction is understood, and the end-product is reliably located, then it is of importance to test the specificity of the reaction. At present, the main controls used are (a) incubation in the absence of the substrate, when a reaction would not normally be expected. It is possible for a positive enzymic reaction to occur through the presence of endogenous substrate at a high enough level; (b) treatment of the sections or small blocks of tissue in distilled water at 90°C for 5–10 min in order to inactivate the enzyme activity; (c) addition of specific inhibitors or known activators to the full incubation medium.

Futher information can be determined by the response of the enzyme to (a) other related or naturally occurring substrates where the reaction employs an artificial substrate; (b) pH changes; and (c) inhibitors, e.g. whether competitive, reversible or irreversible.

An additional check to be made for electron microscopy concerns the effect of stains used to obtain contrast, e.g. lead citrate. It is advisable to examine enzyme end-products in unstained sections to avoid any non-enzymatic deposits of electron-opaque material caused by staining.

E. Length of Incubation

From the foregoing comments, it might be doubted whether reliable enzyme cytochemical tests really exist! The rest of this chapter will try to indicate that a range of methods are available which, if suitably controlled, can yield useful, even quantitative (see Chapter 9) information on a number of cytological and physiological problems.

When incubating sections or small block of tissue, it is worth remembering that a series of incubation times may be helpful. Obviously, this will depend upon the question being asked of the method. Thus, when used for the first time, it should be performed with a tissue that has been well documented in terms of its response to the reaction, as well as the new experimental material. This will give a check on the effectiveness of the incubation medium. Then, a series of incubation times, e.g. 2, 5, 10, 20, 40 min, should be used to determine the speed of visible response from the various cell types in the material to be examined. Remember that even cells morphologically similar may be physiologically different. Equally, the unit volume of cytoplasm in a large vacuolate cell may differ in content from that of a meristematic cell (see Chapter 9). This approach will indicate at the optical microscope level both different responses and different rates of response between cell types. Such information will be helpful in two ways, namely, for tackling enzyme cytochemistry with the electron microscope, and for examining new tissues—not everything behaves like a root meristem!

F. Electron Microscope Cytochemistry

The large range of enzyme reactions available for use with the optical micro-scope cannot all be directly visualized with the electron microscope. The range of possibilities is still limited, as has been reviewed recently by Hall *et al.* (1977; Sexton and Hall, 1978). Unfortunately, many of the reactions depend upon the use of Pb ions to achieve an electron-dense product, and it is necessary to add many stringent controls to avoid any artefacts (including the exclusion of lead staining of the sections). Nevertheless, much has and can be achieved with the currently limited list of methods. The problems of individual methods will be discussed with each group of enzymes.

G. Extrapolation of Methods

Many workers find that a given method works well with a given tissue of a given plant species. However, this does not mean that the method can automatically be transferred to another tissue of the same species (e.g. from root apex to leaf) or to the same tissue of another species (e.g. from root tips of *V. faba* to those of *A. cepa*), and it is essential to check out the methodology on a new tissue before trying any experimental work.

H. Molecules versus Activity

The foregoing general discussion concerns the assay of enzyme activity in tissues. An alternative approach involves immunofluorescence methods. These have been little tried in plants, although Bal *et al.* (1976) have successfully localized cellulase by this method. In view of the extent of application in animal studies, it clearly offers an important approach that should be developed. How-ever, it should be stressed that this method is based upon reacting the section with a purified antibody to the enzyme under study (for general details see Chapter 4) and in consequence will allow the localization of the enzyme mole-cules. It will demonstrate differences in numbers of enzyme molecules in differ-ent cells, but *not* differences in enzyme activities. For instance, providing the enzyme molecules can act as antigens for the antibodies, they will react and be detected. However, since both active and inactive enzyme molecules should be capable of acting as antigens, it will not be possible by this method to decide if all of the enzyme molecules are actually functioning in a given cell. The application of this approach, together with the substrate methods might provide interesting information on the state of affairs, e.g. during differentiation.

II. DIAPHORASES AND DEHYDROGENASES

A. Tetrazolium Salts

The tetrazolium salts were first prepared in 1894 by von Pechman and Runge who also summarised the general properties of the compound. They have become important in cytochemistry because the water-soluble, lightly coloured salts can be reduced by mild agents to water-insoluble, coloured formazans (von Pechmann and Runge, 1894a,b).

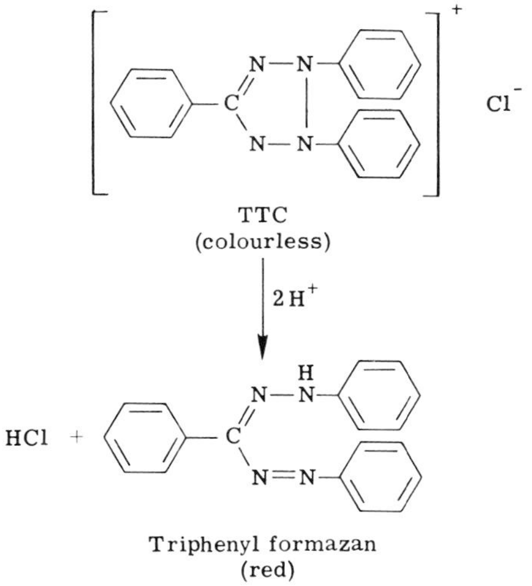

TTC
(colourless)

$2 H^+$

Triphenyl formazan
(red)

A number of tetrazolium salts are now available commercially and their characteristics are given in Tables 2 and 3. The redox potentials help to explain the way in which the tetrazolium salts compete for electrons and their comparative efficiencies, for the more positive the redox potential the more easily reduced is the compound, e.g. NBT is more readily reduced than NT. In the histochemical reaction for dehydrogenase activity, the enzyme catalyses the oxidation of the substrate, the hydrogen ions removed being transferred to the enzyme flavoprotein in the case of succinic dehydrogenase or to NAD(P) and hence to the flavoproteins of these compounds. Normally the flavoproteins would be reoxidised by transfer of the electron to oxygen via the electron transport pathway. In the presence of a tetrazolium salt, however, some of the elec-

TABLE 2.   The Tretrazolium Salts Used in Cytochemistry

Common name	Abbreviation	Formula	Redox[a]	Molecular weight
—	TTC[b]	Triphenyl tetrazolium chloride	−0.49	334,80
Neotetrazolium	NT[c]	2,2'-(p-Diphenylene)-bis(3,5-diphenyl) tetrazolium chloride	−0.17	667,57
Blue tetrazolium	BT[c]	3,3'-(3,3'-Dimethoxy-4,4'-biphenylene-bis(2,5-diphenyl) 2H-tetrazolium chloride	−0.16	727,63
—	MTT[b]	3-(4,5-Dimethylthiazolyl-2)-2,5-diphenyl tetrazolium chloride	−0.11	414,34
—	INT[b]	2-(p-Iodophenyl)-3-(p-nitrophenyl)-5-phenyl tetrazolium chloride	−0.09	505,70
Nitroblue tetrazolium	NBT[c]	2,2'-Di-p-nitro-phenyl-5,5'-diphenyl-3,3'-(3,3'-dimethoxy-4,4'-biphenylene) ditetrazolium chloride	−0.05	817,63
Tetra-nitroblue tetrazolium	TNBT[c]	2,2',5,5'-Tetra-p-nitrophenyl-3,3'(3,3'-dimethoxy-4,4'-diphenylene) ditetrazolium chloride	−0.05	907,63

[a] $E_{1/2}$, 22°C, pH 7.2, in volts.
[b] Monotetrazoles.
[c] Ditetrazoles.

trons are diverted and reduce the salt to the formazan. The sites of acceptance of electrons from the electron transport pathway in plant cells by the various tetrazolium salts are indicated in Fig. 11 (Gahan and Kalina, 1968; Kalina and Palmer, 1968). These sites were assessed by incubating sections of plant tissues or isolated plant mitochondria in the presence of succinate, a tetrazolium salt and one of the inhibitors shown in Fig. 11. Thus, if the reaction is blocked by the inhibitor of the electron transport pathway then the site of pick-up is likely to be

TABLE 3.   Some Characteristics of the Tetrazolium Salts[a]

Salt	Substantivity of tetrazole	Colour of formazan	Size of deposit (μm)	Shape of formazan	Lipid solubility of formazan
MTT	−	Purple-grey	1 × 6	Needle	Soluble
INT	+	Orange-red	1 × 2.5	Needle	Soluble
NT	+	Purple-red	1.7 × 1.7	Granular diffuse	Partial
BT	+	Blue-red	1.5 × 1.5	Granular diffuse	Partial
NBT	+	Deep blue-red	0.5 × 0.5	Granular diffuse	Insoluble
TNBT	+	Brownish red	0.2 × 0.2	Granular diffuse	Insoluble

[a] After Altman (1976).

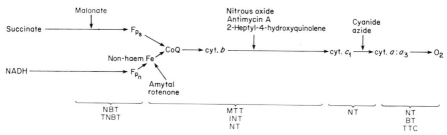

FIG. 11.   Sites of action of inhibitors of electron transport and apparent sites of electron acceptance by tetrazolium salts. (After Kalina and Palmer, 1968; Gahan and Kalina, 1968; Palmer, 1976.)

after the point of inhibition. Conversely, lack of inhibition indicates electron acceptance before the site of action of the inhibitor.

Although tetrazolium salts were used by Lakon (1939, 1942a,b) to demonstrate the viability of maize, wheat, oats, rye and barley, relatively little use has been made of them in plant cytochemistry, and few quantitative studies have been attempted. The first tetrazolium salt produced, TTC, has been found to be unsatisfactory for cytochemistry since the formazan is deposited as large crystals that are water-soluble, so that it does not yield a visible reaction product for succinic dehydrogenase in 10 μm sections of plant tissues (Gahan and Kalina, 1968). A number of different tetrazolium salts have now been developed, and of these NBT and TNBT seem to be the most useful since they are soluble in water, their formazans are insoluble in water and lipids and are produced as very fine crystals that are very substantive to proteins, so reducing the possibilities of diffusion during processing, and yielding a more accurate sub-cellular localization (Table 3). Substantivity of the formazan is paralleled by that of the NBT itself, which can render these compounds unsuitable for quantitative studies with [3H]NBT since an autoradiograph of sections incubated with [3H]NBT will show the sites of both the [3H]NBT and [3H]formazan attached to the section. This problem may be overcome by the addition of 2.5% protamine sulphate to the reaction medium (F. P. Altman, private communication), which blocks the binding of NT to the sections and hence may block NBT. The substantivity of the NBT formazan is also a factor concerning its use in some types of quantitative studies, since it is extremely difficult to extract the formazan completely from a section. Conversely, this aspect is of extreme importance in other quantitative studies (Chapter 9).

B. Fixation

Little information is available upon the effects of fixation on dehydrogenases in plants (Sexton and Hall, 1978). In animal studies, it was found that succinate, malate, isocitrate and β-hydroxybutyrate dehydrogenases could survive a brief (10 min) fixation in formaldehyde as could lactate dehydrogenase (Novikoff and Masek, 1958). After fixation for 24 h lactate and malate dehydrogenases were still active. However, glucose-6-phosphate and 6-phosphogluconate dehydrogenases are very sensitive to fixation, though surviving brief fixation in dilute glutaraldehyde. Fixation for 1 h at 4°C in 4% glutaraldehyde leaves only 13% of lactate dehydrogenase and 20% of isocitrate dehydrogenase activities (Anderson, 1967). Flitney (1966) used 0.6% glutaraldehyde for 1 min at 20°C for succinate, β-glycerophosphate and glucose-6-phosphate dehydrogenases. NADH and NADPH-tetrazolium reductases appear to resist long fixation in formalin at 4°C (McAlpine, 1965). Little resistance by plant dehydrogenases to fixation in Ca–formalin has been observed (Gahan, unpublished data). The observation is of importance when considering NAD(P)-linked dehydrogenase reactions, since, basically, the enzyme reaction is

$$\text{Substrate (oxidized)} + \text{NAD(P)} \xrightarrow{\text{dehydrogenase}} \text{substrate (reduced)} + \text{NAD(P)H}^+ + \text{H}^+ \quad (3)$$

$$\text{NAD(P)}^+ + \text{H}^+ + \text{tetrazole} \xrightarrow[\text{system}]{\text{reductase}} \text{NAD(P)} + \text{formazan} \quad (4)$$

Clearly, if a fixative inhibits the tetrazole reductase system [Reaction (4)] without affecting the dehydrogenase activity [in Reaction (3)], then no formazan will be produced and no reaction will be observed. A way of overcoming this is by the addition of menadione or phenazine methosulphate.

C. Succinic Dehydrogenase

Succinic dehydrogenase is the only dehydrogenase that can be directly demonstrated with the aid of tetrazolium salts and that is not dependent upon NAD(P). Studies of this enzyme (reviewed by Jensen, 1962; van Fleet 1962) have been few in number, and these authors considered that succinic dehydrogenase activity was destroyed in frozen sections and therefore could only be demonstrated in fresh tissues. However, Van den Born (1963), Koenig (1966), Roberts et al. (1966) and Gahan et al. (1967) showed that this enzyme can be demonstrated in frozen sections of plant material. An attempt by Gahan and Kalina (1968) to resolve these discrepancies revealed that succinic dehydrogenase activity could be demonstrated in 10 μm fresh or frozen sections if TNBT, NBT, INT or MTT were used as electron receptors, but not with NT, BT or TTC. If thicker sections of 50–150 μm were used, then all tetrazolium salts yielded a reaction. This agreed with the findings of Van den Born (1963) who obtained a reaction for succinic dehydrogenase in 80 μm sections of *Pinus* using INT and of Sato (1953) who found a reduction of TTC in the presence of succinate in sections of radicle and hypocotyl from seedlings of *Phaseolus vulgaris* that were thicker than 150

μm. It was suggested (Gahan and Kalina, 1968) that this may be related to the redox potential of the tetrazolium salts, though the degree of sustantivity of the formazan is also of importance.

D. NAD(P)-Linked Dehydrogenases

Dehydrogenases, other than succinic dehydrogenases, require the presence of NAD or NADP in order to catalyse a particular reaction. As discussed, hydrogen ions are transferred from the substrate to NAD(P), the cytochemical reaction depending upon reoxidation of the NAD(P)H$^+$ + H$^+$ in the presence of a tetrazolium salt.

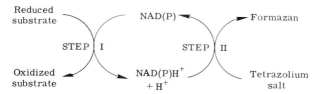

Basically, the reaction effectively indicates sites of NAD(P)H$^+$ + H$^+$/ tetrazolium reductase systems and not the sites of dehydrogenase activities. It also means that the dehydrogenase cannot be demonstrated in the absence of this system (Farber *et al.*, 1956a,b; Gahan and Kalina, 1965; Kalina *et al.*, 1965; Kalina and Gahan, 1965) and that it is only possible to visualize the dehydrogenase activity as a general cell reaction. Thus this is a two-step reaction in which the NAD(P) is reduced (step I) and then reoxidized with the concomitant reduction of a tetrazolium salt (step II). It is important to check that step II is not a rate-limiting step by simply running the reaction with NAD(P)H$^+$ + H$^+$ and a tetrazolium salt and determining if the rate of formazan deposition is faster than that of the dehydrogenese reaction. If step II is rate limiting, this can be overcome by the addition of menadione or phenazine methosulphate (see Section II, G).

E. Enzyme Loss

A further complication arises concerning the localization of the dehydrogenases studied. The majority of dehydrogenases appear to be weakly associated with sub-cellular structures and so in biochemical analysis appear in the supernatant fraction. It has been shown for plant tissues (Gahan and Kalina, 1965; Kalina and Gahan, 1968) that on incubation of unfixed, frozen or razor sections of plant tissues in the medium for a particular dehydrogenase, the enzyme is lost from the section into the incubation medium, although the NADH(P)H$^+$ + H$^+$/tetrazolium reductase system remains particle-bound in the section. The enzyme acts upon the substrate with a consequent reduction of the NAD(P) in the

TABLE 4. Inhibition of Some Enzyme Activities by Various Fixatives

Enzyme	Fixative	Length of fixation	Temperature (°C)	Tissue	Percentage inhibition	Reference
Acid phosphatase	10% Acrolein	2½ h	4	Maize roots	25	Sexton et al., 1971
	3% Glutaraldehyde	2 h	4	Maize roots	16	Sexton et al., 1971
	Acetone	2 h	4	Rat and mouse liver	71	Rabinowitch et al., 1949
	Acetone	24 h	4		78	
	Formal–saline	12 h	4			
		12 h	4		90	
	80% Ethanol	12 h	4		90	
	2% Ca–formal	24 h	2	Rat kidney and liver	90	Holt et al., 1960
	Acetone	12 h	2		25	
	10% Formalin 20–40 min	20–40 min	—		25	Wyllie, 1965
	60% Acetone	20–40 min	—		25	
	Gluteraldehyde	6 h	0–2	Rat liver and renal cortex	81–60	Janigen, 1965
	Glyoxal	6 h	0–2		26–44	
	Hydroxyadipaldehyde	6 h	0–2		17–31	
	Formaldehyde	6 h	0–2		45–61	
	Methacrolein	6 h	0–2		59	
	Acrolein	6 h	0–2		96	
	Crotonaldehyde	6 h	0–2		72–74	

Enzyme	Fixative	Time	Temp.	Tissue	%	Reference
Nucleoside diphosphatase	1% Glutaraldehyde	1½ h	4	Onion roots	79	Goff and Klohs, 1974
	4% Glutaraldehyde	1½ h	4	Onion roots	81	Goff and Klohs, 1974
	1% Formaldehyde	1½ h	4	Onion roots	8	Goff and Klohs, 1974
	4% Formaldehyde	1½ h	4	Onion roots	12	Goff and Klohs, 1974
ATPase	1% Glutaraldehyde	2 h	4	Pea roots	55	Al-Azzawi and Hall, 1977
	5% Glutaraldehyde	2 h	4	Pea roots	73	Al-Azzawi and Hall, 1977
	1% Formaldehyde	2 h	4	Pea roots	0	Al-Azzawi and Hall, 1977
	5% Formaldehyde	2 h	4	Pea roots	32	Al-Azzawi and Hall, 1977
Myrosinase	3% Glutaraldehyde	—	—	Synapis albis roots	2	Iverson, 1973
	4% Formaldehyde	—	—	Synapis albis roots	5	Iverson, 1973
Esterase	Acetone	24 h	0		35	Richterich, 1951
	10% Formalin	5 min			25	
	50% Acetone	5 min			25	Wyllie, 1965
	2% Formal-Ca	24 h	2	Rat liver and kidney	40–50	Holt et al., 1960
α-Glucosidase	Formalin				20	Rutenburg et al., 1960
β-Glucuronidase	Formalin	30 min	4		75	Nachlas et al., 1956a
Peroxidase	1% Glutaraldehyde	2 h	4	Pea roots	14	Al-Azzawi and Hall, 1977
	5% Glutaraldehyde	2 h	4	Pea roots	12	Al-Azzawi and Hall, 1977
	1% Formaldehyde	2 h	4	Pea roots	7	Al-Azzawi and Hall, 1977
	5% Formaldehyde	2 h	4	Pea roots	8	Al-Azzawi and Hall, 1977

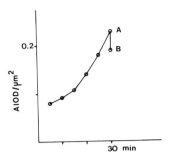

FIG. 12. Graph of arbitrary integrated optical density units (AIOD) of formazan produced per μm^2 of reacted cytoplasm versus time in the radicle of a *Vicia faba* seed (imbibed for 24 h) with the reaction for glucose-6-phosphate dehydrogenase activity. The production of formazan was monitored continuously during the incubation at room temperature for 30 min (A) and was remeasured after removal of the incubation medium and mounting in Farrants' medium (B), showing about a 20% loss of formation.

medium. The $NAD(P)H^+ + H^+$ so formed diffuses back to the section where it is reoxidised with a concomitant reduction of the tetrazolium salt.

In order to detect the amount of dehydrogenase activity within a particular cell, it is imperative to stop the enzyme diffusing from that cell. The addition of 20% polyvinyl pyrrolidone (Balogh, 1965) or 20% polyvinyl alcohol (Altman and Chayen, 1965) to the incubation medium has been shown to overcome these difficulties with animal tissues and more recently, the list of additives has been extended (Altman, 1980) (Table 4). The method may also be applied to plant sections (e.g., Gahan *et al.*, 1979), but one problem concerns the loss of formazan from the more heavily (?) reacted parts of the section on removal of the incubation medium (Fig. 12). This may be more striking with plant than with animal material since the formazans appear to be less substantive in plant cells and are of importance in quantitative studies. Another method has been a modification of the gelatin-film method developed for use with sections of animal tissues (Fahimi and Amarasingham, 1963, 1964; Benitez and Fischer, 1964) in which the compounds of the incubation medium are incorporated in a 5% gelatin solution that is allowed to gel. Strips of the gel are layed on to the sections for the purposes of incubation (Kalina and Gahan, 1968), although here again, there is a slight mechanical loss of formazan on removal of the film from the section.

Whilst the $NAD(P)H^+$-tetrazolium reductase system is apparently particle-bound within the cell, it is to be noted that a second system, which can be shown to be present in the supernatant fraction from biochemical preparations of plant tissues, appears to catalyse the transfer of electrons from $NAD(P)H^+$, to NBT and TNBT, but not to NT, BT, MTT, INT or TTC. Since many studies involve the use of NBT, it is as well to be aware of the presence of this soluble di-aphorase system, which may be partly responsible for the reduction of NBT in the incubation medium so resulting in a random deposition of the formazan on the surface of the section.

F. pH Optima

When reacting for NAD(P)-linked dehydrogenases, measurement is being made on two systems, i.e. the two steps of the overall reaction. This could raise problems since cytochemically the optimal pH for the reaction for glucose-6-phosphate and 6-phosphogluconate dehydrogenases is at about pH 7.8 when there is a maximum rate of formazan production. The pH optima of these two dehydrogenases as measured biochemically can vary considerably, e.g. pH 7.6 for rat liver and pH 8.5 for yeast glucose-6-phosphate dehydrogenases, and pH 7.4 for yeast and pH 9.0 for rat liver 6-phosphogluconate dehydrogenases. Thus, in these circumstances, the pH optimum of the tetrazole reductase system would seem to be influencing the overall pH optimum seen cytochemically.

Most workers operate these dehydrogenase reactions at pH 7.4–7.6 due to the above-mentioned problems plus an additional complication. As the pH rises above neutrality, the NAD(P) and NAD(P)H$^+$ + H$^+$ become more unstable and break down in solution, so that it is advantageous to work as close to neutrality as possible (Pearse, 1972).

G. Tetrazolium Salt/Formazan Inhibition

The use of tetrazolium salts in the study of pyridine nucleotide-linked dehydro-genases may be somewhat limited, since in addition to the difficulties of localiza-tion, the inhibitory effects of the tetrazolium salts or formazans must also be considered. It has been shown (Clark *et al.*, 1965; Sato and Sato, 1965; Kalina and Palmer, 1968) that in addition to uncoupling oxidative phosphorylation, tetrazolium salts, or their formazans, inhibit electron flow between NADH$^+$ and cytochrome *b* at concentrations of 200 μM. Thus, it is not possible to attempt inhibitor studies of the kind reported for succinic dehydrogenase by Gahan and Kalina (1968). This also results in an enzyme reaction in a cell in which, under certain conditions, the rate of reoxidation of NADH$^+$ + H$^+$ is controlled by the rate at which electrons can be passed to the tetrazolium salt.

Nevertheless, it is possible to study a series of dehydrogenases, including those associated with the glycolysis, pentose phosphate and tricarboxylic acid pathways. A fuller description of the range of reactions is given by Altman (1976), though methods are given for sample reactions in Appendix 5.

H. Use of Phenazine Methosulphate and Menadione

One additional step of interest used by Altman on rat liver (1972) and by Gahan *et al.* (1979) on apices of spinach plants in which flowering has been induced concerns the electron flow associated with the pentose phosphate pathway. Here glucose-6-phosphate and 6-phosphogluconate dehydrogenases are involved leading to the reduction of NADP. Some of the electron flow is associated with the normal hydroxylation pathway and some with lipid biosynthesis on the reoxidation of $NADPH^+ + H^+$. Neotetrazolium chloride when used alone will accept only those electrons involved with hydroxylation. If, however, phenazine methosulphate (PMS) or menadione are added to the incubation mixture, all electrons may be trapped through neotetrazolium chloride (Altman, 1972). Thus, the ratio of the amount of formazan produced in the absence of PMS to that produced in its presence will give an indication of the importance of these two pathways in the cells examined.

Phenazine methosulphate has been used in dehydrogenase biochemistry for many years. Dickens and McIlwain (1938) showed that soluble redox dyes of the appropriate redox potential could accept electrons non-enzymically from reduced co-enzymes and prosthetic groups, and transfer them to molecular oxygen, thus

$$D \cdot H_2 + PMS \rightarrow D + PMS \cdot H_2$$

$$PMS \cdot H_2 + R \rightarrow RH_2 + PMS$$

where D is the electron donor and R the electron receiver. Such reactions clearly need to be performed in the absence of molecular oxygen, since otherwise the reduced PMS will be reoxidised by the oxygen rather than the artificial electron acceptor (Raap, 1983). Measurements on rat liver have shown that the PMS-mediated oxidation of NADH is 800 times faster than the oxidation achieved by the liver section alone (Altman, 1976). It follows also that the addition of PMS to the reaction mixture, under anaerobic conditions, overcomes any possibility of the tetrazolium reductase system becoming a rate-limiting step in the reaction for pyridine nucleotide-linked dehydrogenases. It would appear that whilst PMS may not result in obviously enhanced reaction product deposition, the reduced form is sparingly water-soluble and has good substantivity so that diffusion of PMSH is virtually excluded. Thus, tetrazolium salt reduction will occur at the site of PMS reduction (Raap *et al.*, 1983a,b). Some workers consider that 1-methoxy PMS (Hisada and Yagi, 1977) is a better electron carrier than PMS in dehydrogenase cytochemistry and, unlike PMS, it is light stable and photochemically reduces tetrazolium salts only to a minimal extent (Van Noorden and Tas, 1982, 1983). It has been indicated from animal studies that PMS may damage membranes and so affect enzyme reactions, the result of which is that menadione has been substituted for PMS as electron transfer agent.

$$+2H^+$$

$(^-O-SO_2-OCH_3)$ $^-O-SO_2-OCH_3$

I. Ultra-structural Studies

Whilst some progress has been made in the development of methods for electron microscopy in animal tissues, especially by Seligman and his colleagues (reviewed in Pearse, 1972; Altman, 1976), there appears to have been no serious attempt to develop these studies in plants. Two basic approaches are currently available. The first employs ferricyanide as an electron acceptor (Ogawa et al., 1968), and this method has been modified by Kalina et al. (1969). Fresh or hydroxyadipaldehyde-fixed pieces of tissue are reacted in the presence of substrate ferricyanide and Cu^{2+} ions. The latter are chelated with sodium-potassium tartrate yielding an electron-dense product along the crystal membranes.

The second method involves the use of a modified tetrazolium salt, since the commonly available ones do not yield sufficiently electron-dense formazans. Seligman et al. (1967) developed a carbamyl nitro-BT which produced osmium black on reaction with OsO_4.

Osmium black

An alternative approach of Tsou et al. (1968) involved the production of the osmate of 2,2',5,5'-tetra-p-nitrophenyl-3,3'-stilbene ditetrazolium chloride (Os-TNST), which was used on glutaraldehyde-fixed tissues.

Perhaps of more interest is the production of 2-(2-benzo-thiazolyl-(4-phthalhydrazyl)-5-styryl tetrazolium chloride (BSPT). This is a non-substantive monotetrazolium salt of which only the formazan is osmiophilic (Kalina et al., 1972); BSPT is very readily reduced, the formazan chelating OsO_4 even at room temperature. This would appear to be the best tetrazolium salt for use in electron

Os-TNST

microscopy, since the formazan is lipophobic and non-crystalline, giving accurate localization, and can be used in quantification (Altman, 1976). It is not possible to use the salt with some plant tissues, e.g. unfixed embryos and root apices, because the formazan is not substantive and will not stay at its sites of formation in the section (Butcher *et al.*, 1980; Gahan and Dawson, 1981).

III. CYTOCHROME OXIDASE

Cytochrome oxidase is the name of the terminal oxidase in the electron transport pathway that results in the final transfer of electrons from the sequence of cytochrome carriers to molecular oxygen. The original reaction was the NADI test (Graff, 1916) that was used on plant and animal material. Cytochrome oxidase, in the presence of cytochrome c, oxidizes a mixture of α-naphthol and dimethylparaphenylene diamine to indophenol. The method lost favour because there are a number of inherent difficulties in that (a) the colour is not stable; (b) the indophenol dye formed is lipophilic; (c) lignin will yield a false-positive reaction (van Fleet, 1952); and (d) the reactions can occur in the absence of cytochrome c. The lipophilia is of importance since the end-product migrates readily from the site of formation to yield a false localization. The NADI reaction in the absence of cytochrome c is possibly due to the presence of lipid peroxides, which catalyse the non-enzymic formation of indophenol blue. Jensen (1962) suggested adding catalase and peroxidase to the incubation medium to destroy any peroxides present.

Attempts to overcome these basic problems have been made by, e.g. employing 4-amino-1-N,N-dimethylnaphthylamine which resulted in the production of a less lipophilic dye (Nachlas *et al.*, 1958). Aryl amines, which form indamine–azine-type dyes on oxidation and are capable of chelating with a number of metals to form insoluble complexes, have also been tried (Burstone, 1956, 1960).

More recently Seligman *et al.* (1968) showed that 3,3′-diaminobenzidine

(DAB) could also be exploited to demonstrate cytochrome oxidase activity, and which has the added advantage of being usable in electron microscopic studies. The final reaction mixture (see Appendix 5) contains cytochrome c to cover any losses from the tissue during preparation. The reaction appears to involve the reduction of oxidized cytochrome c by DAB, which in turn is reoxidised by the cytochrome oxidase complex (Seligman et al., 1968, 1973; Anderson et al., 1975; Cammer and Moore, 1973):

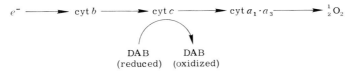

3,3'-Diamenobenzidine will act also in the presence of H_2O_2, and so catalase is added to the incubation mixture to preclude the build-up of H_2O_2. As controls, sections must be incubated in the presence of terminal oxidase inhibitors, such as cyanide, azide or carbon monoxide. To rule out any DAB binding through auto-oxidation in the presence of light at neutral pH and subsequent binding to cytochrome c (Hirai, 1968), it is important to run heat-inactivated sections as controls. This last reaction is sensitive to inhibitors of the terminal oxidase, but not to heat inactivation.

Whilst reactions have been performed upon unfixed material (Ekés, 1971), it has been found that fixation improves preservation of cytological detail (Opik, 1975). If fixation is used, long washing periods seem important to remove residual fixative (Anderson et al., 1975). The use of this method for ultrastructural studies in plants has been well reviewed by Sexton and Hall (1978).

IV. PEROXIDASES AND CATALASES

These are both present in plant tissues and are distinguished in that normally whilst catalase causes the catalysis of hydrogen peroxide to water and molecular oxygen [Reaction (5)]; peroxidase catalyses the reduction of hydrogen peroxide to water by exploiting electron donors other than hydrogen peroxide [Reaction (6)].

$$2H_2O_2 \xrightarrow{\text{catalase}} 2H_2O + O_2 \tag{5}$$

$$XH_2 + H_2O_2 \xrightarrow{\text{peroxidase}} 2H_2O + X \tag{6}$$

Studies on peroxidase have shown that a broad range of electron donors are involved, and XH_2 in Reaction (6) above could be derived from phenols and alcohols. The earliest reaction employed the oxidation of benzidine in the presence of hydrogen peroxide (Isacc and Winch, 1947). Guaiacol (*o*-hydroxyani-sole) was also introduced as an alternative to benzidine. However, both ap-proaches presented a number of difficulties (reviewed in van Fleet, 1952) and, in particular, (a) the false-positive reactions yielded by copper, iron and aldehydes; and (b) the solubility of the enzyme and the reaction products. Part of this dilemma has been resolved by the banning of the synthesis and importation into the United Kingdom of the carcinogenic benzidine!

However, we are still allowed to work with diaminobenzidine, which was introduced as a more efficient reagent for optical and electron microscope studies by Graham and Karnovsky (1966). The following reaction was considered to explain the mechanism (Seligman *et al.*, 1968):

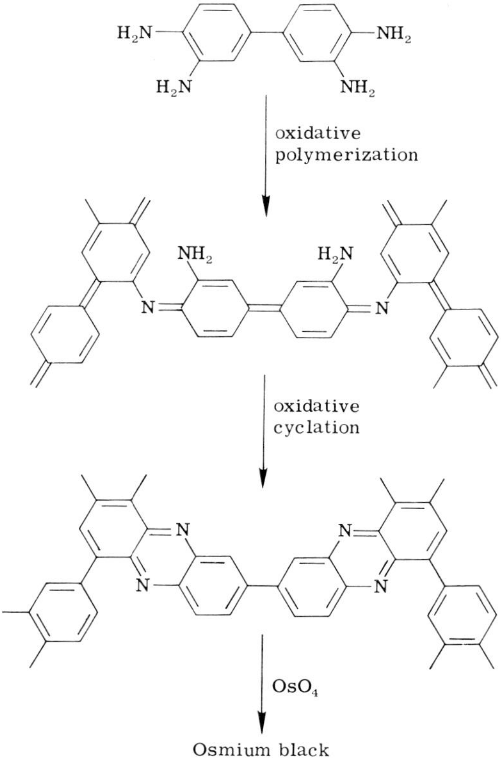

For once we are dealing with an enzyme cytochemical reaction that was original-ly devised for studies with plants! The modified reaction has been applied in detail to plants (reviewed in Sexton and Hall, 1978 (Fig. 13B), and the basic method allows the use of fixation that seems to help in minimising the effects of diffusion of the enzyme and in improving the rate of penetration of DAB into

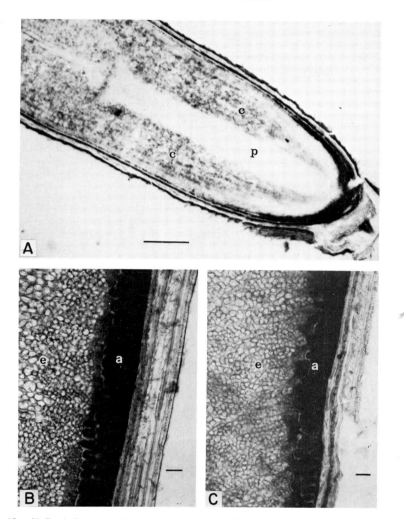

FIG. 13. Unfixed, frozen sections incubated for peroxidase activity. (A) Seed of *Lactuca sativa* reacted with homovanillic acid. c, cortex; p, prostele. (B) and (C) Seed of *Avena fatua* showing aleurone layer (a) and part of endosperm (e) reacted with diaminobenzidene (B) and *p*-phenylene diamine (C) giving very strong reaction in aleurone layer. Scale, 0.1 mm.

tissues, which is normally very slow (Sexton and Hall, 1978). Use of either glutaraldehyde or formaldehyde does not appear to inhibit peroxidase activity to any serious degree (Al-Azzawi and Hall, 1977) and helps the preservation of cell ultra-structure during the reaction.

A number of controls are needed for the peroxidase reaction. Firstly, incubation in the medium lacking H_2O_2 is essential, although endogenous H_2O_2 can be generated by the tissue itself. A variety of methods have been suggested to block endogenous H_2O_2 production, including pretreatment of the tissue sections with buffered 0.05–0.075% catalase for 1–2 h prior to incubation in the test medium, or adding 2 mM sodium pyruvate to the incubation medium to supress peroxide (Fahimi, 1969).

Next, heat inactivation of the enzymes for 5–15 min at 95°C will inhibit most of the enzymes, although some peroxidases may be heat-resistant (Fahimi, 1969). Finally, the nonspecific adsorption of DAB can be tested by placing sections in a H_2O_2-free medium. The sections are washed and then transferred to a buffered medium containing 3×10^{-3} M potassium ferricyanide for 5 min when the DAB will be oxidised (Sexton and Hall, 1978).

In studying catalase activity, essentially the same reaction is employed. Once again, catalase behaves in a similar way to peroxidase with respect to fixation (Sexton and Hall, 1978), though the post-fixation wash would seem of importance (Fahimi, 1973). Thus, whilst long post-fixation washes are recommended for peroxidases, short washing times (about 30 min) are recommended for catalases that seem to be more readily eluted.

The reaction for plant tissues is normally that of Frederick and Newcomb (1969) based on the original method of Novikoff and Goldfischer (1969). The reaction relies on the fact that whilst hydrogen peroxide normally acts as both electron donor and receptor, other hydrogen donors can be shown to be capable of replacing hydrogen peroxide. In consequence, Chance (1950) proposed that the catalase reaction was not simply as shown in Eq. (5), but that

$$\text{Catalase} + H_2O_2 \rightarrow \text{catalase–}H_2O_2 \text{ complex} \xrightarrow{\text{XH}_2} \text{catalase} + 2H_2O + X$$

and so DAB could be acting as XH_2 in this type of reaction. Thus, controls performed for peroxidase activity in the absence of either substrate or DAB must also be made for catalase. Since both peroxidase and catalase are shown by similar reactions, how can one try to distinguish between them? One approach is the use of 3-amino-1,2,4-triazole as a strong inhibitor of catalase and which does not inhibit peroxidase (Margoliash and Novogrodsky, 1958; Recheigl and Evans, 1963). Normally 20 mM aminotriazole will be adequate for the purpose, although there may be some problems with its use since Longo et al. (1972) found only 60–70% of maize catalase to be inhibited at this concentration. However, the use of 100 mM aminotriazole (Drumm et al., 1970) yielded a 90% inhibition of catalase without affecting peroxidase.

A further control may be through the action of the hydrogen peroxide itself, which at a concentration of 1% inhibits peroxidase activity whilst still allowing catalase to operate (Vigil, 1970). This would be best performed on sections of fixed material, since 1% H_2O_2 will normally damage unfixed frozen sections.

Whilst it was thought that peroxides and catalase may be separated by changing the pH of the reaction from pH 7.6 for the former to pH 10.0 for the latter, it should be mentioned that even at the high pH employed for catalase activity, peroxidase may still be active (Hall and Sexton, 1972). Recently, an alternative method has been employed for peroxidase activity in animal tissues and is of interest for plant studies (P. B. Gahan and A. L. Dawson, unpublished data) in that it avoids the use of the carinogenic compound DAB, yields a coloured electron-dense end-product, and the end-product can be coupled with a fluorescent compound that could lead to the reaction being quantifiable (Fig. 13A). The basis of the reaction is the conversion of homovanillic acid from its monomeric to its dimeric form by the action of H_2O_2 and peroxidase.

Monomeric
homovanillic acid
(non-fluorescent)

Dimeric
homovanillic acid
(fluorescent)

The dimer can then be precipitated by lead ions in the presence of either Rhodamine B or Rhodamine 6G and viewed directly by fluorescence or electron microscopy. In addition, the lead complex may be treated with ammonium sulphide and converted to lead sulphide for viewing by bright field microscopy (Papadimitriou et al., 1976). Such a reaction would be of immense value when peroxidase is used to tag antibodies in immuno-fluorescent studies of proteins (see Chapter 4).

Equally valuable in studies on plant tissues is the method of Hanker et al. (1977) in which DAB is replaced by pyrocatechol and p-phenylenediamine in the reaction. The oxidative coupling reactions of some aromatic amines in the presence of phenols yield deeply coloured synthetic melanin-like compounds that are relatively water-insoluble and are osmiophilic. The peroxidation of p-phenylenediamine (PPD) was greatly accelerated by the presence of pyrocatechol. The resulting co-polymer was found to be osmiophilic and bluer than oxidized DAB, thus being available for both optical and electron microscopy. The method was originally designed to be used with horseradish peroxidase, and has proven useful in studies on pea roots and dormant and non-dormant seeds of Avena (A. L. Dawson and P. B. Gahan, unpublished; Fig. 13C).

A less frequently exploited method is that used in studies of monoamine oxidase in animal tissues in which 3-amino-9-ethylcarbazole is reduced to an insoluble red product (Pearse, 1972). This has been little used in plant studies (Rickard, 1982).

V. POLYPHENOL OXIDASES

This is a group of enzymes responsible for the oxidation of polyphenols to quinones, e.g. the browning reaction in apples. They are also known as phenolase, catechol oxidase and tyrosinase. Czaninski and Catesson (1974) have critically reviewed these enzymes and their localization in plants. Most published work has used the dopa test in which dihydrophenylalanine (dopa) is oxidised to dopa quinone.

Ring closure of the quinone occurs spontaneously when reaction with water yields indole-5,6-quinone, which polymerizes to form the pigmented product. This product is capable of reacting with OsO_4 to yield an electron-dense complex for ultrastructural studies.

This group of enzymes can be examined after fixation with aldehydes, although studies on animal tissues indicate that activity is inhibited by fixation for only 30 min in 5% formalin (Rappaport, 1955). Effective inhibition of these enzymes occur with 20 mM sodium diethyldithiocarbamate.

Two problems can occur with this method. The first is that dopa may undergo auto-oxidation in alkaline solutions (Eppig, 1974), though this can be overcome either by adjusting the pH of the normal phosphate buffer to pH 6.8, by using cacodylate buffer at pH 7.4, or by renewing the incubation medium with freshly prepared solution at frequent intervals during incubation.

The second problem concerns the fact that peroxidases are capable of oxidising the polyphenyl oxidase substrates, and if H_2O_2 is generated in the section, false-positive localization may occur. The same approach for the removal of H_2O_2 can be employed as in the reactions for peroxidases.

VI. HYDROLASES

The problems outlined above for all enzyme studies apply to the hydrolases with respect to tissue preparation and the interaction of the reactants with the sections and enzymes contained therein. It is possible to gain information on a broad range of hydrolytic enzymes at both the optical and electron microscope levels, but interestingly, the methods are mostly based upon three general types of reaction. Thus, prior to discussing the individual enzyme tests, a few comments are offered on the basic approaches.

A. The Metal Salt Technique

1. Method

This approach was published independently by Gomori (1939) and Takamatsu (1939) for alkaline phosphatase activity. Essentially, the enzyme acts on the substrate releasing a group such as phosphate, which complexes with calcium or lead ions present in the incubation medium. The resultant product is water-insoluble and should precipitate at the site of the enzyme reaction. The choice of lead or calcium as the trapping agent depends upon the pH of the reaction. Lead phosphate is water-insoluble at an acid pH, but on increasing the pH to above 8.0 it is increasingly mobile in an aqueous medium. At high pH values calcium should be employed and is subsequently replaced by cobalt prior to forming the metal sulphide (Gomori, 1952).

The reaction is most frequently employed with phosphatase activities (Fig. 14), and the cobalt or lead phosphate so produced, whilst being electron-dense and hence observable directly with the electron microscope, is white in colour and hence viewed only with extreme difficulty with the optical microscope. To ameliorate this situation, the cobalt or lead phosphate is converted to a black metal sulphide by interaction with ammonium or hydrogen sulphide solution, respectively. The overall reaction may be expressed as follows:

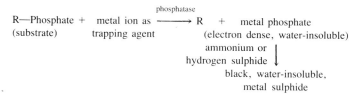

In the case of reactions that employ sulphur-containing substrates, e.g. for cholinesterase activity, with thioacetic acid as substrate in the presence of a metal trapping agent, a black metal sulphide is the direct product of the reaction in which hydrolysis of thiolacetate results in the liberation of H_2S. This can be viewed by either the optical or electron microscopes.

2. Problems of Interpretation

The effects of fixation have already been discussed in general and will be treated additionally for each enzyme. However, the method itself poses some problems due to the use of a heavy metal. Lead ions have an affinity for some tissue components and so can result in a non-enzymic reaction. This may be overcome by an extremely brief (10 s) rinsing of sections in 1% acetic acid solution. The

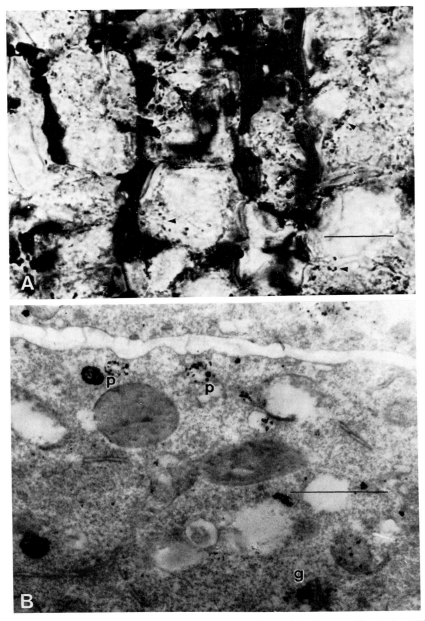

FIG. 14.   Longitudinal, unfixed frozen section of root tip of *Vicia faba* (A) reacted for 4 min at 37°C for acid *p*-nitrophenyl phosphatase. Granular deposits (arrows) indicate phytolysosomal enzyme activity, whilst the diffuse reaction along the cell walls may indicate a transport phosphatase activity.

operative word is brief, since the acetic acid will not distinguish between lead ions bound to the section and the enzymically formed lead phosphate, so that the longer the washing, the more likely will be the loss of lead phosphate.

A nuclear reaction is frequently observed, and this has been considered to be due to a random (non-enzymic) lead deposit in the nucleus (Gomori, 1952) or to diffusion of either the enzyme (Bitensky, 1962) or the reaction product (Bitensky, 1963) to the nucleus with prolonged incubation times. Meticulous investigation of the lead salt reaction by Holt (1959) also showed that the correct ratio of the components in the reaction medium is critical, and variations in this ratio can lead to artefactual deposits of lead in the sections. In the case of plant tissues, there is the distinct possibility of the presence of high concentrations of endogenous phosphate that can also lead to the formation of non-enzymic lead phosphate. Additional problems specific to the handling of tissues with this method for electron microscopy have been well discussed by Essner (1973) and by Sexton and Hall (1978).

From the foregoing remarks, it is evident that control reactions are essential, and must include (a) the omission of the substrate from the full incubation medium; (b) the addition of specific activators or inhibitors to the full incubation medium; and (c) the use of heat-inactivated sections. In addition, it is worthwhile to limit the times of incubation as much as possible in order to achieve an enzyme reaction with a reduced artefactual deposition of metal.

B. The Azo Dye Method

1. Method

This approach has gained favour in view of the wider application of the basic method when compared to that of the metal salt method. It differs from the latter in that whilst in the metal salt method the free phosphate is trapped, in the azo dye technique it is the phenol or naphthol molecules which are trapped.

The azo-dye method developed from an idea by Menten et al. (1944) which depended upon the reaction

$$\text{Ca-}\beta\text{-naphthyl phosphate} \xrightarrow[\text{phosphatase}]{\text{alkaline}} \beta\text{-naphthol}$$

If this reaction was performed in the presence of a diazonium salt, then β-naphthol and α-naphthyl diazonium chloride would lead to the formation of a red dye complex. In general terms, a water-soluble, yellow or colourless phenol derivative or naphthol coupled to a phosphate radicle will be acted upon by the

Scale, 10 μm. (B) Part of root meristematic cell of *Vicia faba* fixed at 4°C for 2 h in 2.5% glutaraldehyde and reacted for acid β-glycerophosphatase activity for 8 min at 37°C. End-product is present in phytolysosomes (p) and Golgi body (g) Unstained section. Scale, 1 μm.

hydrolase to cleave the radical, and the now water-insoluble phenol derivative or naphthol molecule, in the presence of a diazonium salt, will couple to yield to a water-insoluble, coloured product:

$$\underset{\substack{\text{phosphate}\\\text{(yellow, water-soluble)}}}{\text{Naphthol AS-BI}} + \text{diazonium salt} \xrightarrow{\text{phosphatase}} \text{phosphate} + \underset{\substack{\text{diazonium salt complex}\\\text{(coloured, water-insoluble)}}}{\text{naphthol AS-BI-}}$$

The diazonium salt is essentially the product of a primary aromatic (or aliphatic) amine after treatment with nitrous acid at ice-cold temperature:

$$Ar \cdot NH_2 + HNO_2 + HCl \rightarrow (ArN \equiv N)^+ Cl^- + 2\ H_2O$$

Thus, in the reaction of Menten *et al.* (1944) we have

This is known as a simultaneous coupling reaction since both substrate and diazonium salt are present in the incubation medium. The alternative approach is to react the tissue with the substrate and then transfer to a second bath containing the diazonium salt. Such a procedure is termed post-coupling.

Clearly, the azo dye techniques offer greater possibilities than the metal salt method, since the phosphate group can be replaced by alternative groups, e.g. sulphate and glucuronide, and the basic reaction exploited for different enzymes. Other advantages over the metal salt method include

1. Frequent use of shorter incubation times, indicating greater sensitivity.
2. Naphthols are not normally present in plant cells and so the chances of false-positivity are reduced though not eliminated.
3. Azo dyes are much less water-soluble than, e.g. $CaHPO_4$, so reducing the changes of diffusion.
4. Azo dyes are very substantive, i.e. they bind to protein, hence reducing the possibility of diffusion and so giving good localization.

5. Simultaneous coupling reactions permit immediate visualization of the end-product.

6. Quantification of the end-product is much more feasible than with Ca or Pb.

2. General Comments on the Substrates

A big improvement over the original substrate of Menten *et al.* (1944) was the replacing of Ca β-naphthyl phosphate by Na α-naphthyl phosphate (Gomori, 1952). The substitution of sodium for calcium immediately increased the water solubility of the substrate, enabling an optimum concentration of substrate to be employed. A second benefit was greater water insolubility of the azo dye formed with α-naphthol compared to its β-naphthol counterpart, which reduced the problem of diffusion of the end-product.

A major improvement came with the introduction of mono-substituted naphthol phosphates, e.g. naphthol AS, by Rutenburg *et al.* (1958a), and the various complex arylides of 2-hydroxy-3-naphthoic acid by Burstone (1962) reviewed in detail by him. Three of the commonly used substrates are

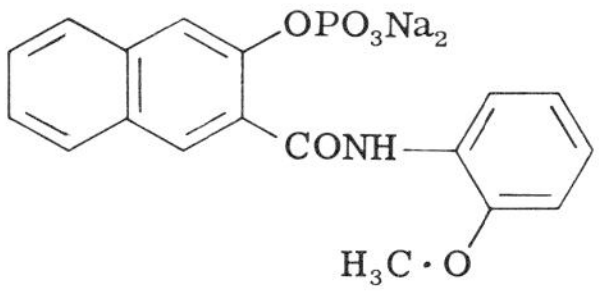

Naphthol **AS**–BI phosphate

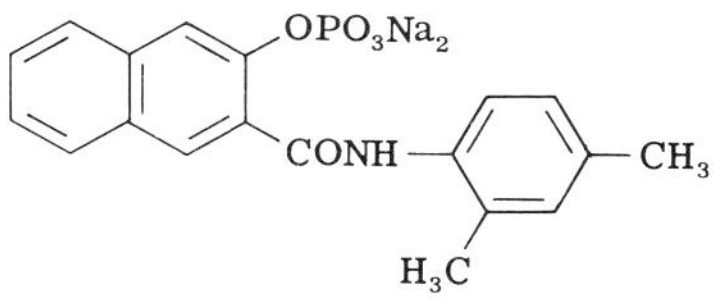

Naphthol **AS**–MX phosphate

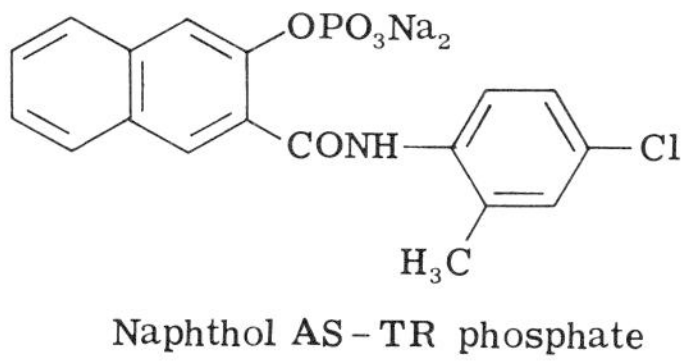

Naphthol **AS**–TR phosphate

These substrates are very stable in acid solutions, the sodium salts being more freely soluble than the free acids. Before waxing too enthusiastic, it is perhaps important to mention the following.

1. The solubility of these substrates in aqueous media is very low, which makes it difficult to achieve an optimal substrate concentration. This difficulty is overcome by dissolving the substrates in a minimal quantity of either acetone or dimethylformamide prior to mixing with the buffer system.

2. They are larger molecules than either α- or β-naphthol and possess a variety of polar groups that tend to result in there being a low substrate level at the site of the enzyme.

3. Hydroxynaphthoic acids have a lower coupling rate than either α- or β-naphthol, e.g. the half-time for coupling with the diazonium salt fast blue B at high pH is about 62 s with a variety of anilides, 300 ms with α-naphthol and 1800 ms with β-naphthol (Pearse, 1968).

4. Perhaps the biggest worry is that they are not naturally occurring substrates, and in consequence reactions need to be controlled very carefully in order to try to define the enzyme or enzymes under investigation.

3. General Comments on Diazonium Salts

In early studies it was necessary to prepare diazonium salts fresh on each occasion, but it is now possible to obtain stable diazonium salts from commercial sources. A number are available, but it is important to remember that their long shelf life is due to the addition of stabilizers that may also be enzyme inhibitors. A favourite diazonium salt for acid phosphatase activity was fast red violet LB, i.e. 5-benzamide-4-chloro-o-toluidine (Burstone, 1962; Pearse, 1968, 1972), but this has now been withdrawn from the market and alternative salts must be used, e.g. hexazotized pararosaniline (Davis and Ornstein, 1959). The recommended replacement by the manufacturers, fast violet B, has not proved as efficient in plant studies as fast red violet LB when used at acid pH in a simultaneous coupling reaction. The stability of these diazonium salts in solution varies, and probably pH 8.2 should be regarded as a limit of stability in the alkaline range. To stabilize further it is necessary to reduce the temperature or to change the incubation medium at frequent intervals.

Given the long lists of diazonium salts, how is a choice made? To date, this appears to have occurred in a somewhat empirical way, and botanists have tended to exploit methods available from animal studies. What appears to be a good clean reaction product may merely be due to the fact that enzyme inhibition has occurred at some sites due to action of the added stabilizer or to active groups present in the molecule, so giving a sharper picture. In addition, the pH of the reaction can influence the degree and rate of coupling. Thus, using fast blue B with α- and β-naphthol, Pearse (1968) found that optimal coupling occurred at alkaline pH values. In other words, the optimal pH for the enzyme reaction may not be the optimal pH for rapid coupling to the diazonium salt. Hence the choice of pH may have to be a compromise between these two differing requirements, or it may be necessary to resort to post-coupling, thereby achieving optimal rates in both cases.

Whilst it is to be noted that the enzyme product is highly substantive, it must also be mentioned that the azo dye may also be lipophilic and readily migrate from its site of formation to any adjacent lipid droplets.

One problem arising from the application of this approach to electron microscopy is that the products are not very electron opaque. Various attempts have

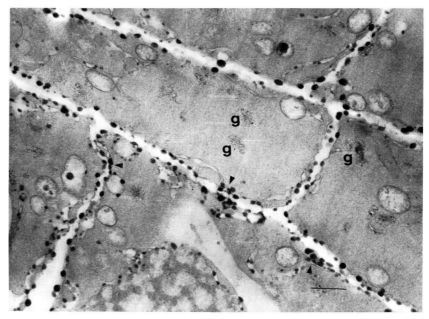

FIG. 15.   Unstained section, of root tip of *Vicia faba* fixed for 2 h at 4°C in 2.5% glutaraldehyde and reacted for esterase activity using naphthol AS-D acetate as substrate and lead phthalocyanin as the diazonium salt. End-product is present in discrete packages in the endoplasmic reticulum and passing through the plasmalemma (arrowheads) and in the Golgi bodies (g). Scale, 1 μm.

been made to overcome this, e.g. by introducing heavy metals into the diazonium salts (Livingstone *et al.*, 1969 Fig. 15), but this has had limited success (McLean and Gahan, 1969). A further possibility seems to be the use of hexazotized pararosaniline as the coupling salt, which when coupled to hydroxynaphthoic acid derivatives yields an electron-dense product. However, whilst this seems successful if naphthol AS-TX phosphate is used as a substrate, naphthol AS-TX yields an end-product which is freely soluble in the dehydrating solutions and embedding resins (Holt and Hicks, 1965; Livingstone *et al.*, 1969), though this can be overcome by using water-soluble Durcupan (Fluka Ltd) for dehydration.

C. Indigo Dye Methods

Method

This approach involves the use of indoxyl derivatives, e.g. acetate and phosphate, as substrates for various hydrolases. It was originally derived for glucosidases and sulphatases (Holt, 1952), the substrate being hydrolyzed to free,

soluble, indoxyl, which is oxidized via its leuco derivatives to the corresponding
indigoid dye. The basis of the reaction is outlined for esterases is as follows:

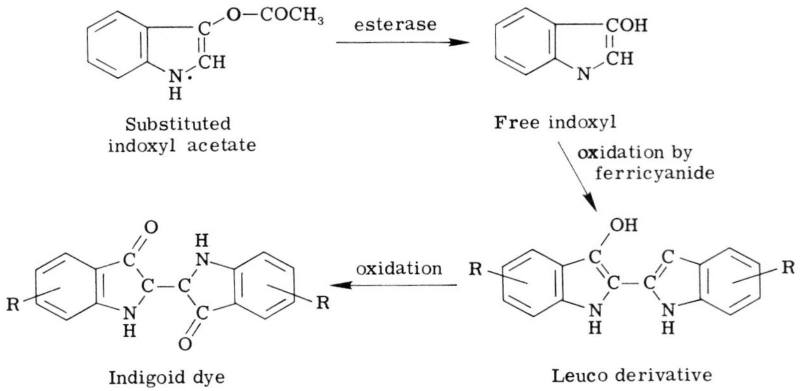

Substituted
indoxyl acetate　　　　　　　　　　　　　Free indoxyl

oxidation by
ferricyanide

Indigoid dye　　　　　　　　　　　　　Leuco derivative

The reaction has been used most successfully with esterases for which the best
substrates appear to be 5-bromoindoxyl acetate and 5-bromo-4-chloroindoxyl
acetate. The oxidation process under cytochemical conditions is somewhat un-
usual in that normally oxidation of indoxyls by ferricyanide yields isatins and
anthranilic acids. However, in the presence of fixed proteins, the indoxyls become linked to the functional groups of the proteins revealed on derivation
through fixation and become oxidized to the indigoid dye. If unfixed protein is
present, then indigoid dyes appear not to form, yielding less product that is more
diffusible.

In spite of its attractions, the method has been little used on plant material
(e.g., McLean, 1969), perhaps because it does not seem to give a localization
that compares with that of azo dye methods, yet it might provide an interesting
method for electron microscopy, since as shown by Holt and Hicks (1966),
electron-dense, indoxyl–azo dye complexes can be formed with hexazotized
pararosaniline:

Indoxyl　　　Hexazotized
pararosaniline

Indoxyl-azo dye
(insoluble)

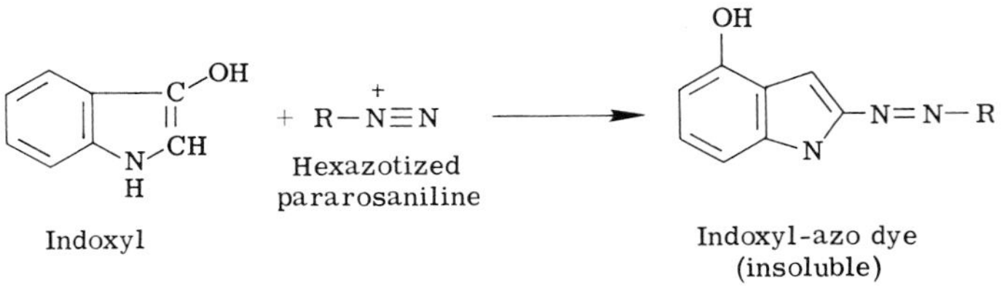

Post-osmication produces an electron-dense complex that seems to consist of the
linking together of the indoxylazo groups from three dye molecules by the
divalent osmium to form an octahedral complex:

D. Alkaline Phosphatase

There is some confusion in the literature concerning this enzyme in plant tissues, since it has never been possible to demonstrate the alkaline phosphatase activity typically associated with animal tissues. Using β-glycerophosphate as substrate, no activity was found by Jensen (1962) or P. B. Gahan (unpublished data), yet in contrast Surrey (reported in van Fleet, 1957) successfully used it in studies on regenerating meristem tissue after wounding, and K. M. A. Sheikh (private communication) found such activity in developing crown gall tumours in tomato. Studies with naphthol AS-B phosphate as substrate have also permitted the identification of an "alkaline phosphatase" activity in tissues of V. faba, especially the embryo (P. B. Gahan and A. L. Dawson, in preparation). However, this activity at pH 10 has proved to be insensitive to levamisol and ouabain and can be stimulated by Mg^{2+}. In these respects, it is unlike the animal alkaline phosphatase, but has some characteristics of cell wall ATPase (Hall, 1971) that can show activity at high pH.

The reaction employed naphthol AS-BI phosphate with a diazonium salt at pH 10.0 in a simultaneous coupling reaction. Long incubation times were required, and, in consequence, it was found necessary to change the incubation medium every 20 min due to breakdown of the substrate at high pH. Too little is known about this activity for much comment on the methodology.

More recently, alkaline phosphatase has been found to be present in onion roots and the mycorrhiza of Glomus mosseae, especially during the infection of the host by the mycorrhiza. Biochemical and cytochemical studies using p-nitrophenyl phosphate, β-glycerophosphate and α-naphthyl phosphate as substrates indicated enzyme activity at pH 8.5, which was inhibited by cyanide,

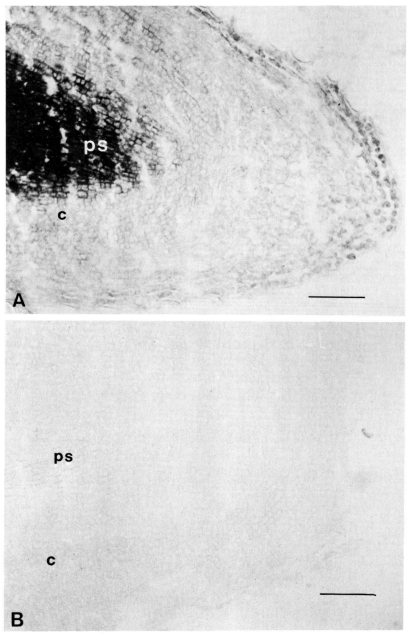

FIG. 16. Longitudinal, unfixed, frozen sections of root tip of *Pisum sativum*. (A) Reacted for 1 h at 37°C for esterase activity using naphthol AS-D acetate as substrate and fast blue BB as diazonium salt. (B) Preincubated for 15 min in acetate buffer pH 6.5 containing 10^{-4} M E600, followed by

cysteine and Cu^{2+}, but was insensitive to fluoride, and was activated by Mg^{2+} and Mn^{2+} ions (Gianinazzi-Pearson and Gianinazzi, 1976, 1977; Gianinazzi *et al.*, 1979). Whilst this implicates an alkaline phosphatase activity, especially in the mycorrhiza of *Glomus mosseae,* the evidence is still equivocal.

E. Esterases

These represent a broad spectrum of enzymes that are widely distributed in plant tissues and are capable of hydrolysing the carboxylic acid esters of alcohols, phenols and naphthols:

$$R\text{-}COOR' + H_2O \leftrightarrow R\text{-}COOH + R'OH$$

At present, five groups of esterases can be considered in cytochemistry:

1. Carboxylesterases, which preferentially hydrolyze aliphatic and aromatic esters. They are inhibited by organo-phosphates, but not by eserine.

2. Arylesterases, which hydrolyze aromatic esters, especially acetates. They are inhibited by sulphydryl agents, but not by organophosphates.

3. Acetylesterases, which hydrolyze both aromatic and aliphatic acetyl esters. They are not inhibited by eserine, sulphydryl reagents or low concentrations of organophosphates.

4. Acetylcholinesterases, which hydrolyze acetylcholine at a higher rate than either aliphatic or aromatic esters. They are inhibited by low concentrations of eserine or organophosphates.

5. Cholinesterases, which hydrolyze preferentially butyrylcholine and aromatic butyrate esters. They are inhibited by eserine and organophosphates.

As is frequently the case, most information available stems from studies on animal tissues, and here it is possible to demonstrate these groups of esterases by means of a number of substrates including α-naphthyl acetate (1,2,4, and 5), naphthol AS-D acetate (1–3), indoxyl acetates (1–5), thiolacetic acid (1–5), acetylthiocholine (3 and 4), butyryl thiocholine (5) and myrystylthiocholine (3). The reactions with α-naphthol acetate and naphthol AS-D acetate are by the azo dye method, indoxyl acetate by the indigo dye method, and the remainder by the metal salt technique.

Each of the main groups of esterases contain a number of enzymes, and at present, the best hope of identification is through the use of inhibitors coupled with polyacrylamide gel electrophoresis. The standard inhibitors are eserine and E-600 (organophosphorus compound that is highly dangerous), both of which have been used at 10^{-4} M (Gahan, 1981) (Fig. 16).

---

incubation for 1 h at 37°C as for (A) plus E600. Note heavy activity in central portion of the meristem (ps, prostele; c, cortex) and almost complete inhibition of activity by E600. Scale, 0.1 mm.

All three methods have been used satisfactorily on plant tissues. The azo dye method for optical and electron microscopy where naphthol AS-D acetate was the substrate employed has been the most popular (e.g., Gahan and McLean, 1969; Livingstone et al., 1969; Knox and Heslop-Harrison, 1970; Williamson, 1973; Beneš, 1974). This was found to be preferable to α-naphthyl acetate, the end-product of which is less substantive, though this can be used with good results on acrylamide gels (Gahan et al., 1970; Sheikh and Gahan, 1976). The thiolacetic acid reaction (Wachstein and Meisel, 1960) has been used with success in a number of plant studies (e.g., Coulomb, 1969b; Berjak, 1968). The indigo dye method has been little exploited, but can be used successfully (McLean, 1969; McLean and Gahan, 1970). Using this approach and eserine and E-600 as inhibitors, evidence for "pseudo" acetylcholinesterase activity was obtained from cells of the pulvinus region in petioles of *Mimosa pudica* (J. McLean and P. B. Gahan, unpublished data) and represents also a carboxyl esterase linked to stele formation (Gahan, 1981).

F. Lipase

Generally, esters of short-chain fatty acids (C_2–C_4) are hydrolyzed by esterases, whilst those of longer chain fatty acids (C_8–C_n) tend to be hydrolyzed by lipases. This is a somewhat contentious area, since there is an overlap *vis-à-vis* substrates and esterase activity.

Lipase activity has been frequently studied in animal tissues using the modified lead salt method (Gomori, 1945; see review by Nagata, 1974). The basis of this reaction is the use of Tween 40, 60 or 80 as a substrate. Tween 80 (polyoxyethylene sorbitan monoleate) has been most favoured and used in the presence of calcium ions. On hydrolysis fatty acids are produced that form insoluble calcium soaps. The calcium is subsequently replaced by lead ions, which are then converted to lead sulphide.

The method does not appear to have been used very successfully with plant tissue, although Yamada (1957) claimed to have been able to do so.

G. Adenosinetriphosphatase (ATPase)

This name is given to a number of enzymes present in plant cells that catalyse the hydrolysis of ATP to yield inorganic phosphate. ATPases from animal systems have been fairly well characterized, which is not the case for these enzymes in plants. Thus, ATPase activity has been demonstrated in some plant tissues and is seen to be associated with both the plasma membrane and the cell wall (Hall, 1969a,b, 1971). In contrast to animal cells, the Mg^{2-}- and K^--activated ATPase systems have not been clearly demonstrated by biochemical means in plant cells, though a K^--activated acyl phosphatase activity has been found cytochemically in prostelar cells of the root (Gahan *et al.*, 1978).

The cytochemical techniques are based upon the lead salt method of Wachstein and Meisel (1957). The inorganic phosphate freed by the action of ATPase on ATP is trapped by lead ions present in the incubation medium. Some criticism has been levelled at the method because it is considered that lead in the medium (a) inhibits the enzyme activity and (b) catalyses the non-enzymic breakdown of ATP (Rosenthal *et al.*, 1966; Moses and Rosenthal, 1968; Tice, 1969). However, the studies of Novikoff (1967, 1970) would seem to refute this view, and Hall (1969b) considered the influence of lead ions to be of little significance in inducing artefacts in plant tissues.

Whilst the reaction may be performed on unfixed, frozen or razor sections, Al-Azzawi and Hall (1977) showed that fixation in 1% glutaraldehyde fixation for 2 h did not affect it significantly.

Clearly, when working with a lead salt technique controls are of the utmost importance, and should include a no-substrate and a heat-inactivated section control. In addition, the effects of Na^+ and K^+ can be tried, though a typical inhibitor to use is ouabain, which seems to act specifically upon ATPase activity (Ernst, 1975). Post-osmication of sections reacted for electron microscopy should be interpreted with care, since not all electron-dense structures may be enzymatically active (Van Steveninck, 1979).

H. Nucleoside Phosphatases

A range of nucleoside phosphatases have been localized by lead salt methods using a series of nucleoside mono-, di- and triphosphates as substrates (Pearse, 1972). Such reactions have been performed successfully on plant cells, especially for IDPase, which in animal cells is considered to be a marker for Golgi bodies. In *Allium cepa* roots IDPase would seem to be sensitive to glutaraldehyde fixation (Goff and Klohs, 1974), though successful studies performed on other plant tissues would indicate that enough activity remains for the method to be viable.

I. Glucose-6-Phosphatase

This is also demonstrable by the lead salt method using glucose-6-phosphate as substrate. The enzyme has been localized successfully in plant tissues by this method (Hall, 1977; Gahan *et al.*, 1978) and appears to be heat-sensitive, being inhibited by incubating sections for 15 min at 37°C in acetate buffer at pH 5.0 (Beaufey, 1972). Specific inhibitors for this enzyme include sorbitan-6-phosphate and *o*-hydroxy-phenylacetic acid.

J. Adenyl Cyclase

Studies on animal tissues indicate that this enzyme can be demonstrated by a lead salt method using 5^1-adenylylimidodiphosphate (AMP-PNP) as substrate (Howell and Whitfield, 1972; Wagner and Bitensky, 1974). Normally, adenyl cyclase acts on ATP to form cAMP and pyrophosphate. The presence of such an enzyme is clear-cut in animal tissues, though its presence in plant tissues is readily disputed (reviewed in Amhrein, 1977). Nevertheless, by employing the cytochemical method of Wagner and Bitensky (1974) it has been possible to demonstrate the presence of an activity resembling adenyl cyclase in cells of maize roots (Al-Azzawi and Hall, 1976) and in bean roots and embryos (P. B. Gahan and A. L. Dawson, in preparation).

The reaction involves

$$5^1\text{-Adenylylimidodiphosphate} \xrightarrow[\text{cyclase}]{\text{adenyl}} cAMP + \text{imidodiphosphate} \xrightarrow{Pb^+} \text{lead complex}$$

The rate of hydrolysis of AMP-PNP by adenyl cyclase is slower than that of ATP, and so longer incubation times are needed if the former is used.

In a reaction of this kind, a number of controls are necessary in addition to those discussed previously for the lead salt methods. Firstly, purity of the substrate is important since the presence of ATP will also yield a positive reaction through the effects of ATPase. Secondly, since cAMP is continuously degraded to 5^1-AMP by cAMP phosphodiesterase (Sutherland and Rall, 1958), and because 5^1- nucleotidases can further degrade 5^1-AMP to adenosine and inorganic phosphate, it is important to include an inhibitor of the phosphodiesterase in the incubation medium. To this end, theophylline is usually employed, through it can be replaced by aminophylline or methylxanthines (Butcher and Sutherland, 1962). Sodium vanadate has been used in biochemical studies to inhibit simultaneously ATPase activity and activate adenyl cyclase activity (Schwabe et al., 1979). This is of no use with the cytochemical method, since vanadate complexes with lead to form lead vanadate.

K. Acid Phosphatases

Originally the name was used to describe an enzyme that hydrolyzed a range of phosphate esters at an optimum acid pH. This is too general a description, since it encompasses a wide range of enzyme activities with pH optima between 4.5 and 6.5. In view of this, and because of the frequent employment of non-physiological substrates in biochemical and cytochemical studies, a form of nomenclature arose in which the activities were described according to the substrate employed, e.g. acid β-glycerophosphatase, acid naphthol AS-BI phosphatase, acid p-nitrophenylphosphatase. Even this only allowed "group names" to be applied, since it is clear that more than one enzyme can work on a given substrate of the type commonly employed with plant tissues (e.g., Gahan *et al.*, 1970; Sheikh and Gahan, 1967; Johnson *et al.*, 1973; Gahan *et al.*, 1978). This is still not a satisfactory classification, though it aids in comparing published data.

Acid phosphatases in plant cells can be demonstrated by the lead salt method (e.g., Gahan, 1965a; Gahan *et al.*, 1978), the azo dye method (Burstone, 1962) and the bromoindoxyl method (P. B. Gahan and J. McLean, unpublished data). It is difficult to recommend one method rather than another since the commonly used substrates, e.g. β-glycerophosphate, *p*-nitrophenylphosphate and naphthol AS-BI phosphate, each demonstrate a multiplicity of acid phosphatases and, in addition, do not necessarily demonstrate the same enzymes (e.g., Gahan *et al.*, 1978). Thus, it is possible to arrive at a situation where one substrate may show the presence of acid phosphatase activity whilst another used on the same tissues will not (e.g., Gahan and McLean, 1967). In consequence, when starting to work with a new tissue, it is of value to try more than one substrate.

1. Fixation

Whilst a number of studies have been performed on the effects of fixation on acid phosphatases in animal tissues (Table IV), there have been few on plant tissues. Sexton *et al.* (1971) showed that fixation for 2 h in 3% glutaraldehyde slightly affected acid β-glycerophosphatase activity in roots of *P. sativum*, leaving 84% of the enzyme activity available. However, 10% acrolein destroyed 75% of the enzyme activity. Clearly, more work is needed in this area of study of plant tissues, especially in terms of the sensitivity of one enzyme rather than another in a range demonstrable with a single substrate.

2. Controls

If more than one enzyme is involved, what controls can be devised for studying acid phosphatase reactions? There is no simple answer, but the following suggestions may be of some help. Control reactions may be performed at two levels. The first concerns the validity of the reactions themselves, which were described in general terms in Section VI,A–C. Some further specific points may be of help with the two most frequently used methods. In the case of the lead salt method if sodium β-glycerophosphate is used as the substrate, the reaction can normally be inhibited by the addition of 10 mM sodium fluoride to the full incubation medium. If this inhibitor is used with *p*-nitrophenylphosphate as substrate, total inhibition will not be achieved, and, in fact, there are signs of an activation of the enzyme in some cell types (Gahan *et al.*, 1978). In general however, some 90% of the total activity will be inhibited, though Hall (1969a) reports as little as 70% inhibition. This difference of enzyme sensitivity to the fluoride ions demonstrated with the two substrates may be a reflection of the additional enzymes shown with p-nitrophenylphosphate as compared with β-glycerophosphate (Gahan *et al.*, 1978).

In studying the azo dye reaction, it has been found too that total inhibition of the acid phosphatase activity cannot be achieved with 10 mM sodium fluoride in either animal or plant cells. A recent study of isolated rat liver parenchymal cells (Middleton and Gahan, 1979) has shown only a 90% inhibition. Studies by Maggi and Carbonell (1969) indicated that acid phosphatase activity that was fluoride resistant was associated with the ribosomes in young mouse kidney cells. In contrast, acid naphthol AS-BI phosphatase activity in plant cells can be completely inhibited with 10 mM sodium molybdate. Unfortunately, this inhibitor cannot be employed with the lead salt method, since the conditions of the incubation media are ideal for the formation of lead molybdate (Vogel, 1951), and all of the lead will be removed from the incubation medium (McLean, 1969), yielding a false negative reaction.

The second level of control concerns the actual identification of the enzymes involved in the reaction. Not enough work has been performed to establish the certain identity of these enzymes by polyacrylamide gel electrophoresis of isolated enzyme fractions. However, an important step forward in the cytochemical demonstration of these enzymes concerns the use of more specific inhibitors, e.g. ouabain, in an effort to identify the distribution of known enzymes when using the broad-spectrum substrates. This can be further aided by the use of activators, such as K^+, Na^+ or Mg^{2+} ions. It is pertinent to mention that p-nitrophenylphosphate can act as substrate for those enzymes seen with β-glycerophosphate plus nucleotide pyrophosphatase (Kole *et al.*, 1976), K^+-activated acyl phosphatase (Gahan *et al.*, 1978), glucose-6-phosphatase (Gahan *et al.*, 1978), $5^1,(3^1)$-ribonucleotide phosphohydrolase (Polya and Ashton, 1973) and nucleotide phosphotransferase (Brawerman and Chargaff, 1955). The azo dye reactions are no different, and, as in the case of lead salt methods, more specific activators and inhibitors should be tried as aids to identification.

One point of warning when using the azo dye and lead salt methods concerns the use of buffers, and in particular their molarities. Thus, 0.05 M acetate buffer is satisfactory for the lead salt method of Gomori (1952), but the molarity is too low to buffer the Burstone (1962) azo dye method. Conversely, the 0.2 M acetate buffer of the azo dye method will inhibit the Gomori reaction.

A number of approaches have been employed in the electron microscopic study of acid phosphatases, and these have been well reviewed by Sexton and Hall (1978). One fundamental point that emerges from these studies is that although each method has been used, apparently satisfactorily, with a given tissue, there have been few attempts to exploit any one method on a range of plant tissues, with the exception of the lead salt method. Where this has been done, e.g. the method of Livingstone *et al.* (1969), it has worked satisfactorily on root apices of *Vicia faba* (Gahan and McLean, 1969), but has not seemed adequate when used with strawberry receptacles (Beadle *et al.*, 1974). One further point is that the reactants have often failed to penetrate the tissues adequately, with the result that the reacted material has been readily trimmed from the block during preparation for cutting, sections then being removed from unreacted tissue. This is an easy way of obtaining false negative control material! From these brief remarks, it is apparent that the electron microscopic cytochemistry to acid phosphatases, and indeed of hydrolases in general, is at the beginning. There is no totally reliable method that has been shown to be suitable for a broad range of tissues. Until this stage is reached, great care should be taken in the application of high-resolution methods to the study of acid phosphatases, even when using the lead salt technique.

L. Nucleotide Pyrophosphatase

One of the enzymes demonstrated by the general acid phosphatase reaction can also be shown by means of an azo dye reaction employing thymidine-5^1-monophosphonaphthol AS-BI ester as substrate (Sierakowska *et al.*, 1978). The reaction relies on the following steps:

the final product being visible for viewing with the optical microscope (Fig. 17).

M. Glycosidases

These are hydrolases that split glycosidic linkages in true glycosides, *N*-glycosyl and *S*-glycosyl compounds.

1. β-*Glucuronidase*

This is perhaps the best studied glycosidase for cytochemistry and is involved in the hydrolysis of β-glucuronides.

The earlier methods, well reviewed in Pearse (1972) and Burstone (1962) involved either the use of azo dyes or of a Prussian blue reaction. Subsequently, Fishman and his collaborators produced a method that has been little applied to

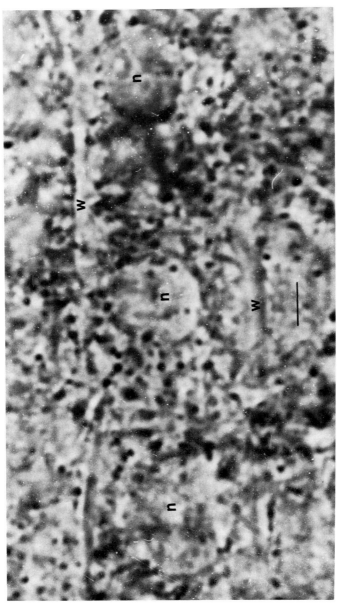

FIG. 17. Longitudinal, unfixed frozen section of coleoptile from embryo of *Avena fatua* incubated for 30 min at 37°C for nucleotide pyrophosphatase activity. n, nucleus; w, wall. Dark granules indicate sites of enzyme activity. Scale, 10 μm.

plant tissues (Ashford and McCully, 1973; Beneš et al., 1973) though it has been used extensively with animal tissues. The method uses naphthol AS-BI-β-D-glucuronic acid as the substrate that is hydrolyzed to yield naphthol AS-BI, which in turn is coupled to hexazotized pararosaniline (Fishman et al., 1964a,b; Fishman et al., 1967; Hayashi, 1964; Hayashi et al., 1964). Other diazonium salts can be used, including fast dark blue R or the diazotate of lead phthalocyanin. This has been little applied to plant tissues, but has the potential advantage of yielding a more accurate localization of end-product than the earlier methods, and also gives an electron-dense end-product with either lead phthalocyanin or hexazotized pararosaniline. In addition to varying the diazonium salt, two substrates have been employed, namely, naphthol AS-β-D-glucuronic acid (Livingstone et al., 1969) and naphthol AS-BI-β-D-glucuronic acid (Smith and Fishman, 1968; Bowen, 1973).

No information on the effects of fixation upon this enzyme are available for plant tissues, but it has been reported that 75% inhibition occurs with 30-min fixation in formalin at 4°C in animal tissue (Nachlas et al., 1956a,b).

Suitable controls include omission of the substrate from the incubation medium or the addition of potassium hydrogen saccharate (Campbell, 1949) or of 1,4-saccharolactone to the full incubation medium. Furthermore, by varying the pH of the medium it should be possible to differentiate between the various forms and localizations of β-glucuronidase (Hayashi et al., 1964).

2. Myrosinase

This enzyme is also known as β-thioglucosidase and catalyses the hydrolysis of thioglucosides to yield glucose, bisulphate and isothiocyanate. Both enzyme and substrates are present in all species of the Cruciferae. The general reaction for this enzyme is

$$\text{R—C—S—C}_6\text{H}_{11}\text{O}_5 + \text{N—O—SO}_3 \xrightarrow{\text{myrosinase}} \text{R—N=C=S} + \text{C}_6\text{H}_{12}\text{O}_6 + \text{H}^+ + \text{SO}_4^{2-}$$

Glucosinolate / Isothiocyanate / Glucose

and the histochemical reaction produced by Iverson (1970, 1973) uses sinigrin as the substrate, i.e. in the above reaction, the R of the glucosinolate is $\text{H}_2\text{C}=\text{CH—CH}_2\text{—}$.

The reaction occurs in two steps in which the enzyme liberates aglucone, which in turn spontaneously and non-enzymatically decomposes to isothiocyanate and sulphate in a neutral solution (Ettlinger and Kjaer, 1968). The sulphate is precipitated with lead ions.

Myrosinase appears to be completely inhibited by 3% glutaraldehyde, whereas 4% formaldehyde, if anything, slightly stimulates the enzyme extracted from the roots of Sinapis alba (Iverson, 1973). Studies of the effects of lead ions on the purified enzyme indicate only about a 10% inhibition.

3. β-*Glucosidase*

This enzyme is present in plant tissues, but has been little studied cytochemically (Avers, 1961; Ashford, 1970). An azo dye method is available and is based upon a simultaneous coupling procedure of Rutenburg *et al.*, (1958a). The diazonium salt recommended is fast blue B, although Ashford (1970) working on plant tissues found red violet LB and fast garnet GBC to be satisfactory. Hexazonium pararosaniline is claimed to be even better (Bowen and Evans, 1966).

In the reaction, 6-bromo-2-naphthyl-β-D-galactopyranoside is acted upon in the presence of both β-galactosidases and β-glucosidases, the two enzymes being distinguished by differential inhibition. Thus, acetone completely inhibits glucosidase activity, while only causing a 15% loss of β-galactosidase activity. Alternatively, 1.0 M sodium chloride completely inhibits glucosidase activity without apparently affecting galactosidase activity.

4. α-*Glucosidase*

The method of Rutenburg *et al.* (1958b) employs 6-bromo-2-naphthyl-α-D-glucopyranoside as substrate in a reaction similar to that for β-galactosidase. However, analysis is only possible at the histological level, since the end-product is not very substantive.

N. Sulphatases

This group of enzymes is present in plant tissues and catalyses the cleavage of sulphate esters

$$ROSO_3^- + H_2O \xrightarrow{\text{sulphatase}} R \cdot OH + H^+ + SO_4^{2-}$$

They have been localized cytochemically in plants using both an azo dye method (Olszewska and Gabara, 1964; Walek-Czernecka, 1965) and with a lead salt method (Poux, 1967; Coulomb, 1969b).

Since the first reported attempts to localize myro-sulphatase by incubating sections in a solution of sodium myronate and saturated barium chloride to yield barium sulphate as the end-product, much attention was given to the use of azo dye complexes (Seligman *et al.*, 1949; Rutenburg *et al.*, 1952; Surrey and van Fleet, 1955). The production of hydroxynaphthoic acid anilides (naphthol AS-BI sulphate and naphthol AS-OL sulphate) has improved the resolution of the method that could in turn lead to the development of high-resolution methods for sulphatases. However, some tissues contain sulphatases that will hydrolyse 6-benzoyl-2-naphthyl sulphate but not the naphthol AS series of sulphates. This rather limits the applicability of the azo dye approach.

Goldfischer's (1965) lead salt method for sulphatases is based upon the Gomori acid phosphatase reaction, but using *p*-nitrocatechol sulphate as substrate, and was first applied successfully to plants by Poux (1967). On hydrolysis in the presence of lead ions, the reaction yields an insoluble precipitate of lead sulphate that can be converted to black lead sulphide. The method has the advantage of being applicable to both the optical and electron microscope.

A further difficulty in localizing the sulphatases is that there are at least three groups of sulphatases—aryl sulphatases A, B and C—of which A and B are thought to be lysosomal and C microsomal. A and B have pH optima at about pH 6.0, whereas C has its optimum at pH 8.0 (Roy, 1962). Thus, variation of the pH may be of value here in separating A and B from C. An alternative method was introduced by Kawiak et al. (1964) based upon the hydrolysis of $[^{35}S]p$-nitro-phenylsulphate. The $^{35}SO_4^{2-}$ so liberated was precipitated in situ in the form of the barium salt, this being visualized autoradiographically.

If the lead salt method is chosen for high-resolution studies, it should be remembered that post-staining the sections with lead citrate, apart from introducing lead into the picture over and above that obtained with the enzyme reaction, will cause a loss of the end-product that is soluble in alkaline solutions (Kalimo et al., 1968).

O. Deoxyribonuclease

Two approaches are available for this group of enzymes, one being a lead salt method and the other a somewhat novel approach for hydrolases—the substrate film method which is limited to optical microscopy only. The latter method, proposed by Daoust (1965) requires that the substrate, DNA, is incorporated into a gelatin film. The dried film is placed in contact with the sections and incubated, after which the sections and film are separated. The film is stained with toluidine blue, sites of enzyme activity showing as unstained areas. This method is only of value at the gross histological level. An additional difficulty is that it is not easy to control the pH of the reaction and so distinguish between the various forms of the enzyme.

An alternative method that has been applied successfully to plant tissues (Walek-Czernecka, 1962; Coulomb, 1969c; Gahan et al., 1974) is that of Aronson et al., (1958) and modified by Vorbrodt (1961). Essentially the reaction is two step and employs two enzymes:

$$\text{DNA} \xrightarrow[\text{step I}]{\text{acid DNAse}} \text{polynucleotides} \xrightarrow[\text{step II}]{\text{acid phosphatase}} \text{phosphates}$$

The incubation medium is similar to that for the Gomori reaction except that DNA is used as the substrate, and acid phosphatase is added to the incubation medium. The DNase hydrolyses the DNA to polynucleotides from which the acid phosphatase splits off phosphate groups. The phosphate is then precipitated as lead phosphate. Little is known about the kinetics of the reaction. If rate I is faster than rate II, the visualization will be controlled by step II and so may permit a false localization due to diffusion of the polynucleotides away from their site of formation. If rate II is faster than rate I then a more reliable reaction should be obtained, as should occur with added acid phosphate.

Controls to the lead salt reaction are of great importance and, in addition to the heat-inactivated sections and no-substrate controls, must include incubation (a) with DNA, but without acid phosphatase; (b) without either DNA or acid phosphatase; and (c) in either the full incubation medium or the no-substrate control, or control (a), all with the addition of 10 mM sodium fluoride. Other inactivators of DNase may also be employed, e.g. citrate and arsenate.

P. Acid Ribonuclease

A gelatin film method similar to that for DNase is also available (Daoust, 1965), but the same limitations on the application of that method apply here also. Alternatively, the lead salt method for deoxyribonuclease may be modified by substituting RNA for DNA (Coulomb, 1969c).

Q. Cellulase

This multi-enzyme complex is widely present in plants, and is responsible for the hydrolysis of cellulose and other $\beta 1 \rightarrow 4$-linked glycans. Two approaches have been adapted for this enzyme. The first of these involves the immunocyto-chemical localization of cellulase activity by means of a labelled antibody raised against cellulase (Bal et al., 1976; see Chapter 4). The second method is the localization of cellulase through the reduction of cupric salts to cupric oxide by glucose produced through the action of cellulase. The method employs carbox-ymethylcellulose as a substrate. Whilst this has given reliable results with pea epicotyl material (Bal, 1974), it has not proved very reliable with sections of root of Vicia faba (A. L. Dawson and P. B. Gahan, unpublished data). Some prob-lems associated with this method would appear to be the following: (a) the rate of penetration of the substrate may be slow so leading to an accumulation at the cell surface; (b) any hydrolase yielding reducing substances could result in a positive reaction; (c) since there is always high endogenous substrate level present, all "no-substrate" controls are likely to be positive; and (d) the reaction product is soluble and hence likely to diffuse during the incubation period.

R. Proteases

Curiously, in spite of their importance in plant physiology, this group of en-zymes has been quite neglected in plant cytochemistry. Such optical microscope studies as have been performed have exploited the various available amino acid derivatives of β-naphthylamine that are hydrolyzed by peptidases using an azo dye method:

$$\text{L-Leucyl-β-naphthylamine} \xrightarrow[\text{diazonium salt}]{\text{peptidase}} \text{leucine} + \text{β-naphthylamine–diazonium salt complex}$$

Results with β-naphthylamide derivatives have proved unsatisfactory due to the slow coupling rates achieved, which allow diffusion away from the site of enzyme activity of the free β-naphthylamine. Better resolution is achieved with derivatives of 4-methoxy-β-naphthylamine, which yields a faster coupling rate. This can be used successfully with plant tissues.

More recently, Smith and Van Frank (1975) have devised a series of substrates based on the use of 4-methoxy-β-naphthylamine. This is an extremely flexible system since (a) coupling to fast blue B yields a visible colour reaction for optical microscopy; (b) coupling to hexazotized pararosaniline yields a coloured product for optical microscopy that can be rendered electron dense for electron microscopy; and (c) coupling to 5-nitrosalicylaldehyde creates a molecule that is fluorescent. At present these substrates are only available from the United States and are very costly. They have as yet not been applied successfully to plant tissues.

A little exploited method for animal proteases involves placing a section of tissue directly onto a fogged photographic emulsion, e.g. Kodak AR 10 stripping film (Adams and Tuquan, 1961; Greenoak and Maggi, 1971). The proteases in the section digest the gelatin of the emulsion causing a loss of silver grains. Thus, sites of enzyme activity in the section will become visible through the blackened film. Better specificity could be achieved by making emulsions of specific substrates or by impregnating the existing emulsions with known inhibitors of proteases. A further gain in the resolution of the method should be obtained by using frozen, ultra-thin sections covered with a monolayer of fogged liquid emulsion, prepared in the same way as for high resolution autoradiography (Chapter 9). A further approach as yet unexploited in plants is the use of specific proteinase inhibitors that can be tagged directly with a fluorescent or enzyme marker molecule or against which antibodies may be raised and used to identify the inhibitor trapped on the enzyme molecules. A start has been made in this direction with studies on animals (Sakai *et al.*, 1979).

6. Group IV: Lipids

I. INTRODUCTION

Due to the lack of many specific cytochemical methods for lipids, especially phospholipids, little information has been gleaned in botany by the application of cytochemistry, when compared to biochemical studies. In particular, the work on cytoplasmic lipids has been very sparse, and as late as 1930, lipids were listed as just another component of the cytoplasm (Strasburger, 1930). Guilliermond (1941) devoted a chapter to lipids in plant cells, but this was confined to studies of lipids that were present as droplets or granules when viewed with the ultramicroscope or after staining with Sudan dyes, indophenol blue or osmic acid. This unsatisfactory situation was due in part to the fact that lipids were very much the least studied group of the major biological compounds until the 1960s onwards. Thus, with little known about their biochemistry, it was difficult for any serious development to occur in the biochemistry of lipids.

If a significant contribution has been made, it is perhaps in the study of nuclear phospholipids. Berg's (1951) failure to detect lipids on chromosomes was found to be due to the form of tissue preparation involved, and chromosomal lipids were demonstrated by their uptake of 3,4-benzpyrene (Chayen et al., 1957). Using alternative methods of tissue preparation to those employed by Berg, chromosomal lipids have now been demonstrated by the use of a number of cytochemical methods, including the acid haematein test, the osmium tetroxide−α-naphthylamine (OTAN) reaction, Sudan black B, aniline blue-orange G, and the 3,4-benzpyrene method (Chayen et al., 1957; La Cour and Chayen, 1958; La Cour et al., 1958; Idelman, 1957, 1958a,b; Cave and Gahan, 1970; Serra and Seixas, 1962). Thus, by employing methods involving both chemical and physical reactions, lipids have been demonstrated on the mitotic and meiotic chromosomes and chromatin of interphase nuclei from a number of plant species (Figs. 18 and 19).

Some workers have noted differences in the staining behaviour of chromosomal lipids during mitosis. Thus, Serra and Seixas (1962) employing the Sudan black B reaction (Serra, 1958) showed that whilst early mitotic chromosomes of *Vicia faba, Allium cepa,* and *Agapanthus umbellatus* gave an intense reaction, by the end of prophase and metaphase, it was limited to an outer

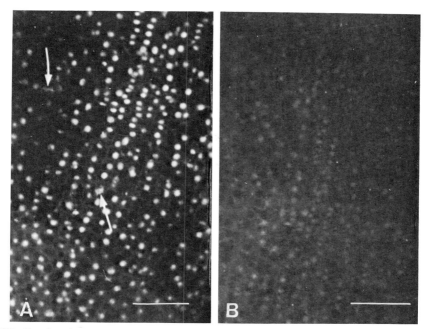

FIG. 18.   Longitudinal section of root tip (*Allium cepa*) fixed in Lewitsky's fluid and stained with 3,4-benzypyrene for lipids (A). Note the strong fluorescence of the nuclei and chromosomes (arrow) after excitation with ultra-violet light. (B) Control stained with caffeine solution. Scale, 50 μm.

pellicle region of the chromosomes. The heavy reaction was again evident at telophase. They interpreted their results to indicate a loss of lipid from the chromosomes during division as indicated by measurements of the dry mass of the chromosomes by interference microscopy (Richards and Bajer, 1961). A cyclic staining behaviour was also noted by La Cour and Chayen (1958). Thus, examination of roots from *Fritillaria falcata*, *Scilla siberica*, *S. campanulata*, *Trillium grandiflorum*, *Paris polyphylla* and *Vicia faba* fixed in Lewitsky's fluid (1931) revealed heterochromatic regions of the interphase chromosomes that stained for lipids, but from mid-prophase to early telophase the chromosomes reacted uniformly throughout. The discrepancies between the two series of experiments may be explained by the type of fixation employed and the staining procedures used. Thus, it was also clear that mitotic chromosomes of *Vicia faba* and *Allium cepa* stained for lipids at all stages from early prophase to the end of telophase after fixation in either Lewitsky's fluid or formal–calcium–Reinecke salt (La Cour *et al.*, 1958), when employing the acid haematein reaction or 3,4-benzpyrene method. Studies of the effects of various fixatives (La Cour *et al.*, 1958) and biochemical findings (Chayen and Gahan, 1959; Chayen *et al.*,

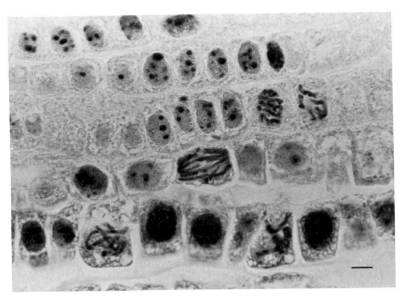

FIG. 19.   Longitudinal section of root tip from *Allium cepa* fixed in Lewitsky's fluid and stained with the acid haematein test. Phospholipids stain darkly, including chromosomes. Scale, 0.1 mm.

1959a,b; Gahan, 1961, 1965b) indicated that a number of phospholipid fractions exist in chromosomes and that depending on the mode of tissue preparation employed and the colour reaction used, these various fractions may be demonstrated partially or completely.

One criticism of such work is that the positive phospholipid reaction on the chromosomes is due to the presence of fragments of nuclear membrane remaining attached to the chromatin following dissolution of the nuclear membrane at the end of prophase (Du Praw, 1970), coating the metaphase chromosomes with a phospholipid-containing material.

Studies on the incorporation of lipid precursors into chromosomal lipids are sparse, and little information is at present available. One difficulty concerns the choice of precursor and its ease of entry into the plant organ. The preliminary findings of P. B. Gahan and C. F. Cave, 1968, unpublished data) suggest that choline and thanolamine may prove of value in such studies, though the methods used for tissue preparation clearly affect the results obtained. Nevertheless, using [^{14}C]- and [^{3}H]ethanolamine as a precursor in roots of *Vicia faba*, it has been possible to demonstrate the labelling of lipids in both mitotic chromosomes and interphase nuclei (Viola-Magni *et al.*, 1984). Since the autoradiographic studies were performed on semi-thin sections, it is unlikely that the interphase chromatin was labelled by cross-fire from nuclear membrane label or from adjacent cytoplasmic organelles. Thus, the autoradiographs confirm the evidence from color-imetric cytochemistry that lipid components are present in chromatin.

The nuclear membrane can be shown clearly to react with lipid stains (e.g., La Cour *et al.*, 1958), and studies on the nucleolus also show the presence of phospholipids in these structures (La Cour *et al.*, 1958; Serra and Seixas, 1962). With a number of phospholipid reactions the nucleoli react strongly, and also readily incorporate ethanolamine and choline (Cave and Gahan, 1970), though there appears to be no correlation between the incorporation of the precursors and the cell cycle. The studies of Serra *et al.* also indicate the presence of phos-pholipid on the spindles of cells in meiosis from *Agapanthus umbellatus* and in mitosis from roots of *Vicia faba* and *Allium cepa,* as well as in the centromeres. Few fundamental cytochemical studies of lipids have been made on the cytoplasm of plant cells (e.g., Beneš, 1964; Hébant, 1970).

II. CYTOCHEMICAL INVESTIGATION OF LIPIDS

Bloor (1943) suggested a general description of lipids as compounds that are (a) insoluble in water but soluble in solvents such as chloroform, ether and benzene; (b) actual or potential esters of fatty acids; and (c) utilized by living organisms. However Adams (1965) pointed out that this definition included steroid hor-mones but excluded water-soluble gangliosides. He preferred the definition of lipids as substances "normally utilized by the organism, that are long-chain fatty acids with glycerol, cholesterol, sphingosine or higher aliphatic alcohols".

Most histochemical methods for plant lipids have been adapted from studies on animal tissues (Jensen, 1962), and such methods are well reviewed by Adams (1965), Pearse (1968) and Bayliss-High (1977). The difficulties in demonstrating lipids at the cell level include (a) the lability of some compounds, such as fats, which can be readily lost during tissue preparation; (b) the close binding of most phospholipids to proteins or polysaccharides which act as a mask, so preventing the visualization of the lipid components; and (c) the lack of specificity of the methods which, in many cases, concern the reactive group in the lipids, e.g. NH_2, which is also present in other compounds.

A. Tissue Preparation

Before discussing lipid histochemical methods, it is pertinent to reconsider the techniques of tissue preparation. Sections can be prepared from either fixed or unfixed tissues. Unfixed material is best sectioned by razor since this is least likely to disturb the lipid forms in the cells. However, for the production of a large number of adequately thin serial sections, frozen sections may provide an alternative approach. Although Gahan *et al.* (1967) were unable to detect any severe damage to the lipid sites, this may have been due to insufficiently sensitive assay procedures, for it is well known that freezing causes the splitting of some bonds between lipid and proteins. If unfixed sections are used, then it must be remembered that the first reagent with which the section comes into contact may, or may not, extract some material from the sections. This is because some lipids are rendered hydrophilic by their attachment to protein or polysaccharide fractions. The most widely used fixative for the preservation of lipids is formal–calcium (Baker, 1944, 1958), the calcium being added to prevent phospholipids from forming "myelin" figures when in contact with an aqueous solution (Wolman and Weiner, 1965). Formalin, however, does not fix, but merely preserves or retains lipids, and Baker (1960) considered a post-fixation in potassium dichromate necessary to ensure fixation of the lipids, a procedure introduced by Ciaccio (1909). Against this use of fixation is the fact that certain phospholipids are slowly dissolved by aqueous solutions of formaldehyde (Brante, 1949; Hammar, 1924; Millot and Giberton, 1927; Weil, 1929). In addition, there is strong evidence that formal–calcium removes lipoprotein, not merely from the cytoplasm, but also from the chromosomes (Chayen *et al.*, 1958; 1959a,b; Cave, 1971). It is also important to remember that hydrophobic lipids can crystalize with prolonged exposure to formalin (Baker, 1958) and so will fail to stain, as they may also do if unfixed, frozen sections are left to dry overnight at $-25°C$. Thus, in preparing tissues for lipid studies, care must be taken to assess the changes wrought by the preparatory technique. It is imperative to avoid the use of lipid solvents as much as possible, and if embedding is necessary, freeze-drying, freeze-substitution, and water-soluble embedding materials are an advantage. The use of acetone as a fixative, dehydrating agent and embedding solvent (Chayen and Gahan, 1958) reduces the changes considerably, and some polar lipids have been shown to be retained in paraffin sections after processing the tissue through acetone and benzene (Elleder and Lojda, 1973).

B. Identification of Lipids

Fundamentally, lipids may be demonstrated either by physical methods, which are based on the selective solubility of dyes in the lipids, or by chemical methods based on direct chemical interaction between dye and lipid.

Whilst some lipids have characteristic birefringent properties, this is not a very useful guide to lipids in cells, since other compounds and structures such as cell walls are also birefringent when viewed with polarized light. Moreover, some lipids that are birefringent lose this property after processing.

1. Histophysical Methods

The histophysical methods include the staining of hydrophobic compounds, such as unsaturated triglycerides, sterol esters and fatty acids, with oil red O (Lillie and Ashburn, 1943; Lillie, 1954) or other Sudan dyes. The latter dyes are usually employed as saturated solutions in 70% ethanol or acetone, but ethylene glycol, propylene or triethyl phosphate have also been used (Baker, 1946; Chiffelle and Putt, 1951; Gomori, 1952). Waxes, fats, oils and free fatty acids are stained red by Sudan III and IV, whilst Sudan black B stains all lipids that are liquid and hydrophobic together with phospholipids insoluble in the dye solution. The physical state of the lipid is much involved since oils will accumulate Sudan dyes more readily than will solid lipid formations, which may not easily become coloured. Of the solvent systems employed, isopropanol for oil red O and 70% ethanol for Sudan black B have proved the most suitable.

Sudan black B appears to stain all classes of lipids that are in a liquid state and hence contain some unsaturated groups, though not all unsaturated lipids may be liquid at staining temperatures. This means that the dye can stain both hydrophobic and hydrophilic lipids. It was believed that the dye reacts by true physical absorption into the lipids, but the interaction between the dye and phospholipids may be due to a salt linkage (Terner et al., 1963), a suggestion confirmed by chromatographic studies. Two fractions can be suggested (Beneš, 1964; Lansink, 1968), one of which is physically absorbed by neutral fats and the other which is a basic dye, reacting with phospholipids and producing a metachromatic shift. Bayliss and Adams (1972) have further suggested that bromination of the material prior to staining with Sudan black B reduces the solubility of lecithin and free fatty acids during staining and also converts crystalline cholesterol to the bromo derivatives, which are liquid at room temperature and hence readily stainable.

Auramine O is a potentially interesting fluorescent dye for studying unsaturated, acidic waxes and certain precursors. Its more general use awaits further exploitation with a broader variety of material (Heslop-Harrison, 1977; Considine and Knox, 1979).

Fluorescent dyes appear to be of more interest in lipid studies since the methods seem to be more sensitive than those relying upon direct observation of the coloured dye. The more successful dyes include phosphine 3R (Popper, 1944), rhodamine B (Strügger, 1938), auramine O (Heslop-Harrison, 1977; Considine and Knox, 1979) and 3,4-benzpyrene (Berg, 1951; Chayen et al., 1957; Fig. 18). Dyes are used as aqueous suspensions, the lipid sites readily absorbing the dye from the solvent. This exemplifies the need to prepare the dyes in a solvent which favours the migration of the dye to the lipid site. If, for example, the dye is dissolved in an organic solvent, it is unlikely that it will be available to the lipid site and hence will remain partitioned in the solvent. All lipid sites in the cell including sterols react with 3,4-benzpyrene, whereas phosphine 3R reacts with all lipids except free fatty acids and sterols.

Nile blue sulphate is a water-soluble dye yet it behaves in a way similar to the Sudan dyes. It consists of two components, namely, a red oxazone being soluble in ''fats'' and which colours waxes, fats and oils, and a blue oxazine reacting chemically with free fatty acids and phospholipids (Cain, 1947). A disadvantage of Nile blue sulphate is that the basic dye can also stain nucleoprotein in addition to lipids.

The relationship between the lipid sites and the organic solvents is such that once a lipid is coloured, the preparation can only be mounted in a water-soluble medium or in aqueous solution. Dehydration of the preparation will result in the loss of the dye.

2. Histochemical Methods

The use of histochemical methods for the detection of lipids shows the limitations of this approach. Firstly, one must aim for chemical specificity, and here it is extremely difficult to evolve a procedure that will allow the attachment of a coloured component to a complete lipid molecule, especially in the case of the more complex phospholipids. An alternative method is to determine reactions for component parts of the lipid molecules.

$$
\begin{array}{ll}
\mathrm{CH_2O-F_1} & \mathrm{CH_2O-F_1} \\
| & | \\
\mathrm{CHO-F_2} & \mathrm{CHO-F_2} \\
| \quad \mathrm{O} & | \quad \mathrm{O} \\
| \quad \| & | \quad \| \\
\mathrm{CH_2O \cdot P \cdot O \cdot CH_2 \cdot CH_2 \overset{+}{N}(CH_3)_3} & \mathrm{CH_2 \cdot O \cdot P \cdot O \cdot CH_2 \cdot CH \cdot COOH} \\
| & \quad\quad | \quad\quad\quad\quad | \\
\mathrm{O_-} & \quad\quad \mathrm{OH} \quad\quad\quad \mathrm{NH_2}
\end{array}
$$

Phosphatidylcholine   Phosphatidylserine

F_1 = saturated fatty acid
F_2 = unsaturated fatty acid

It is possible in the case of phosphatidylcholine, for example, to obtain a reaction for an unsaturated fatty acid and for choline. If both reactions occur at the same site then one might deduce the presence of the molecule. This approach has its limitations, for example, in the case of phosphatidylserine in which one can perform a reaction for unsaturated bonds (in the fatty acid) and for the amino group of the serine. However, if the serine is linked to a peptide chain then the reaction will be negative. Similarly, if the H_2N- of serine does react, there is no way of proving that the reaction is specific for serine and not for the same group in another amino acid. It will be seen that most lipid-staining reactions are essentially a compromise between reacting the whole molecule and the parts of the molecule.

A second point concerns the availability of the lipid in the cell. Free fats present few problems providing that they are not lost from the section during the reaction. In contrast, the phospholipids are invariably linked with protein or polysaccharide, to varying degrees. Thus, the lipid can be linked to protein and yet be readily stained. Conversely, the protein can form a relationship with the lipid so that the latter is masked. When this occurs, it is necessary to use an agent, such as heat, to alter the binding of the lipid to its masking agent and allow the penetration of the dye to the lipid site.

In all studies, it is essential to have a series of controls to the reactions employed. It is relatively easy to test the specificity of the reaction with a particular chemical grouping. However, as already discussed, the reactive groups present in the lipid molecules are also possibly present in other molecular groups such as proteins. To overcome this difficulty, many workers resort to the extraction of the lipids as a means of control. This is not altogether satisfactory since those lipids more closely linked to proteins are less readily available for extraction by lipid solvents. Moreover, it is possible to obtain an enhanced reaction after extraction due to the unmasking of some solvent-resistant lipids (Chayen *et al.*, 1959b).

This topic is carefully considered in relation to animal studies by Adams and Bayliss (1975), though very few attempts have been made to exploit this approach in plants (Cave, 1971). A number of solvent systems can be employed to remove lipids from sections, such as acetone; chloroform–methanol (2 : 1, v/v); or HCl–chloroform–methanol (1 :66 : 33, v/v). The major problem is that the efficiency of the extraction will be affected by (a) the methods of tissue preparation employed; (b) the complexing of lipids to other cellular components such as protein that will render them resistant to extraction; and (c) the degree of mutual solubility of the various types of lipids in a given solvent system. Thus, it is not possible to obtain a complete lipid extraction from a given tissue section, and attempts to do this may result in rather confusing pictures after staining with lipid dyes.

Enzyme digestion methods may also be employed, but, partly due to the lack of purity of most of the available lipases and phospholipases, this approach has not proved to be very satisfactory. Although this is an unsatisfactory state of affairs, the best approach seems to be a combination of a number of reactions and controls on the suspected lipid sites.

a. OSMIUM TETROXIDE. Of the more established methods, that of osmium tetroxide is probably the oldest: this substance is thought to be reduced by the cis unsaturated groups of lipids to yield a black compound. The reaction may be blocked by pretreating sections with bromine. The mechanism appears to depend upon the formation of bridged bis-osmates through the reaction of osmium tetroxide with unsaturated fatty acids (Cain, 1950; Lison, 1953; Wigglesworth, 1957).

$$
\begin{array}{c}
\mathrm{H}\ \big|\ \mathrm{C-O} \qquad \mathrm{O} \qquad \mathrm{O-C}\ \big|\ \mathrm{H} \\
\diagdown\ \underset{\overset{\|}{\mathrm{Os}}}{} \diagup \\
\mathrm{H}\ \big|\ \mathrm{C-O} \qquad\qquad \mathrm{O-C}\ \big|\ \mathrm{H}
\end{array}
$$

It has been suggested that an osmium–fatty acid ester may first be formed, when a lower osmium oxide is ejected to form the bridged bis-osmate. This may not be a correct explanation since the second step seems to be precluded through the fact that the OsO_4–fatty acid ratio is 1 : 2 (Korn, 1966a-c, 1967).

Many workers have indicated an interaction between proteins and mucopolysaccharides (Bahr, 1954; Porter and Kallman, 1953; Rogers, 1959; Wolman 1957). This resulted in a suspicion that the osmiophilia of unit membranes in electron micrographs does not represent the lipids of the membrane. This interpretation was confirmed by the studies of Korn, (1966b, 1967) and Adams *et al.* (1967).

b. ACID HAEMATEIN. Perhaps one of the most widely used stains for phospholipids is the acid haematein reaction (Baker, 1946; 1947). After fixation in formal–calcium, the tissue sections are mordanted in a dichromate–calcium reagent, the dichromate oxidizing the lipids and itself being reduced to an insoluble compound that combines with haematoxylin to yield a blue-black colouration. As a control, Baker (1947) suggested extraction with hot pyridine prior to performing the acid haematein reaction on sections of material that had been fixed in weak Bouin's fluid. A reaction that appeared in the test slide, but was absent from the control slide, was considered to be due to the presence of a phospholipid. In a detailed discussion, Adams (1965) concluded from studies on pure samples that only sphingomyelin and lecithin were strongly stained. This is in agreement with the findings of Bourgeois and Hack (1962) that only choline-containing lipids are appreciably stained by the acid haematein reaction. Roozemonde (1971) working on grey and white matter from the central nervous system found conflicting results and concluded that the method stained polar lipids in a certain physicochemical state rather than those with a specific chemical configuration.

In some cases, e.g. with nuclei, a stronger reaction can be obtained after extraction with pyridine than before such an extraction. Chayen *et al.* (1959b) suggested that far from extracting nuclear phospholipids, the hot pyridine was merely unmasking them. Moreover, the extraction procedure was seen to remove large amounts of protein. It was considered that the extraction in hot pyridine did not constitute a reliable control. Lillie (1954) found that on pre-treating paraffin sections with bromine in carbon tetrachloride, C=C bonds could be blocked. Long *et al.* (1963) showed that after treatment of unfixed sections with bromine–water, the acid haematein test did not react, and they suggested that the bromination procedure might usefully be employed as a control. A second feature of this study was the demonstration of the involvement of double bonds in the reaction. Adams (1965) was opposed to this, claiming no blocking of the reaction by bromination and hence no involvement of the double bonds. That he worked with fixed tissues and used shorter periods of bromination than did Long *et al.* (1963) may account for this difference. The acid haematein reaction can be successfully blocked in plant tissues by pre-treatment in bromine–water (Gahan, unpublished data) and would appear to be a possible control. Thus, the basis of the acid haematein test seems to be (a) reduction of $Cr_2O_2^{2-}$ to Cr_2O_5 mediated by the unsaturated bonds of the fatty acids, and attachment of the chromate ions to the phospholipid molecule, possibly adjacent to the phosphate group; (b) the formation of the haematein "lake" at the sites of the chromate ions (Baker, 1958); and (c) removal of loosely bound "lake" by differentiation.

c. OTAN METHOD. There are many other lipid reactions that have been used with animal tissues to detect phospholipids, steroids, sterols and other lipids (reviewed in Adams, 1965; Adams and Bayliss, 1975). However, although most of these do not appear to have been applied to plant tissues, one which has been used successfully (Cave and Gahan, 1970) is the OTAN reaction (Adams, 1959). Formalin-fixed, frozen sections are treated for 18 h with 1% OsO_4–1% $KClO_3$ (1 : 3) in a tighly stoppered bottle. This is followed by treatment with α-naphthylamine for 20 min at 37°C. The reaction results in esters of cholesterol and triglycerides staining black as the result of the Marchi test (1886) in which if $KClO_3$ and OsO_4 are used together, the $KClO_3$ can penetrate hydrophilic lipids reducing the double bonds, which are thus prevented from blackening with OsO_4. In contrast, $KClO_3$ cannot enter the hydrophobic lipids and so the OsO_4 enters the molecules and interacts normally with the double bonds, resulting in a blackening of the sites. The non-blackened osmium tetroxide is then reacted with α-naphthylamine to yield an orange-red dye at the sites of the hydrophilic lipids (phospholipids) (Adams and Bayliss, 1975). This is not an absolutely reliable test since it was shown that only liquid esters react as predicted. More saturated ones such as oleate colour orange rather than black.

This is recommended as a general purpose reaction to distinguish between hydrophilic phospholipids and hydrophobic triglyceride esters, cholesterol esters and fatty acids.

At present there appear to be no satisfactory electron microscopy cytochemical tests for lipids in plant tissues, although the method of Kalina and Pease (1977) employing tannic acid to stabilize saturated phosphatidylcholine, may provide a starting point for further tests.

d. PLASMALOGENS. One group of lipids that are somewhat difficult to detect are the plasmalogens. These compounds essentially have the structure

$$CH_2O-CH=CH-(CH_2)_x-CH_3$$
$$CHO-\underset{O}{\overset{\parallel}{C}}-(CH_2)_y-CH_3$$
$$\underset{\underset{OH}{|}}{CH_2O-\overset{O}{\overset{\parallel}{P}}-O}$$

KOH →

$$\begin{array}{l} H_2C-O \\ \quad\quad\quad\diagdown \\ \quad\quad\quad\quad CH-(CH_2)_x-CH_3 \\ HC-O\diagup \\ | \\ \quad\; O \\ \quad\; \parallel \\ CH_2O-P-O\text{-nitrogen base} \\ \quad\quad\; | \\ \quad\quad\; OH \end{array}$$

Lyso-plasmalogen   Acetal phosphatide

Feulgen and Rossenbeck (1924) first drew attention to these compounds when they observed cytoplasmic compounds that reacted with Schiff's reagent in sections not exposed to hydrolysis in 1 N HCl. Feulgen and Voigt (1924) showed that the reaction could be abolished by pretreating the sections with sodium bisulphite or phenylhydrazine, indicating the presence of aldehyde groups. Later work by Feulgen and his associates showed these plasmals to be derived from a lipid precursor and plasmalogen. They later suggested the structure to be that shown above. The evolution of the histochemical methods for plasmalogens has been carefully reviewed by Cain (1949) and by Pearse (1968).

There has been much controversy over the validity for the reaction for plasmalogens. Hayes (1949) considered that for a plasmal reaction to be valid the technique should include a brief fixation in 10% formalin; be subjected to a short treatment with $HgCl_2$ if working with frozen sections, which appears to form higher fatty acid aldehydes from acetyl phosphatides; and be adequately controlled. However, unfixed material will show a strong reaction whilst fixation may diminish the response.

Due to the uncertainty of the basis of the reaction and doubt concerning the ability of the reaction to demonstrate all plasmals, it may be only of value in demonstrating the possible sites of plasmalogens.

e. MASKED LIPIDS. In general, the lipid methods mentioned above will only show those lipids that are available to the stain, but not those that are in some way masked, e.g. by protein binding to the lipid. A number of procedures have been devised for the demonstration of "bound" lipids, and the most commonly used agent is heat. This can be achieved by pre-incubation of the sections in distilled water at 60°C for varying periods of time followed by the staining reaction, or by staining in the reaction medium at 60°C. Berenbaum (1958) extended this to the Sudan black B method in which the stain is ignited on the section. In all methods, the heat would seem to be acting by altering the binding of lipid to protein, so facilitating the entry of the stain to the lipid sites. In studies on animal tissues, various ions have been used as unmasking agents (Wolman, 1955; Maggi, 1965), but this approach has been little used in plant studies. Unmasking of lipid sites may occur also through more naturally occurring events such as freezing or desiccation (P. B. Gahan, unpublished).

III. ELECTRON MICROSCOPE METHODS

Little work in this direction has been performed upon lipids in plant tissues and what studies that have been made with animal tissues have not been very encouraging (reviewed in Adams and Bayliss, 1975). Perhaps the advent of ultracryotomy with unfixed specimens, so removing the problems encountered by the loss of lipids through fixation and embedding, may help to advance this area of study.

IV. AUTORADIOGRAPHY

This approach is possible with plant tissues (Cave and Gahan, 1970; Viola-Magni *et al.*, 1984), but the basic problems apply as in the case of electron microscopy. The use of fixatives and many embedding processes result in the loss of labelled lipids from the sections and tissues, and perhaps more dangerous, may result in a redistribution of the label in the tissue. To a certain extent, these problems can be overcome by using unfixed, frozen sections, but the difficulty here is in designing the experiment in such a way that the non-incorporated precursor is not retained in the tissue.

V. SUBERIN

Special reference is made to this typical plant component since it has been shown to be composed of two-thirds aromatic phenols, and one-third long chain aliphatic acids (Kolattukudy, 1975) resulting in its having lipid-like properties in terms of its reaction with some of the lipid reagents. Clearly, it can be demonstrated by reaction through its phenol component (see Chapter 7). Thus, when irradiated with ultra-violet light suberin will fluoresce yellow if mounted in 0.02 *M* phosphate buffer at pH 9.1 and viewed with fluorescein filters.

Suberin is resistant to concentrated sulphuric acid and will stain with Sudan blue (Jensen, 1962). It has also been considered to react with gentian violet (Faulkner and Kimmins, 1976) though the specificity and mechanism for reacting are far from clear.

7. Group V: Carbohydrates

I. INTRODUCTION

The biochemical classification of carbohydrates by Jeanloz (1960) and Gott-schalk (1962) resulted in the ordering of a long series of compounds, many of which are not found in plants. However, the definition of carbohydrates as "polyhydroxyketones or polyhydroxyaldehydes or compounds which can be hydrolyzed to these substances using dilute mineral acid" (Hall *et al.*, 1974) allowed the identification in plants of a series of compounds falling into the main groups of monosaccharides, oligosaccharides and complexes of these with, for example, proteins or lipids to form (a) polysaccharide–protein complexes, such as chitin–protein; (b) glycolipids, and (c) glycolipid–protein complexes, both occuring in membranes; and (d) cerebrosides. Whilst the biochemical aspects of these compounds in plants have been intensively studied, little use has been made of cytochemical methods to gain information concerning the *in situ* behaviour of carbohydrates in processes, such as division and differentiation. The examples listed below are by no means exhaustive, but serve to indicate the range of studies and the possibility of bringing a dynamic dimension to the consideration of carbohydrates.

The early colorimetric studies by Jensen and Ashton (1960) on roots of *Allium cepa* were based upon a joint application of the periodic acid–Schiff (PAS) reaction for polysaccharides and a series of extraction procedures scheduled by Buroughs and Bonner (1953). Thus, four serial sections were assessed by PAS staining after (a) no treatment; (b) extraction with 0.5% ammonium oxalate at 90°C for 12 h; (c) as in (b) extraction for 12 h at 25°C in 4% sodium hydroxide; and (d) as in (c) but followed by 12 h at 25°C in 17.5% sodium hydroxide. Section (a) showed all of the available polysaccharide material, section (b) had water-soluble and pectic substances removed from the walls, section (c) had lost pectic substances and hemicelluloses, whilst section (d) had only cellulose remaining. The data so obtained indicated that the cell walls of the apical initials contained each of these groups of carbohydrates, but that they were present in low amounts.

Early in the development of the cells, differences appeared in the wall composition depending upon the type of tissue being developed. Whilst initially the protodermal cells were similar to those in the cortex, upon radial enlargement of the cells of the protoderm, the walls were found to be low in non-cellulose polysaccharides and cellulose, and high in pectic substances and hemicellulose. These differences were lost during elongation of the protodermal and cortical cells. During early development, the vascular cell walls had a low non-cellulosic polysaccharide and cellulose content, but a high content of pectic substances and hemicelluloses. With further differentiation, the hemicelluloses became more important.

Studies at the ultra-structural level concerning the localization of pectin in the cell walls were made. Dark-grown roots of *A. cepa,* 1 mm in length, were reacted with hydroxylamine to produce pectic hydroxamic acids. A further reaction with ferric ions yielded electron-opaque, insoluble ferric complexes, after which the roots were embedded and sectioned for electron microscopy. Dense deposits of iron were found in the region of the middle lamella and in an area near the surface of the primary wall. The pectin of the immature cross walls appeared continuous with the inner reacting layer of the longitudinal wall, whilst that of the more mature transverse walls became associated with the middle lamella pectin of the longitudinal wall. Middle lamella pectin was found to be soluble in hot water in contrast to that of the longitudinal and transverse walls that represented the residual fraction. All of the electron-opaque material was removable with hot versene.

Hemicelluloses have been considered by Northcote and his collaborators in a classic conjoint biochemical and autoradiographic study that helped to elucidate the manner in which plant cells manufacture wall substances and transport them to the cell wall. Excised roots of *Triticum* were incubated in D-[6-^{3}H]glucose at a concentration of 5 mCi/ml for 5 min prior to fixation in potassium permanganate and preparation for high-resolution autoradiography (Northcote and Pickett-Heaps, 1966). At this stage, almost all of the label was associated with the dictyosomes. Feeding for 10 min revealed a similar situation in the root cap cells. If the 10 min feeding pulse with [^{3}H]glucose was followed by a chase for 10 min with non-radioactive glucose, labelling was found in the dictyosomes, the cell wall and in vesicles passing their contents into the cell wall by reverse pinocytosis. A pulse of 10 min followed by a chase of 30 min showed most of the dictyosomes to be unlabelled, but the walls heavily labelled, a situation further enhanced when a pulse of 10 min was followed by a chase of 60 min. Biochemical analysis of the labelled material after feeding for 15 min revealed that more than 70% of the label was present as galactose. The authors suggested that their results were consistant with the idea that a pool of precursors for the synthesis of polysaccharides containing galactose, galacturonic acid and arabinose was present in the dictyosomes. This material was passed to the cell walls via vesicles derived from the dictyosomes. Similar results were obtained by Wooding (1968) working on the incorporation of [^{3}H]glucose into the walls of the vascular tissue of 1-year-old sycamore seedlings.

In addition to the autoradiographic studies, Pickett-Heaps (1967, 1968) attempted to utilize a modified PAS reaction for polysaccharides at the ultra-structural level in root tips and coleoptiles of wheat seedlings. Golgi cisternae and vesicles in the root cap cells and those of the epidermis gave a strong reaction for polysaccharides with an increasing intensity the further were the vesicles from the Golgi bodies. During cell plate formation both small (Golgi?) vesicles and large (phragmoplast) vesicles also stained strongly for polysaccharides. These latter findings confirm the earlier optical microscope observations of PAS reactive material at the newly forming cell plate by Olzsewska *et al.* (1966).

Whilst lectins were first considered in relation to their ability to cause ag-glutination of animal erythrocytes (phytohaemagglutinins), they have now been shown to be more than agglutinins and can be described as those proteins or glycoproteins of plant, animal or bacterial origin that bind to cell surfaces through specific carbohydrate-containing receptor sites (Callow, 1975). They are known to exert toxic effects (Jaffe, 1969), agglutinate cells and induce mitosis (Nowell, 1960). However, of particular interest in histochemistry is the capacity of lectins to bind to specific carbohydrate sites, since this makes possible the identification of carbohydrate molecules on membranes and in cell walls (Table 5).

Little information is available on the role of lectins in plants or their distribu-tion, although recent immunofluorescent studies of the distribution of *Datura* lectin in *Datura stramonium* have shown it to be associated with the plasmalem-ma and particulate material without being confined to any single type of struc-tural organelle. Moreover, there appeared to be a negligible association of the lectin with the cell wall (Yeoman *et al.,* 1979). Callow (1975) lists the possible functions of lectins and concludes that "through their specific carbohydrate-binding properties, lectins may play an important role in a variety of recognition phenomena".

Lectins may be employed cytochemically to detect various carbohydrate resi-dues, some of which are listed in Table 5. The lectins can be tagged with a fluorescent compound, such as fluorescein isothiocyanate, used directly upon sections to localize the various lectin-binding sites, and visualized by fluores-cence microscopy. Alternatively, sections may be treated with the lectins and the sites of the lectins determined by means of specific fluorescent-labelled anti-bodies raised against the lectins, and also by employing the "sandwich" technique.

The reaction can be controlled to a certain degree by the addition of simple sugars that block the binding sites, e.g. the addition of methyl-X-D-man-nopyranoside to block the binding of concavalin A (Con A) by yeast mannans (So and Goldstein, 1968) or the blocking of Con A sites on the stigma surface pellicle of *Helianthus annuus* by methyl α-D-glucoside (Vithanage and Knox, 1977).

This approach has been extended to electron microscopy when, employing ultra-thin frozen sections of yeast cells, it has been possible to visualize the binding of lectins with an appropriate marker, glycosylated-ferritin (Vian, 1979).

TABLE 5. Some Lectins and Their Affinities

Lectin	Molecular weight	Affinity
Concanavalin A (from jackbean)	102,000	(i) o-Methoxy-α-D-mannopyranosyl-
		(ii) Non-reducing δ-D-glucopyranosyl-
		(iii) δ-D-Mannopyranosyl-
		(iv) β-D-Fructofuranosyl-
		(v) δ-D-Arabinofuranosyl-
Helix pomatia agglutinin	?	N-Acetylgalactosamine
Peanut agglutinin	106,000	(i) Galactose
		(ii) Lactose
Soya bean agglutinin	120,000	(i) N-Acetyl-α-D-galactosaminide
		(ii) α-D-Galactopyranoside
		(iii) β-D-Galactopyranoside
Ulex europaeus agglutinin	46,000	α-1-Fucose
Wheat germ agglutinin	36,000	(i) N-Acetyl-D-glucosamine
		(ii) di-N-Acetylchitobiose

Thus, the α-mannosyl residues and N-acetylglucosamine residues were localized with Con A and wheat germ agglutinins, respectively, and visualized in the electron microscope with mannosyl and chitobiosyl ferritin. The methodology is well discussed by Knox and Clarke (1978).

Clearly, this approach offers interesting possibilities in carbohydrate cytochemistry, but if it is to become a routine method there are still some technical difficulties to be overcome, such as specificity and ease of penetration of the lectins into electron microscopic specimens.

A recent innovation for the optical microscope has been introduced for the staining of neutral polysaccharides (Yamada, 1978) in animal tissues. Here a lectin binding method is combined with the periodic acid-based reaction, the lectin (Con A) demonstrating α-D-glycosyl and α-D-mannosyl residues, being visualized with the DAB reaction for the tag, peroxidase (brown). The periodic acid–m-aminophenol–fast black K indicates 1,2-glycol groups of the neutral polysaccharide (blackish purple).

II. CYTOCHEMICAL INVESTIGATION OF CARBOHYDRATES

Carbohydrate cytochemistry, like that of lipids, has been somewhat neglected in spite of the fundamental importance of these compounds in plant cells. Most of the quantitative methods that are available take the form of micro-chemical analyses, which have been well documented by Jensen (1962). The remaining colorimetric methods, although mostly qualitative in character, are relatively specific if adequate controls are performed. The main difficulty in localizing carbohydrates lies in the fact that although varied in form, the methods of identification are limited because these compounds are so basically similar to one another in chemical structure.

A. Polysaccharides

Few methods are available for polysaccharides and the most reliable appears to be the periodic acid–Schiff (PAS) reaction (Hotchkiss, 1948; McManus, 1948). This reaction (PAS or PARS if a reducing bath is included in the reaction procedure) depends upon the oxidation of the 1,2-glycol linkage within the sugar molecule, usually with periodic acid, resulting in the formation of two free aldehyde groups:

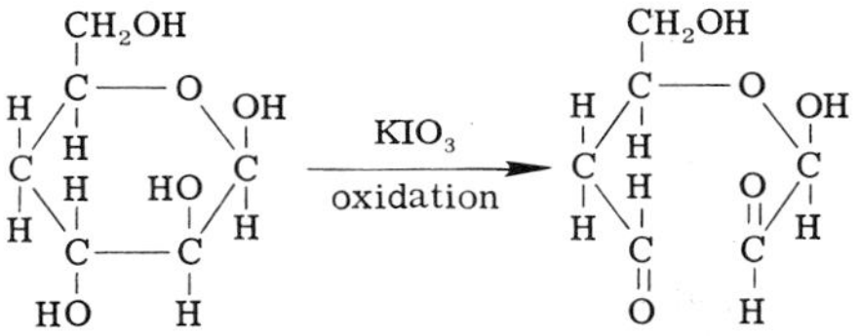

Any periodic acid remaining in the section after the period of oxidation can be reduced with the aid of a potassium iodide–sodium thiosulphate bath. The aldehyde groups so formed are demonstrated by reaction with Schiff's reagent to yield a pink coloration. For this reaction to occur, the hydroxyl groups of the sugar must be free (Hale, 1957), and if they are substituted or involved in further linkages they will not react. This is the proposed explanation for the inactivity of DNA and RNA in this reaction. Some substitutions seem to permit a reaction, such as when a hydroxyl group is replaced by an amino group, a carboxyl group or an alkyl amino group (Hale, 1957). This could explain the reaction with chitin. Nicolet and Schinn (1941) suggested that the presence of hydroxyamino acids, such as serine and threonine, at the end of chains or of hydroxyserine at any position in the chain may yield a positive PARS reaction, though Glegg *et al.* (1952) found that proteins containing large amounts of serine and threonine did not react with gelatin films containing these amino acids. Lhotka (1953) indicated that amino acids were only PARS positive after long periods of oxidation, and normally only relatively short periods (10 min) are used.

Basically, the PARS reaction indicates the sites of aldehyde groups, and it is incumbent upon the investigator to prove that the aldehydes are associated with carbohydrate molecules. This can be achieved in a number of ways, and a suggested scheme as used by Gahan (1965c) is as follows:

1. Free aldehydes are demonstrated by staining with the Schiff reagent. That the reaction is due to aldehydes can be shown by the absence of reaction in the sections pretreated with a saturated solution of dimedone in 5% acetic acid at 60°C for 18 h, the dimedone blocking aldehydes but not ketones.

2. Pretreatment of the sections with dimedone followed by the PARS reaction may be used to indicate carbohydrate aldehyde groups as distinct from the aldehyde groups already present in the section.

3. Formation of aldehyde groups within carbohydrate molecules is further tested by (a) dimedone blockade, (b) periodic acid oxidation, (c) a reducing rinse, (d) dimedone blockade of aldehydes formed during (b), (e) reacting with Schiff reagent.

4. Acetylation or benzoylation followed by the PARS reaction. Absence of colour due to substitution of the hydroxyl groups, as opposed to a colour in the absence of acetylation or benzoylation is indicative of the presence of a polysaccharide.

Whilst dimedone blockade has proved effective on plant material (Gahan, 1965c), Bayliss and Adams (1976) indicate its uncertainty with animal tissues and prefer phenylhydrazine, since this is most resistant to the action of periodic acid in (1) and (3) above.

Having established that the reaction is due to a polysaccharide, further analysis may be performed as suggested by Jensen (1962). Since all carbohydrate components of the cell wall appear to react equally well with the PARS reaction, he suggested that selective extraction might facilitate the assessment of individual components. Thus, three slides are extracted with 0.5% ammonium oxalate at 70°–80°C to remove pectic and water-soluble substances. Two of these slides are further extracted with 4% sodium hydroxide at 25°C to remove hemicelluloses, and one slide is finally extracted with 17.5% sodium hydroxide at 25°C leaving only cellulose. All slides are subjected to the PAS reaction and a comparison made to indicate the amount and localization of the various cell wall components. Although this is not an ideal procedure, it does allow some assessment to be made in the absence of a more specific reaction.

Alternative forms of control include the treatment of sections with various enzymes, such as pectinase and cellulase, that digest specific components. The pectinase group has been known since 1898 and includes methylpectinesterase and polygalacturonase as two major enzyme components. The former enzyme is thought to hydrolyse methyl ester groups adjacent to free carboxyl groups in polygalacturonides and is highly specific, acting only upon polygalacturonides (MacDonnell *et al.*, 1950). The latter enzyme, polygalacturonase, occurs primarily in fungi and bacteria and amongst animal sources in snail stomach (Faberge, 1945). Poly-α-1,4-galacturonide glycanohydrolase, the usual commercially available enzyme obtained from *Aspergillus niger,* acts by breaking glycosidic links of de-esterified parts of polygalacturonide chains. Cellulases are highly specific β(1→4)-endoglucosidases, but only recently have relatively pure products become commercially available. Hemicellulases are also commercially available, but the purity is often dubious.

Thus, treatment of sections with these enzymes may be followed by reaction with the PARS test and compared with sections treated with the enzyme carrier solution (often a buffer) alone and subjected to the PARS test.

Starches may be identified by the classic method of Couentou (1825) in which it appears that iodine is accumulated in the centre of the helical starch molecules. On staining a preparation in potassium iodide−iodine solution, the shorter-chain starch molecules yield a more reddish colour, whilst the longer chains yield a deeper blue colour. Hence, starch that is in the process of being formed tends to stain red to violet due to the shorter chain length of the molecules as does amylopectin because of the branched-chain configuration of the molecules. The presence of starch grains can be identified by their characteristic birefringence pattern when viewed with polarized light (Chapter 9).

It should be noted that unlike ordinary starch, the starch present in the sieve tubes of the phloem stains brownish-red rather than blue-black. Studies on this special starch from *Phaseolus vulgaris* indicate it to be a highly branched molecule of the amylopectin type having many α(1→6)-linkages at the branch points (Palevitz and Newcombe, 1970).

Inulin is a polysaccharide occurring in the storage organs of many Compositae, Campanulaceae and many monocotyledonous plants. It is comprised of fructofuranose units linked from C-2 to C-1 with a glucose molecule at one end of each polysaccharide chain. Unlike starch it is present in solution, though it is readily precipitated if the tissues are fixed in ethanol, when characteristic sphaerocrystals of inulin can be seen. A similar affect can be achieved by treating inulin-rich tissues with glycerin (Fahn, 1974). If the precipitated inulin is soaked for 2 min in alcoholic phloroglucin, mounted in concentrated HCl and warmed, the inulin disappears and is replaced by a red-brown precipitate.

Cellulose, is routinely identified in cell walls by means of the zinc chloriodide and iodine sulphuric acid tests. However, these tests seem to be nonspecific in that hemicelluloses will also colour blue, whilst if lignin is present no colour forms (Waley *et al.*, 1952). The introduction of optical brighteners to cytochemistry has resulted in the ability to demonstrate cellulose, including newly formed cellulose, by means of staining with the fluorochromes, Calcofluor and Photine HV (Hughes and McCully, 1975; Tampion *et al.*, 1973).

The failure to stain with toluidine blue has also been used as an indicator of cellulose when present with other carbohydrate components that do stain (O'Brien et al., 1964; Parups and Moinar, 1972). Pectic compounds have been localized by their ability to stain with 0.02% ruthenium red (Johansen, 1958) when present in high concentrations. Consequently, failure to react may not necessarily indicate an absence of these substances. Many studies have been made on the staining mechanism of ruthenium red, since it was introduced as a means of enhancing the electron-opacity of animal cell membranes (reviewed in Luft, 1971a,b). As a pectin stain, however, Sterling (1970) has indicated that the staining group in ruthenium red is the ruthenium ion and the associated complex of four ammonia molecules. Staining will occur when the host molecule has two negative charges 0.42 nm apart, which will accommodate the staining group. It is believed that the staining sites are intra-molecular, and that the staining can be intensified if the cell walls are de-esterified, since carboxyl groups with strong negative charges on the oxygen atoms will be re-established (Sterling, 1970). Work on animal tissues where the dye appears to bind to the carboxyl groups of polysaccharides associated with the plasma membrane, e.g. ruthenium red binds selectively to glycosaminoglycan (heparin) in mast cells, led to the suggestion that at low pH the carboxyl groups are dissociated, and the co-ordination ion of the stain may form a salt linkage with the anionic groups.

$$\left[\begin{array}{c} H_3N \quad NH_3 \; H_3N \quad NH_3 \; H_3N \quad NH_3 \\ H_3N-Ru-O-Ru-O-Ru-NH_3 \\ H_3N \quad NH_3 \; H_3N \quad NH_3 \; H_3N \quad NH_3 \end{array} \right]^{6+} \cdot 6\,Cl^- \; + 6\,R\cdot \underset{\underset{O}{\|}}{C}\cdot O\cdot H^+ \longrightarrow$$

$$R.C.-O-\underset{H_3N}{\overset{H_3N}{Ru^+}}-O-\underset{H_3N}{\overset{NH_3\;H_3N}{Ru^{2+}}}-\underset{H_3N}{\overset{NH_3\;H_3N}{Ru^{2+}}}-\underset{NH_3}{\overset{NH_3}{NH_3}} \longrightarrow$$

$$R-\underset{O}{\overset{O}{C}}-O-\underset{H_3N}{\overset{C=O}{Ru}}-O-\underset{H_3N}{\overset{R}{Ru}}-O-\underset{H_3N}{\overset{R}{Ru}}-O-C-R$$

An alternative method for esterified pectin is that based upon the reaction of alkaline hydroxylamine hydrochloride with the methyl esters of pectin to produce hydroxylamic acid, which in turn yields a red complex with ferric ions (Reeve, 1959). Not only does this method permit a distinction between non-esterified and esterified pectins, but is also quantifiable (Gee et al., 1959; Reeve, 1959). A further advantage is that the ferric complexes are electron-opaque and so the method may be employed for electron microscopy (Albersheim *et al.*, 1960) unlike ruthenium red, which, although very useful in animal studies, has proved relatively unsuitable with plant tissues. This is possibly due to its different mechanism of reaction preventing the interaction of osmium tetroxide and ruthenium red as had been proposed for animal tissues (Luft, 1966, 1971a). Ruthenium red is not, however, always a reliable method for the detection of pectin and needs careful controls.

The copper phthalocyanin dye (alcian blue 8GX) was introduced by Mowry (1960) for the cytochemical detection of free and protein-bound glycosaminogly-cans in animal tissues. More recent studies have indicated that alcian blue will bind irreversibly and quantitatively to glycosaminoglycan molecules (Tas, 1977a,b). Although used for many years in studies of mucopolysaccharides in animal tissues, alcian blue has been little applied to plant tissues. Beneš and Uhlírová (1966) and Beneš (1968) attempted to study its sites and mode of staining and concluded from studies varying the pH and using model films and pectinase digests that alcian blue stains for pectin probably by salt linkage of the dye with the free carboxyl groups of the pectic compounds. On this basis, this method, like ruthenium red, would not seem to stain esterified pectins.

Toluidine blue has also been employed to identify pectins in that the meta-chromatic reaction yields a pink coloration (O'Brien *et al.*, 1964).

Until recently, callose, a $\beta1,3$-glucan, was localized with aniline blue. Linskens and Esser (1957) have shown that decolourised aniline blue may also serve as a vital fluorochrome under certain conditions, yielding further information about the localization of callose (Smith and McCully, 1978). This method has been applied with good results for studying the induction of callose deposition in stigmas following pollination by foreign pollens (Vithanage and Knox, 1977). However, more chemically specific methods are required if callose is to be studied satisfactorily.

B. Chitin

Chitin reacts specifically using a method described by Roelofson and Huette (1951) in which the specimen is autoclaved in 23% potassium hydroxide to convert chitin to chitosan, which can then be stained with potassium iodide in 1% sulphuric acid to yield a violet colour. A brown reaction is considered to be negative. This is controlled by treating the autoclaved material with 2% acetic acid in which the chitosan, but not cellulose, is soluble.

C. Lignin

This is not a carbohydrate, but it is perhaps pertinent to discuss its cytochemistry along with the other cell wall components. Due to the presence of double bonds, lignin strongly absorbs ultra-violet light and so can be distinguished readily from the other cell wall components that do not absorb (Wardrop and Bland, 1959). At present no specific cytochemical test exists that will demonstrate lignin under all conditions. Recourse is still made to the routine histological stains, such as Azure B at pH 4.0 and phloroglucin-HCl, or the positive reaction of lignin with Schiff reagent (McLean and Cook, 1941), though lignin has been shown to stain bright blue-green with toludine blue (O'Brien et al., 1964). Phloroglucinol-HCl appears to react with the cinnamaldehyde end groups of lignin, whilst a red stain is thought to occur with the chlorine–sulphite test of Campbell et al. (1937) by reaction with lignin containing syringyl groups (Wardrop, 1971). It may be worth mentioning that commercially available samples of Azure B should be checked for purity (Marshall, 1979).

D. Tannins

Tannins are glycosides containing polyhydroxyphenols or their derivatives. Chemically, they are colourless, non-crystalline compounds that form colloidal solutions in water. They can be precipitated by basic lead acetate or 1% aqueous caffeine solution. The anhydrous derivatives of tannins, the phlobapenes (Gortner and Gortner, 1949), are yellow, red or brown amorphous substances that are very readily visualized in sectioned material, being present as either granular masses or variously sized bodies. Treatment of colourless tannins with ferric salts results in the formation of a blue-black colour that can be used as a test upon sections, but which is better known as a reaction employed in the manufacture of ink. When stained metachromatically with toluidine blue, tannins have been reported to stain green-bright blue (Kinzel et al., 1961; O'Brien et al., 1964) due to the presence of the polyphenols.

E. Polyphenols

Polyphenols are aromatic compounds containing hydroxyl groups attached directly to the nucleus, their classification depending upon the number of hydroxyl groups present. As such, the presence of polyphenols may be identified through a number of reactions. These include the use of ferric chloride (Svendsen, 1951; Mace, 1963) as discussed for the identification of tannins, and which has been used in light, and scanning and transmission electron microscopy (Brissan et al., 1976, 1977). Mace (1963) used Gibb's (1927) test to detect the presence of polyphenols in tomato roots, when the blue ammonium salt of indophenol forms by interation of the polyphenols with 2,6-dichloro-p-benzoquinone-4-chloroimine. A simpler approach is the nitrous acid test (Vorsatz, 1942) in which sections are immersed in a mixture of equal volumes of 10% aqueous sodium nitrate, urea and acetic acid for a few minutes. Sodium hydroxide (2 N) is then

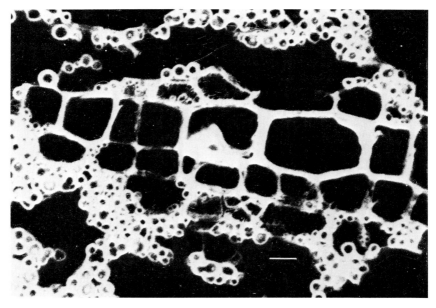

FIG. 20. Unfixed, frozen section of cassava root illuminated by 340–380 nm wavelengths. Auto-fluorescence of material identified biochemically as due to scopoletin. Scale, 0.1 mm.

added and a yellow to red colour will develop if polyphenols are present (Reeve, 1950). Diazotized sulphanilic acid can be used as a general phenol reagent on tissue sections if the pH is adjusted to a final 4.7 when the reaction time is short to achieve the yellow-orange colour, and the breakdown of the reagent and hence a high background staining is avoided (Wistar and Bartlett, 1941; Mace, 1963). Autofluorescence on excitation with ultra-violet light may be used, but is not specific (Fig. 20).

III. AUTORADIOGRAPHY

Whilst autoradiography cannot be used to demonstrate directly the components present in a cell, it may be used to follow the incorporation of, for example, [14C]glucose or [3H]glucose or $^{14}CO_2$ into various carbohydrates. If this is coupled with a biochemical analysis to determine the nature of the radioactive material seen with the autoradiographs, a fairly detailed analysis can be achieved of the localization and synthesis of various carbohydrates (see for example, Northcote and Pickett-Heaps, 1966).

Autoradiography of water-soluble compounds (Chapter 10) also opens up the possibility of studying the localization of the free monosaccharides in tissues as well as the transport pathways involved.

IV. ELECTRON MICROSCOPE CYTOCHEMISTRY

Surprisingly, there have been few attempts to study carbohydrates by electron microscope cytochemistry. Apart from autoradiographic methods, the approach to carbohydrates is limited. A method developed for use with animal tissues has been successfully applied to plants; this is the modification of the PARS reaction in which after periodic acid oxidation of fixed, embedded and sectioned tissues, the sections are reacted with a silver–methenamine reagent (Rambourg, 1968; Pickett-Heaps, 1968). This yields an electron-dense silver deposit at the site of aldehydes instead of the magenta colour observed with the light microscope after reacting with Schiff reagent. The cleanliness of the glassware used in this reaction is of particular importance. Like the PARS reaction, the silver–methenamine method demonstrates only aldehyde groups, and the investigator again must confirm that the aldehydes are associated with carbohydrate molecules. This is made the more necessary because the fixative itself is an aldehyde that will react in this test. Glutaraldehyde is synthesized from acrolein, and some batches of the fixative contain high concentrations of this starting material. Acrolein links to tissue through a reaction between its ethylene group and the NH_2, $=NH$ or SH groups of proteins, or the imidazole of histidine, leaving its aldehyde group free to react with the reagent. The silver–methenamine test will also show pre-existing aldehydes as well as other reducing groups such as 5-hydroxytryptamine. Whilst Rambourg (1968) does not describe any controls to the reaction, the scheme offered for the PARS reaction may also provide a basis of control for the silver–methenamine test.

An alternative approach that has also been applied successfully to plant cell walls (Jewell and Saxton, 1970; Roland, 1978a,b) is the method of Thiéry (1967), which would seem to have a greater specificity than that of the silver–methenamine method mentioned above. This is a modification of the methods based upon the use of thiocarbohydrazide and thiosemicarbohydrazide (Seligman et al., 1965; Hanker et al., 1964). These two compounds were introduced in order to block aldehyde groups but being powerful oxidizing compounds, they could reduce OsO_4 very readily, so forming an electron-opaque "osmium black". Thus, it was possible with this approach to identify the aldehyde groups produced by periodic acid oxidation of the carbohydrate molecules. Thiéry (1967) modified the method by replacing osmium tetroxide with silver–proteinate to yield the final electron-opaque product after binding thiosemicarbohydrazide to the aldehyde groups.

8. Vital Dyes

I. INTRODUCTION

Vital dyes were introduced into animal studies by Trembley (1774), and although frequently used in cytological investigations, were not employed on plant materials until much later (Pfeffer, 1886). Subsequently, they were used routinely (e.g., Guilliermond, 1941), but the introduction of more sophisticated forms of microscopy has meant that their recent use has been minimal. A good, brief, historical account is given by Baker (1958).

The development of new technology allowing rapid assays of large numbers of cells has recently re-stimulated interest in the vital dyes and especially the fluorescent dyes because of their value in flow fluorimetry. As yet, this approach has been applied mainly to animal cells and has been little exploited in botany.

It is important to remember that vital dyes offer a means of making a number of simple observations on living cells, especially in terms of both their physiology and cell damage and death. Some examples, which may be cited, include the use of triphenyltetrazolium chloride for seed germinability (Lakon, 1942a,b; Mattson *et al.*, 1947); mauvine, dahlia and methyl violet on staminal hairs of *Tradescantia* (Campbell, 1888); neutral red, neutral violet and cresyl blue for cell viability and vacuole studies (Guilliermond, 1941); Evans blue for cell viability studies (Gaff and Okang'o-Ogola, 1971); and Rhodamine B and 6G for translocation studies (Strügger, 1938).

The value of vital dyes has already been established, and a number of those involved are listed in this chapter because they may be of help in establishing simple cytochemical characteristics of living plant cells. Before doing this, a few comments are pertinent concerning the handling of vital dyes.

Baker (1958) lists three requirements for vital dyes, namely the ability to (a) enter cells of various types; (b) pass through the cytoplasm without killing the cells; and (c) colour pre-existing cell inclusions distinctively, or to colour the whole of the cytoplasm of particular cells. In cytochemical terms, (a) and (b) still hold, and (c) may be modified so that cell inclusions may be specifically coloured allowing information to be gained concerning the chemistry of that inclusion.

Most dyes will kill cells if used at the concentrations normally employed in histology, but by reducing the concentration significantly, it is possible to avoid killing the cells and yet obtain information about them. Clearly, as the dye accumulates in a cell, its concentration increases so that ultimately the cell will be killed. However, the initial stages of the reactions leave the cells in a viable state. Most useful vital dyes are basic dyes exhibiting varying degrees of toxicity. Thus, chick fibroblasts have been cultured for 24 h in the presence of 0.001% 3,4-benzpyrene (Chayen *et al.*, 1959) and root systems exhibit mitotic activity if grown in the presence of 0.02% or more of neutral red (Becker, 1929). After immersion for 18 h, 0.001% Janus green will kill root systems (P. B. Gahan, unpublished data), though wheat seeds may be successfully germinated in the presence of 0.0005–to 0.001% of this dye (Guilliermond, 1941).

II. COLOURED DYES

A. Janus Green B

This is a basic dye with an adsorption maximum at 610–623 nm and a molecular weight of 511. It is soluble in both water (5.2% at 26°C) and ethanol (1.1% at 26°C), though for vital staining it is used as an aqueous solution. A 0.1% aqueous stock solution is prepared, which is diluted 100 times prior to use. A few drops of the solution are placed on the cells or sections to be studied and a coverslip added. After 10 to 20 min the mitochondria in living cells will become coloured blue-green, whilst the cytoplasm remains clear. In contrast, dead cells stain blue-green throughout. Lazarow and Cooperstein (1953) made a detailed study of the process and found the dye to be absorbed everywhere in the cell and then reduced to the colourless leucobasic form. At mitochondrial sites, the dye is maintained in its blue, oxidized form due to the action of cytochrome oxidase. In dead cells, the differential capacity to reduce and oxidise is lost and the cells merely absorb the blue dye.

B. Evans Blue

Evans blue differs from the better-known Trypan blue only through the position-ing of the sulphate groups. It is a water-soluble, acid dye having a molecular weight of 960, and has been used as a vital dye in animal studies since 1940 (Brunschwig *et al.*, 1940). Whilst both Evans blue and Trypan blue were used as vital dyes to stain various cells, more recently they have been employed to test cell viability by dye exclusion since the dye penetrates and stains only those cells that are dead or damaged. Intact, viable cells prevent the dye from entering and so remain unstained. The use of Evans blue was modified for plant studies (Gaff and Okang'o-Ogola, 1971) when a 0.1% aqueous solution was used to bathe the plant cells for 5 min, after which, a cell count was performed to determine the percentage of viable cells. Evans blue was found to be more satisfactory than Trypan blue for use with plant cells.

C. Neutral Red

A weakly basic dye having an absorption maximum at 540–542 nm and a molecular weight of 300. It is soluble in both water (5.6% at 26°C) and ethanol (2.5% at 26°C). In aqueous solution it is red at acid pH, shifting to yellow at pH 6.8–8.0. It has been employed as a vital dye since 1894 and frequently has been used together with Janus green B (Conn, 1969). Though considered by many to be the vital dye of choice in animal studies (Baker, 1958), it has been of immense value in botanical studies for checking cell viability. Normally this dye is accu-mulated into the vacuoles of viable cells that are the only structures to appear red. If the cells are dead or damaged then the whole cell will stain.

Neutral red has been employed in many ways since its introduction to plant studies, and more recently Basham and Bateman (1975) have used 0.01% neutral red in 20 mM phosphate buffer at pH 7.5 containing 600 mM KNO$_3$ and 1 mM CaCl$_2$. After staining for 20 min, the material is rinsed with the same solution but with the neutral red omitted.

D. Neutral Violet

This is a weakly basic dye of a molecular weight of 408 and absorption maximum at 533 nm. It is sparingly soluble in water (3.3% at 26°C) and ethanol (2.2% at 26°C) and is similar to neutral red in its staining behaviour, being used as a 0.001–0.002% aqueous solution (Guilliermond, 1941).

E. Brilliant Cresyl Blue

The structure of this basic dye which has a molecular weight of about 333 is still disputed, but would seem to be as follows:

The dye is water-soluble and with an absorption maximum in the range 624–628 nm. It has been used as a vital dye with animal tissues since 1927 (Irwin, 1927) and subsequently for plants in a similar manner to neutral red (Guilliermond, 1941). It was used as a 0.005% solution in Schoen's medium (a minimal salt medium containing glucose and asparagine) and, in the case of yeast cells, maximal uptake occurred at pH 9.5, staining the vacuoles.

III. FLUORESCENT DYES

Fluorescent dyes were introduced into botany at the end of the nineteenth century, employing such compounds as auramine O (Vinassa, 1891), but the use of such compounds as vital dyes came about much later through initial attempts to study translocation pathways. Thus, rhodamine B and 6G were introduced by Strügger (1938) as vital dyes, though they have become more popular through their use as fluorescent labels for antibodies. More recently, a large number of new fluorescent compounds have appeared on the market and, after careful screening, seem to be of value as vital dyes in cytology and cytochemistry.

A. Rhodamine B

A basic dye with a molecular weight of 479 and a maximum absorption at 556.5 nm, Rhodamine B is very sparingly soluble in water (0.8% at 26°C) and in ethanol (1.5% at 26°C). It fluoresces when excited by ultra-violet light.

B. Rhodamine 6G

This is the ethyl ester of Rhodamine B having a molecular weight of 479, absorption maximum of 492 nm, and is excited with ultra-violet light.

C. Tetracycline

This antibotic has a molecular weight of 444 in its anhydrous form and is sparingly soluble in water (0.17%) and ethanol (<2%). It has absorption maxima at 220, 268 and 355 nm in 0.1 N HCl.

This dye has not been greatly used in plant studies, but its use in localising sites of newly deposited calcium in bone may make it of interest for calcification studies in plants (Milch *et al.*, 1961), e.g. as chlorotetracycline for detecting Ca–calmodulin complexes (Chandler and Williams, 1978).

D. Fluorescein and Fluorescein Diacetate

Fluorescein

Fluoroscein is an acid dye of molecular weight 332 and not of much value as a stain. However, on excitation with ultra-violet light it yields a greenish yellow fluorescence, and is detectable in low concentration. It has been used in botanical studies for some time (Hercik, 1939; Williams and Green, 1935) and more recently as a vital dye in the form of the diacetate for the determination of the viability of cultured plant cells and isolated protoplasts (Heslop-Harrison and Heslop-Harrison, 1970; Widholm, 1972). Fluorescein diacetate is added to acetone at a concentration of 5 mg/ml, and this is further diluted with 0.05 M phosphate buffer at pH 5.8 to give a final concentration of 0.01%. The reaction mixture is used by staining the material for 5 min, and then examining with a fluorescence microscope. The viability of the cells is checked by their ability to accumulate fluorescein, due to enzymic cleavage of the acetate. The free fluorescein is able to leave the cell and hence the concentration of fluorescein remaining in the cell is dependent upon its capacity to replace the lost dye. Dead cells cannot cleave the ester and so will not fluoresce.

E. Fluorescein Isothiocyanate

This is formed from the diacetate and whilst not itself a vital dye, is used as a fluorescent label for antibodies in immunocytochemical studies.

F. Phenosafranin

This is the simplest of the safranin molecules that normally are methyl, ethyl or phenyl derivatives of phenosafranin. It has been introduced as a fluorochrome for viability studies on plant cells and protoplasts in culture, and works on the dye exclusion principle, staining only dead or dying cells (Widholm, 1972). Normally, the cells are stained for 5 min in 1% phenosafranin in 0.05 M phosphate buffer at pH 5.8, prior to examination by fluorescence microscopy.

G. Acridine Orange

A basic dye, normally obtained as a zinc chloride double salt and having an absorption maximum at 497 nm. Whilst it has been used primarily in nucleic acid studies (see Chapter 3, Section II,B), a 0.0001% solution has been used as a vital dye for animal cell cultures and some plant cell studies where it appears to be accumulated into vacuoles in living cells, e.g. fungal spores (Wilson *et al.*, 1978).

H. 3,4-Benzpyrene

This is more frequently used as a lipid stain, but at a similar concentration can be used as a vital dye when it tends to be accumulated into available lipid sites in the living cell (Allison and Malucci, 1964).

I. Auramine O

$$(CH_3)_2N——C——N(CH_3)_2$$
$$\underset{NH_2}{\|}$$
$$+$$
$$Cl^-$$

This sometime drug is a basic dye with a maximum absorption value at 380 nm and a molecular weight of 304. It is very sparingly soluble in water (0.7% at 26°C) but more soluble in ethanol (4.5% at 26°C). In addition to its role in fluorescent Schiff reactions for DNA (Chapter 3, Section II,C), it can be used to stain sites that appear to correspond to unsaturated, acidic waxes and cutin precursors (Considine and Knox, 1979).

J. Fluorescent Brighteners

These are compounds developed for use in commercial processes as, for example, additives to washing powders and are increasingly being exploited in cytology and cytochemistry. Of those tested, Calcofluor M2R New (Hughes and McCully, 1975) has been used as a vital dye to detect cellulose in plant tissue cultures. An alternative compound for this purpose is Photine HV (Tampion *et al.*, 1973), which is used as a 0.1% aqueous solution reacting in 30 s.

9. Physical Techniques and Quantification

I. INTRODUCTION

In the earlier chapters, methods have been indicated that allow the localization of a range of molecules and chemical groups in cells and tissues. Examination of the sections reacted for a specific substance may show that the different cell types within the section react differently, or that cells that are morphologically similar do not necessarily react in the same way for a given cytochemical test. It is possible to describe these differences in a general way, but this is not adequate if specific conclusions are to be drawn concerning any variations. It may be that the differences represent real variations between these cells, or they may be due to technical deficiences. In order to determine the degree of differences existing between cells or the amounts of material, a number of quantitative cytochemical and cytophysical methods may be employed. Some of these have already been considered in the earlier chapters.

It is important to remember that however good the method of quantification, it is useless if applied to a poorly understood cytochemical method. The following comments are based upon the assumption that the measuring techniques will be applied to reactions, the chemistry of which is understood, and the effects of tissue preparation and of the method itself upon the substance under investigation will be taken into account.

Before going on to consider the various ways in which quantification may be achieved, it is pertinent to ask the question, What is it that we are trying to quantify? Essentially we can make two kinds of measurement. The first concerns absolute measurement in which assays can be made of the total amount of a given ion or molecule present in a section, cell or structure, e.g. RNA, DNA, structural protein or the dry mass of a given object. The second approach concerns comparative measurement that may involve the comparison of absolute amounts discussed above, or simply counts of the total number of cells or organelles that are positive or negative for a specific cytochemical test. With this type of measurement, however, we are trying to estimate orders of difference in response between tissues, cells or organelles in the same or different tissues, before and after a particular treatment, or at different stages of development.

In general, whether we are assessing absolute amounts or making comparisons, there are some general points to be considered; i.e. (a) effects of fixation on the substance under study; (b) effects of the cytochemical reaction on the substance under study; and (c) whole cells versus sections. Points a and b have been dealt with in Chapters 2–7, but point c needs some further discussion.

A. Whole Cells and Protoplasts

When dealing with whole cells or isolated protoplasts, a number of parameters can be readily obtained, such as the dimensions of the cell or protoplast, the size and volume of the nucleus or nucleolus, the total amount of nuclear DNA, or total cell dry mass or protein against which to standardize the particular measurements to be used for comparison, e.g. differences in activity of a given enzyme between two specimens. Thus, providing that the technical problems can be overcome for applying a particular reaction to whole cells or protoplasts, a fairly direct means of comparison is available for a variety of studies. However, the majority of comparative studies will result in the need to examine the cells *in situ* in their tissues, and hence in tissue sections, in order that the cells retain the level of activity relevant to their position in the tissue. Material that permits microdissection and single cell biochemistry presents a different, but limited approach.

B. Tissue Sections

In view of the vacuolated nature of many plant cells, problems of quantification arise that are greater than and different from those frequently encountered in similar quantitative studies on animal tissues. The basic problem with sections of plant material is that, even if it is possible to produce serial sections of uniform thickness, this is not enough to ensure comparability between sections of cells adjacent to each other in the same tissue or similar cells from different specimens.

A brief glance at a diagram of a ''typical'' plant cell will indicate the problem (Fig. 21), and this is further clarified by concentrating on two planes of sectioning (A and B). In the case of section A, the whole field may be comprised of three layers, the cell wall that is covered by a layer of cytoplasm and possibly superimposed by a vacuole, the cytoplasm and vacuole being enclosed by cell wall. Section B, a simpler situation, represents a section of cell wall enclosing cytoplasm that in turn encloses vacuolar space. The cytoplasm may or may not include part of or the whole nucleus. Obviously, if it is proposed to make a comparison of total protein between these two sections, this is not too difficult, but if it is intended to make a comparison of enzyme activity then the fundamental problem arises as to the basis of comparison.

Normally, sections are not of an absolutely even thickness, but even allowing that they can be, there will be obvious differences in the amounts of cytoplasm

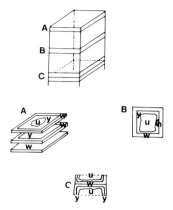

FIG. 21. Diagram of "typical" plant cell showing three planes of section (A–C) and possible variations in the content of the cell section in each plane (see text). n, nucleus; u, vacuole; w, cell wall; y, cytoplasm.

available to react for the enzyme between A and B. This problem will be compounded if sections are cut in different planes. For example, thicker sections are needed for studies on material with large cells containing large vacuoles, e.g. artichoke tubers and cassava roots, than smaller compact cells with little vacuolar structure, e.g. apical meristems, if enough cytoplasm is to be obtained for the reaction to be visualized. In the thicker sections the situation seen in section A may be compounded by A being superimposed upon its mirror-image (Fig. 21 C). It is not difficult to visualize other intermediary situations. This leads to the problem of accurate comparison of activities or amounts of substance in unit volumes of cytoplasm or nucleus or wall or vacuole.

In a sense autoradiography can help to overcome this problem since by using ^{3}H- or ^{125}I-labelled material, only electrons emitted from a maximum depth of 1 μm will be registered by the photographic emulsion and hence will minimise the problem of section thickness. Thus, estimation of areas of the structure of interest will permit calculation of unit volumes containing the labelled material, so enabling the autoradiographic analysis to be based upon a unit volume of, for example, cytoplasm. However, there are limited applications of ^{3}H and ^{125}I autoradiography in cytochemistry as a whole, and this does not solve the problem completely.

A number of alternative solutions are open, depending upon the types of problem under investigation. In the case of non-enzymic reactions, total amounts of nuclear DNA may be measured in sections (Carrière and Patterson, 1962), and total dry mass of the cell may be calculated by interference microscopy. However, measurements relating to cell walls or cytoplasm may well need section thickness measurements in order to calculate volume.

C. Measurement of Section Thickness

A general view of this subject was given by Lange and Engström (1954), and, clearly, the simplest approach available to every microscopist involves the exploitation of the calibrated fine focus adjustment of the microscope. This is achieved by focussing on the upper and lower surfaces of the section, the thickness being calculated from the degree of turn required of the fine adjustment control. Accuracy will be improved if the objective used is of high numerical aperture, which will yield a shallow depth of field. Lange and Engström claimed an error of 10% when working with sections 5 μm thick.

A number of more complicated methods have been published, and many of them require additional apparatus such as the mikrokator and its modifications (Glimstedt and Hakansson, 1951; Hallén, 1956). Whilst under ideal conditions, an accuracy of 0.12 μm is claimed, it will not be possible for everybody to have access to this equipment which employs a profile microscope. More ready access may be had to interferometric methods (see Section II,B). The thickness of the specimen is determined from the optical path difference between two rays, one passing through the specimen and the other passing through the mounting medium adjacent to the specimen. The problem is that the refractive index of the specimen must be known. There are several ways of obtaining this information using two interference measurements, but they are not very useful if one is investigating section thickness during the course of a cytochemical analysis, since they involve the use of two mounting media of different refractive indices. Goldstein (1967) proposed a "two-aperture" technique in which the first measurement is made using axial parallel light and the second using an oblique beam of light exploiting the marginal rays from a wide-angle condenser. A further method involves multiple beam interferometric measurements of the upper side of the slide and the lower surface of the cover-slip, but this would not necessarily indicate true specimen thickness, especially if cell walls were cut unevenly with respect to the cytoplasm. Two recent innovations include the use of a surfometer (Pearse and Marks, 1976) and Cejtronic probe (Halkjaer-Kristensen and-Ingemann-Hansen, 1978). The latter seems of more interest with plant material since the probe rests on the microscope stage and can sensitively measure section thickness to 0.1 μm by difference on focussing the upper and lower surfaces of the specimen. A simpler method involves the use of interference measurements of sections 0.3–45 μm thick. Here, an incident illumination objective incorporating a beam-splitter and adjustable reference mirror is used to generate interference fringes (Section II,B) by reflection from the upper surfaces of sections mounted on glass slides (Robertson et al., 1983). If we are interested in quantifying enzyme activity, then this presents a little more difficulty. When no special equipment is available, and the problem entails differences between, for example, sections of the same tissue treated differently or different cell types within the same section, then measurement of the minimal incubation times required to observe the reaction may be of value (Gahan and Maple, 1966). Thus, differences are measured on a basis of time and do not depend entirely upon the volume of cytoplasm. The differences in speed of reaction indicates not just amounts of enzyme reacting, but may also offer indications as to the availability of the enzyme molecules to react which may be relevant in studies on, for example, hormone treatments.

Some tissues may present the possibility of microdissection of individual cells from thick sections, in which case an advance may be made over the above possibility by applying the approach of Lowry *et al.* (1953; see Chapter 1) to the analysis of both enzyme activity and total tissue protein, so enabling enzyme activity to be expressed on the basis of unit protein per cell (Croxdale, 1983).

Unfortunately, microdissection does not lend itself to all types of tissues, and resort must be made to microdensitometry and/or quantitative fluorescence microscopy. Most workers merely measure the amount of end-product present in a section, a given tissue or each cell and work on the assumption that comparisons may be made between cell types and tissues.

At the cellular level, it is possible to express the measurements as end-product per unit area of reacted cytoplasm. This can be achieved by setting the integrating microdensitometer to measure only cytoplasm containing end-product and to ignore those non-reacted areas (which may also include nuclei, cell walls and vacuoles). The machine will be able to measure both reacted area and end-product, and this means that the time of incubation when the maximum number of enzymically active sites are reacting can also be determined. In addition, by plotting product per unit reacted cytoplasm against time of incubation, it is also possible to calculate the rate of enzymic response by the cell (Fig. 22). Such a method depends upon contant section thickness, and whilst this may be achieved with some tissues, such as primary meristems, large, vacuolated cells do not

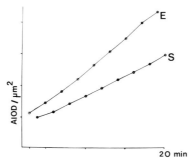

FIG. 22.   Plot of absolute integrated optical density units (AIOD) per μm^2 of reacted cytoplasm versus time of incubation for glucose-6-phosphate dehydrogenase activity at 30°C in an unfixed, frozen section of a seed of *Avena fatua*. S, scutellum; E, embryo.

always handle in a way which will permit this approach to be employed. One way to overcome this is to calculate the rate of the reaction on the linear part of the curve when the maximum reactive area of field measured is saturated. Thus, determining the rate of reaction between two time points on the curve and comparing with rates similarly obtained from other sections should permit comparison regardless of section thickness variation, e.g. calculations based on Fig. 22 would compare

$$k_{\text{scutellum}} = \frac{t_{17 \text{ min}} - t_{11 \text{ min}}}{6} \quad \text{with} \quad k_{\text{embryo}} = \frac{t_{18 \text{ min}} - t_{12 \text{ min}}}{6}$$

The slope of the linear regression line for the plot of reaction product versus time of incubation also can be used to determine the rate of activity. Data can be more readily handled by a computer linked to the microdensitometer (Middleton *et al.*, 1984). Alternative measurements may need to be considered in which a double measurement must be made. This can be either of cytoplasmic dry mass or of total cytoplasmic protein and the enzyme activity. In this way, enzyme activity can be expressed per unit dry mass or protein, and hence a more reliable basis for comparison be achieved. Two types of measurement may be made in the following ways: (a) enzyme activity versus dry mass; and (b) enzyme activity versus total protein.

1. Enzyme Activity versus Dry Mass

Cytoplasmic dry mass may be measured by means of interference microscopy prior to reacting the section for the enzyme reaction. Enzyme end-product may then be assayed on the same cells using either interference microscopy or integrating microdensitometry. Automated interference microscopy is now available on commercial models, which makes this a more realistic approach for routine measurements.

2. Enzyme Activity versus Total Protein

The section can be reacted for enzyme activity and the end-product measured by integrating microdensitometry. The enzyme end-product can then be removed from the section which is reacted for total protein and the colour response again measured by integrating microdensitometry.

This approach may be aided considerably by the current development of fluorescent dyes for total protein estimation and the production of enzyme substrates yielding fluorescent end-products. Thus, by reacting the section for both enzyme activity and total protein, and using fluorochromes that emit light at distinctly different wavelengths, it is possible to perform both measurements simultaneously, so minimizing the handling procedures involved and hence reducing the possibility of artefacts, e.g. through the loss of material from sections, which may occur whilst measuring dry mass.

Developments in automated analysis now permit selective measurements to be made on specific parts of the cell, so that newer measuring devices can be instructed to measure only those zones required, regardless of irregular outlines. This is of value when selectively measuring the cytoplasm in a given cell. At present such equipment is expensive and is only available in specialist laboratories, but the advent of microprocessors should shortly make it possible for this equipment to become routinely available.

II. METHODOLOGY

As has already been discussed, there are a variety of approaches to quantification, each method having its own particular uses. Two main approaches are available, i.e. (a) modified biochemical methods (already discussed in Chapter 1); and (b) microscopical measurements. Each of the microscopical measurements may be employed in different ways, and the remainder of this chapter will consider each of these methods, their "mode d'emploi" and the ways in which they can be exploited.

The light microscope has been well described in a number of works (e.g., Hartley, 1965; Barron, 1966), but, from the point of view of cytochemistry, the most important modifications are those that increase the resolution of the instrument and allow measurements to be made. Minimal modifications are needed to achieve fluorescence, polarized light, phase contrast and interference microscopy and simple instruments can be achieved in the laboratory. However, attempts to increase resolution did result in drastic changes in microscope construction, as will be seen later.

Resolution may be defined as the ability to distinguish two adjacent point sources, and so the resolving power of the microscope may be considered as the minimum distance at which it is possible to observe two adjacent points as two distinct entities. Resolution is directly proportional to the wavelength of the illuminating light, and inversely proportional to the mean of the numerical apertures of the objective and the condenser.

It may be expressed mathematically as

$$R = \frac{0.61\lambda}{NA}$$

where R is the resolving power, λ is the wavelength of light, and NA is half the sum of the numerical apertures of the condenser and objective when that of the condenser is equal to or greater than that of the objective.

For the light microscope, the maximum NA has been achieved in terms of lens design and the construction of objectives and condensers so that resolution is directly limited by the characteristics of light itself. Thus, if the two points observed are closer together than 0.24 μm it will not be possible to distinguish them individually with the light microscope. Attempts to overcome this limitation have been made by the use of monochromatic ultra-violet light, involving the use of a quartz optical system. Further attempts to reduce the wavelength of the illuminating source resulted in an extension into the fields of X-ray and electron microscopy. Each of the developments will be considered.

A. Integrating Microdensitometry

The light microscope has been coupled to a monochromating system together with a refined photometer recording device such that accurate measurements of dye product present in a cell or organelle can be made.

This method is invaluable in measurements of (a) nucleic acids; (b) polysaccharides; (c) structural proteins; and (d) enzyme reaction product and will be useful in (e) lipid cytochemistry. In the case of (a)–(c), measurements can be used to indicate total amounts of each substance present at a chosen site, and this may soon be extended for use with (e). In the case of (d), not only may total amounts of reaction product be measured, but, by continuously monitoring the progress of the enzyme reaction, it is often possible to measure the rate of the enzyme response. The basic requirements are (a) the reaction for the compound assayed is specific; (b) the number of molecules of dye linked to one molecule of the compound assayed is constant and ideally is in a ratio of 1 : 1; and (c) the amount of light absorbed by the dye is proportional to the number of absorbing molecules present per unit thickness and so must obey the Beer–Lambert laws.

Any determination of light absorption involves two measurements, namely, the intensity of the incident or background light (I_o) and the intensity of the incident beam reduced by passing through the specimen (I_s). The percent of light transmitted by the specimen (I_s/I_o) is the percentage transmission (%T). Light absorption ideally depends on the number of absorbing molecules in the light path. Thus, as the number of molecules absorbing within the specimen is increased, e.g. by increasing the specimen thickness, the transmission decreases logarithmically. Transmission is a reciprocal log function of the number of absorbing molecules. Consequently, the optical density, or extinction (E), is defined by

$$E = \log_{10}\frac{1}{T} = \log_{10}\frac{I_o}{I_s}$$

Hence the molecular absorption laws hold when the extinction bears a linear relation to the number of absorbing molecules. The relationship between the extent of light absorption and the layer thickness of a pure compound is given by Lambert's law (1760), namely, equal fractions of the incident radiation are absorbed by successive layers of equal thickness of the light absorbing substance, that is

$$I_s = I_o \, 10^{-El}$$

where l is the passage through 1 cm.

If the absorbing substance is in solution, the relationship between I_o and I_s is given by Beer's law (1852)

$$I_s = I_o \, 10^{-Ecl}$$

where c is the concentration of the solution.

In practice a graph of E versus the concentration of stained material should be linear. However, Beer's law does not hold in cases of molecular interaction, such as dyes that form aggregates at high concentrations where the aggregates have different absorption characteristics from solutions of single dye molecules.

Beer's law can be assumed to hold for a particular stain where absorption curves from lightly and darkly stained regions of the specimen are similar, but does not require stoichiometry between a dye and the substrate to which it is bound (Swift and Rasch, 1956). Since Lambert's law requires that the successive layers of light absorbing material must be of equal thickness, it follows that where the dye is unevenly distributed through the specimen, this law will not be valid.

In addition to providing a check on the biological material, the Beer–Lambert laws also enable a check to be made upon the apparatus. If a series of standard samples of increasing dye concentrations of known amounts are measured, there should be a linear response of dye concentration versus absorption recorded by the apparatus.

The basic system required for such measurements includes a microscope, a monochromator and a photometer (Fig. 23). A simply constructed system is described by Swift and Rasch (1956).

Thus, the amount of light passing through the specimen (I_s) is recorded, as is the light passing through a similar area of clear slide (I_o). The extinction can be calculated from the two measurements and will bear a direct relation to the

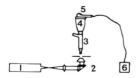

FIG. 23.   Diagram of basic components of a microdensitomer. 1, monochromator; 2, condenser; 3, drawtube; 4, bellows supporting 5, photocell; 6, galvanometer.

number of absorbing molecules in the light path. When such a measurement is referred to calibration curves, the specific amount of the compound present in the specimen can be obtained. Alternatively, the measurement may be utilized in arbitrary units for comparative studies (for example, see Deeley et al., 1957).

The readings can be affected by a number of errors, including light scattering by the specimen, stray light in the apparatus, too large a bandwidth of light, which affects the validity of the Beer–Lambert laws, mal-alignment of the apparatus, variable shape and thickness of specimen, and the irregular distribution of the material to be measured in the particular structure.

A more elaborate form of apparatus has been introduced in order to eliminate some of the inaccuracies (e.g., Figs. 24 and 25).

The first big step forward came with the instrument designed by Deeley (1955). This included a specimen crushing condenser to yield a more even distribution and thickness of material to be measured, and a scanning pho-

FIG. 24.   Integrating microdensitometer (Vickers M86).

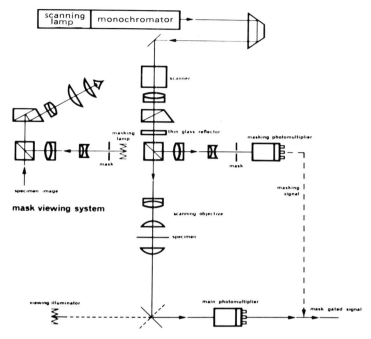

FIG. 25.   Diagram showing optical pathways of the Vickers M86 integrating microdensitometer.

tometric mechanism whereby only small areas of the specimen were measured at any one moment, the individual measurements during the scanning of the specimen being electronically integrated and the final summation being recorded. To improve the accuracy further, a double-beam system was incorporated so that I_s and I_o could be determined simultaneously.

With modern commercial instruments it is possible to overcome many of the problems initially encountered or at least to reduce them to levels of low interference. One of the biggest problems concerned the heterogeneous distribution of the coloured structures in the biological material, and a crushing condenser was not the answer to all situations. The problem is that with a spatial heterogeneity of the specimen, the light absorbance is no longer proportional to the total projected area multiplied by the mean of the individual absorbances of each separate point of the specimen. Such a measurement will yield a value that is lower than the true value. Two alternative approaches have been developed to overcome this problem. The first of these is the two-wavelength method, where the extinction values are determined at two wavelengths, and the ratios between the extinctions calculated. Where the ratios from the different regions in the specimen are dissimilar, it is concluded that there is distributional error between the measured areas. The extent of the differences can be calculated and a correction factor applied (Mendelsohn, 1966).

The second, and perhaps more satisfactory, method to eliminate distributional errors is the use of scanning and integrating microdensitometry. The area of specimen measured at any one moment is limited by a field stop so that it will be small enough to be homogenous. Welford (1972) showed that the spatial resolution of a scanning system is limited by the particular objective aperture and wavelength of light used, when the measuring spot has a diameter of less than half the theoretical limit of resolution, i.e. less than 0.125 μm with green light and a good $100 \times$ oil immersion objective. Since this results in an inadequate amount of light reaching the photodetector, the measuring spot is usually a little larger than the finest theoretically resolvable specimen detail. Under these circumstances, the resulting second-order or residual distribution error can be ignored except for the most exacting work (Goldstein, 1971, 1977a).

Some errors occur if the specimen is incorrectly focussed or if the specimen is thicker than the depth of focus of any objective, so that very thick sections should normally be avoided, and smear or squash preparations should be well flattened.

Strong light or glare can also influence measurements of specimens incompletely or non-uniformly fill the illuminated field. Some light from illuminated, specimen-free areas will find its way into the image of the remainder of the specimen and give higher transmittances than is actually the case. Glare can be minimised by restricting the area of the specimen illuminated and maintaining a clean optical system. The remaining glare can be estimated by measuring the apparent transmittance of an opaque object, whilst some microdensitometers can be set to compensate for glare (Goldstein, 1970).

The reader is referred to the article by Goldstein (1977a) for further aspects of this technique.

B. Measurement of Refractive Index and Dry Mass

The phase contrast and interference microscopes can be used, respectively, for the measurement of refractive indices and dry mass of cells. Measurements of refractive indices in plant studies are somewhat rare though useful, and those of dry mass are somewhat limited. The latter is due to the few laboratories possessing interference microscopes and the fact that, until recently, it was a long and laborious process to make such measurements. The development of scanning microinterferometry now makes the measurement of dry mass a more routine and rapid event (Goldstein, 1977b). The current drawback is, that with most systems, measurements on sections are confined to the edges of the sections due to the ghost image that forms and overlaps the section image. This can be overcome by scoring across sections to make edges, but it should not be long before this problem is overcome in terms of new optical design and dry mass measurements applied to sections in the way they are to isolated cells and organelles. Interference microscopy can be used to measure the total dry mass of a cell, or by the use of specific extraction or digestion procedures, to determine the concentration of a given compound such as DNA or RNA.

1. Phase-Contrast Microscopy

When light waves pass through an object, some of these waves will have their direction changed and be retarded by as much as $\frac{1}{4}\lambda$ (diffracted light), whilst other waves will pass through unaltered (direct light). This results from the differing refractive indices and thicknesses of various points in the object. Thus some light waves will emerge from the object out of phase with others due to the differences in the optical paths of the light waves:

$$\text{Optical path} = \text{refractive index} \times \text{object thickness}$$

Initially these differences are not detectable by the eye, but the phase-contrast microscope overcomes this problem by enhancing such differences.

Dark or *positive* phase contrast is achieved by the addition of two facilities to the light microscope. Firstly, there is an annular diaphragm inserted in the condenser to give restricted illumination of the object. Secondly, a diffraction plate is inserted at the back focal plane of the objective where the diffracted and direct waves are separated. Phase retarding material is present on this plate such that the diffracted waves become retarded by a further $\frac{1}{4}\lambda$ giving a total retardation of $\frac{1}{2}\lambda$, and so being completely out of phase with the direct light. The direct and diffracted waves will tend to cancel out each other so that the object will appear darker than the surroundings (Fig. 26).

An alternative form of phase-contrast is *bright* or *negative* phase-contrast in which the direct light waves are retarded at the level of the back focal plane of the objective. Thus, both the direct and the diffracted waves will be equally retarded so that recombination in phase results in a bright object on a dark background.

Expensive phase-contrast microscopes are available for very precise studies, but light microscopes can be converted to phase-contrast both simply and cheaply (Ross, 1967).

The phase-contrast microscope is better known for its use in examining living, unstained preparations, yet it provides an extremely sensitive form of micro-refractometer, having been used to measure changes in refractive index and concentrations of solids in cell structures during such activities as cell division and fungal spore development by Joseph (in Barer, 1956). This technique involves the immersion of cells in an isotonic solution, the refractive index of which can be varied by small amounts. The optical path difference or phase change (ϕ) can be determined from

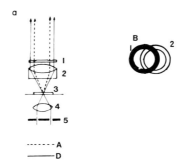

FIG. 26. Phase contrast microscope. (a) Light pathway. D, direct light; A, retarded or accelerated light; 1, phase ring at back focal plane of 2 (objective); 3, specimen; 4, condenser; 5, condenser phase ring. (b) Rings observed when setting up microscope and which need to be superimposed to achieve maximum contrast. 1, phase ring in back focal plane of the objective; 2, phase ring in condenser.

$$\phi = (n_1 - n_2) \, t$$

where n_1 and n_2 are the refractive indices of the object and mounting medium, respectively, and t is the thickness of the object. Thus, if the mounting medium is varied until the object becomes invisible or has minimum contrast when viewed by phase-contrast, then the refractive index of the mounting medium will be equal to that of the object and ϕ will be equal to zero. Variation of the mounting medium by small amounts can be readily achieved with protein solutions which, for every 1% increase in concentration, change their refractive index by a fixed amount termed the specific refractive increment. This is calculated to be approximately 0.99180 for most proteins. Since the solid content of the cytoplasm has been considered, perhaps erroneously, to be primarily comprised of protein, the specific refractive increment of protoplasm is considered to be 0.00180. The refractive index of a protoplasmic structure (p) is related to its concentration of solids by

$$p = n_8 + aC$$

where a is the specific refractive increment, C is the concentration of solids in g/100 ml of solution, and n_8 is the refractive index of a dilute salt solution which is calculated to be about 1.334.

2. Interference Microscopy

A more accurate and direct form of measurement of phase changes and hence of dry mass of cellular contents can be achieved by means of the interference microscope (Barer, 1956a,b; Barron, 1966; Ross, 1967; Chayen and Denby, 1968). Whilst in phase-contrast microscopy, the interfering light waves are separated by passage through the specimen, the interference microscope employs the deliberate separation of the interfering beams. A number of systems have been designed to achieve this purpose (Barron, 1966). Thus light from a source is divided into a beam that passes through the object and a reference beam that by-passes the object, the two beams being recombined prior to entering the eye-piece.

When using monochromatic light, a system of interference bands are gener-ated across the specimen on the introduction into the field of a constant phase gradient such as a quartz wedge. The spacing of the fringes corresponds to equal increments of one wavelength optical path differences between the beams. When a local phase change is introduced into one of the interfering beams a deforma-tion of one or more of the fringes will occur. The linear distribution of this displacment yields a direct measure of the retardation introduced by the object. This information can be used to calculate the dry mass of an object since the concentration of solids is related to the phase change ϕ by

$$\phi = aCt$$

Thus, if ϕ is determined by interference microscopy, C by immersion refrac-tometry, and $a = 0.00180$, then t is given by

$$t = \frac{\phi}{aC}$$

C. Polarized-Light Microscopy

This minor transformation of the light microscope has resulted in the production of a measuring device that has been available since the nineteenth century (Planchon and Hugounen, 1884). Whilst better known to geologists and mate-rials scientists, it has been of immense use in studies on cell walls, inclusions such as starch grains, and the composition and structure of membranes, and can be exploited to confirm the presence of a variety of structures without recourse to staining.

Ordinary light vibrates in all planes at right angles to the direction of propaga-tion. Some substances such as glass do not significantly alter the direction of vibration of light waves and are said to be *isotropic* or single-refracting. Other substances have the capacity of dividing a beam of unpolarised light into two beams that vibrate in mutually perpendicular plans. Such materials are termed *anisotropic* or birefringent.

In polarized-light microscopy, it is necessary to generate a single beam of polarised light through the optical system. In order to achieve this, a polarizer is inserted between the light source and the condenser, and consists of a Nicol prism or dichroic plate of some form. A second polarizing device (the analyser) is inserted above or below the eye-piece.

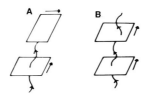

FIG. 27.   Polarized-light microscopy. (A). Analyser at right angles to polarizer so that light vibrating in the plane of the polarizer will be blocked by the analyzer. (B) Analyzer and polarizer in the same plane so that light from the polarizer is permitted to pass through the analyzer.

When the prisms are inserted in the system and at right angles to each other (Fig. 27A), no light will be discernable. The prisms are then said to be crossed. If the analyser is rotated through 90°, the field will now appear bright since the light permitted to pass through the polarizer will also pass through the analyser (Fig. 27B).

If biological material is placed in the path of the polarized light with the analyser set at right angles to the polarizer, it is possible to see some light refracted from the object, although theoretically none should be visible. This is due to the ability of certain structures that have a specific molecular orientation to rotate the pathway through which the light is vibrating from the original to that of the analyser. If the effect is due to true birefringence this should be lost on rotating the object through 45°–90°.

Rotation of the object on the microscope stage through 360° will cause it to appear light and dark alternately. The dark position is known as the *extinction.* The angle between the extinction positions is 90°, and maximum brightness will be achieved at 45° from the extinction position. An explanation for these observations is that on examining an anisotropic object, in one position of extinction, one of the two vibration directions is parallel to the vibration direction of the polarizer so that any light passing through both polarizer and object becomes blocked by the analyser. If the specimen is rotated through 90°, the second vibration from the object will also be blocked by the analyser. However, with the object at an intermediate position such that neither of its vibration directions coincides with that of the polarized beam, the object resolves the incident plane polarized light into two mutually perpendicular components vibrating at right angles to each other, each component vibration being partially transmitted by the analyser since this will not be completely crossed for either. The object will then appear bright on a dark background, yielding the maximum brightness position at 45°. The two beams into which the one beam of polarized light is divided by the biological object in the 45° position may travel with different velocities during the period of transmission within the object, and light waves travelling in the position corresponding to the higher refractive index travel more slowly than those in the faster plane of lower refractive index. The relationship to each other at the point of emission from the specimen is known as the *relative retardation,* which may be expressed in terms of difference of wavelength (in nanometers) or in terms of angle (one wavelength = 360°). The value of the measurement of retardation depends upon (a) specimen thickness and (b) the difference between the two refractive indices. For strongly birefringent materials, such as calcite, the birefringence may be as high as 0.01, whereas birefringence of biological materials is much less than this, e.g. for living muscle fibres it is 0.0025. It is important to know if birefringence is negative or positive, which can be determined by finding the slow and fast axes of transmission by inserting a compensator below the analyser. This is a birefringent material with known fast and slow axes. The biological object is moved to its position of maximum brightness between the crossed polarizer and analyzer. The compensator is rotated to a position where the brightness of the object is enhanced when the slow ray of the compensator is oscillating in the same plane as the slow ray of the biological material. The fast axis will lie therefore at 90° to this position. The sign of birefringence is designated positive or negative depending upon whether the slow axis of the object is parallel (positive) or perpendicular (negative) to some previously selected dimension or direction of the object.

The type of birefringence in biological systems can be either *crystalline, form, strain* birefringence, or a combination of these. Crystalline birefringence is due to the regular anisotropic atomic arrangement, whilst form birefringence reflects the regular arrangement of submicroscopic particles whether or not they are crystalline. Strain birefrigence is observed when a system of unoriented particles is stretched in such a way that the particles become oriented as in the case of rubber. Crystalline birefringence may be distinguished from form birefringence by immersing the specimen in solutions of different refractive indices. If the refractive indices of the specimen and solution are identical and the birefringence is lost, the object is considered to show form birefringence. Crystalline birefringence will be unaffected by changes of refractive index in the mounting medium.

In order to perform simple observations, it is enough to insert a rotatable analyser and polarizer in a standard microscope, but for analytical work it is important to have available a specially designed polarising microscope with strain-free optics and a rotating stage (Oster, 1956; Ruch, 1956; Barron, 1966).

Observations are best made on living cells or razor sections of unfixed material, though unfixed frozen sections may be used (Fig. 28). In general, fixation and embedding interfere considerably with the molecular orientation within structures so that birefringence properties may be lost, e.g. from primary cell walls.

D. Ultra-violet Light Absorption Microscopy

The use of ultra-violet light instead of white light offers two advantages. Firstly, by shortening the wavelength of light employed, resolution is increased. Sec-

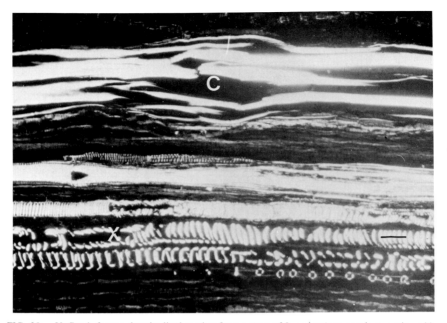

FIG. 28.   Unfixed, frozen, longitudinal section from a stem of *Lycopersicon esculentum* viewed by polarized light and showing birefrigence properties of secondary walls of the xylem elements (X) and of wall thickenings of collenchyma (C). Scale, 50 μm.

ondly, the absorption of specific wavelengths of ultra-violet light by certain compounds allows the identification of these compounds if measurements are made before and after extraction or digestion of these compounds, e.g. DNA, RNA, and proteins.

Ultra-violet light absorption cytochemistry makes use of the property that certain chemical groupings, such as covalent unsaturated groups, e.g. —C=C—, C=N, C=O, have specific absorption in the region of the spectrum above 220 nm where the general absorption due to protein ends. This property alters the identification of the chemical grouping and the measurement of their numbers in the cell. Although there are many biological compounds that absorb, few such compounds make any significant contribution to cellular absorption, so allowing the possibility of ultra-violet studies.

The notation for the absorption law is

$$A_\lambda = \log_{10}\frac{I_o}{I} = kcl \qquad (1)$$

where A is the absorbance (extinction of older terminology) at wavelength λ, I_o is the incident intensity, and I is the transmitted intensity. The absorptivity is k

(extinction coefficient), c is the concentration in grams per litre, and l is the length of the absorption cell, or the thickness of the biological structure in centimeters. Despite many attempts to produce an adequate method for the measurement of specimen thickness, none has been fully successful. In consequence, Walker (1956) has suggested the modification of Eq. (1) of

$$m = \frac{Aa}{k} \tag{2}$$

where m is mass in grams and a is the area in 10^{-3} cm^2. If it is accepted that 0.1 is the lowest absorbance that can be measured with reasonable accuracy in an area of 1 μm^2, it is possible to calculate from Eq. (2) the smallest mass that has to be present with the projected areas of 1 μm^2 independent of the thickness. This is equal to 5.0×10^{-14} g for mass absorptivity of 20 (Walker, 1956).

The measurement of compounds in the cell may be complicated by a similarity of the absorbance between various compounds, and so it may be necessary to remove one or more of these by enzyme digestion or acid extraction. This could introduce errors due to the specificity of the extracting agents and their activities on other compounds in the cell. An alternative approach is to change the chemical environment of some molecules and so alter their absorption. Thus, ascorbic acid, which has a similar absorption maximum to that of nucleic acid, may be assayed in the presence of the latter by measuring the total absorption and remeasuring after oxidizing the ascorbic acid to dehydroascorbic acid with copper ions (Chayen, 1952, 1953). The difference in absorption will be due to the ascorbic acid.

Whilst it is possible to obtain ultra-violet absorption curves of many compounds, it is important to remember that often the spectra are altered by conditions such as changes in pH. For a full discussion of these problems the reader is referred to Walker (1956).

A range of systems have been devised for ultra-violet absorption microscopy, but essentially the components required are those shown in Fig. 29. The various

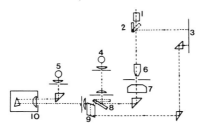

FIG. 29. Ultra-violet light microscopy; all optical components are made from quartz. 1, eye piece; 2, reflector; 3, camera; 4, white light source for viewing the specimen; 5, hydrogen lamp; 6, objective; 7, condenser; 8, reflector; 9, beam splitter; 10, monochromator.

systems are fully discussed by Walker (1956) and Chayen and Denby (1968). The fundamental differences from the visible light microscope are the use of (a) monochromated ultra-violet light; (b) a quartz reflecting condenser; (c) quartz slides and cover-slips; (d) a quartz objective; and (e) a prism rather than a mirror. These are necessary because short wavelength ultra-violet light is filtered out by glass lens systems. A visible light source is still required for alternative viewing since the eye cannot detect specimens illuminated by ultra-violet light.

For the purpose of quantification, two photoelectric cells connected to amplifying systems and galvanometers replace the camera in a similar manner to that described for microspectrophotometry. Alternatively, the image is photographed simultaneously with a step-wedge, and densitometer traces are made across the photographic image, relating the film density to a calibration curve derived from the image of the step-wedge.

A number of errors can be introduced by this procedure due to both the components of the microscope and the biological material, as is fully discussed by Walker (1956).

Tissue preparation is important since, as for all forms of assay, the more preparation involved, the more errors are likely to be introduced. Although ultra-violet irradiation is ultimately lethal to living cells, it is possible to examine cells by this method, though obviously whilst the initial observations are of living cells, as the study progresses, the length of irradiation increases and the cells gradually become "sick" until the irradiation proves lethal (Davies, 1950). Whilst for some compounds, such as DNA, fixed tissues may be used, unfixed frozen sections may prove more useful in other studies when the effects of fixation may be avoided.

E. Fluorescence Microscopy

Fluorescence microscopy was developed from ultra-violet absorption microscopy by Köhler (1904), but was not utilised extensively as a biological tool until some 20 years later. Many components fluoresce when irradiated with light of short wavelength, absorbing light energy of one wavelength and emitting it at a wavelength displaced towards the red end of the spectrum (Fig. 30).

1. Fluorescence

Fluorescence may be considered as being in two forms, i.e., primary and secondary fluorescence. Primary fluorescence is the autofluorescence or natural fluorescence of tissue compounds and in some cases is extremely weak. Secondary fluorescence is usually more powerful and is achieved by staining with fluorescent dyes or fluorochromes.

Originally used to detect naturally fluorescent substances and the passage of fluorescent dyes through plants and into plant cells, fluorescence microscopy is

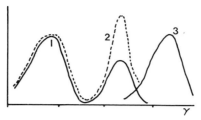

FIG. 30. Fluorescence spectra. 1, absorption spectra; 2, relative excitation efficiency; 3, fluorescence spectrum displaced towards red end of spectrum.

valuable in a variety of ways in histochemistry. Apart from its use in immunofluorescence cytochemistry, it is used to identify nucleic acids, proteins, carbohydrates and lipids reacted with fluorescent dyes, for the localization of fluorescent vital dyes, and for the detection of certain compounds in plants due to their characteristic primary fluorescence, e.g. cutin, chlorophyll and lignin. In addition, fluorescent tracers may be followed through the plant as in the earlier physiological studies of Strügger (1937). Clearly, this adaptation of the light microscope has an important role to play in plant histochemistry.

2. The Microscope

Although microscope manufacturers have produced relatively complicated and expensive fluorescence microscopes, it is possible to construct an efficient system at very little expense. The fundamental requirements are shown in Fig. 31.

Many different lamps are available for such work, the most efficient at present available being the HBO 50 and HBO 200 of Phillips, and quartz halide lamps. If the generally available mercury lamps are used, care should be taken since they emit ultra-violet light, which is harmful to the eyes, and ozone, which can also

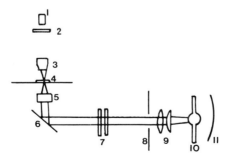

FIG. 31. Simple fluorescence microscope. 1, eye piece; 2, secondary or barrier filter; 3, objective; 4, specimen; 5, condenser; 6, mirror; 7, primary or excitation filters; 8, field diaphragm; 9, field lenses; 10, lamp; 11, reflector.

be dangerous if the worker receives too large a dose. Although the quartz–iodine lamps are considered to be safe since they only emit excitation light of sufficient intensity above 450 nm, care should be taken in using them.

More recent fluorescence microscopes employ an alternative form of illumination known as epi-illumination. This is a big improvement since the specimen is illuminated directly from above so that the light does not have to pass via a mirror, condenser or specimen. Hence a needless loss of illuminating intensity is avoided, and observed fluorescence can be maximized (Figs. 32 and 33).

Care must be taken in selecting filters if a high contrast is to be maintained, the most important features being that light of the required wavelength from the lamp should pass through the exciter filter but not the barrier filter, so giving a completely black background, yet the light from the specimen should pass through the barrier filter. The choice of wavelength for the excitation of fluorescence, and hence the choice of exciter filters, depends upon (a) the excitation and fluorescence spectra of the material to be studied; (b) excitation and fluorescence spectra of any substances giving interfering fluorescence; (c) spectral characteristics of available light sources; (d) characteristics of available filters; and (e)

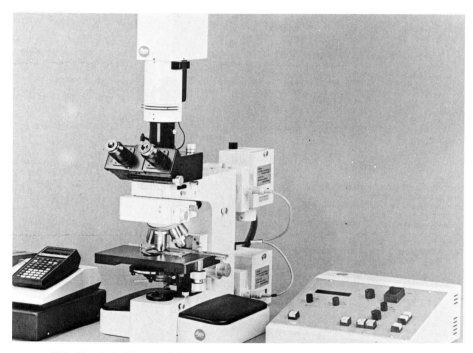

FIG. 32.   Leitz Ploemopak fluorescence microscope with epi-illumination system.

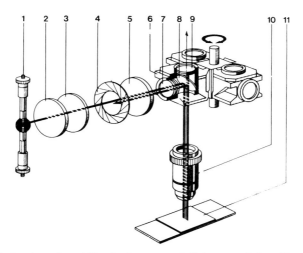

FIG. 33.   Optical pathway for epi-illumination system. 1, light source; 2, heat filter; 3, red suppression filter; 4, field diaphragm; 5, lens; 6, filter system with exciting filter, dichroic beam-splitting
mirror and suppression filter; 7, exciting filter; 8, dichroic beam - splitting mirror; 9, suppression
filter; 10, objective; 11, specimen.

the transmission properties of optical glass. For a fuller discussion of these
problems the reader is referred to Ploem (1977).

   When studying primary fluorescence it is important that the fluorescence of
other components in the system, such as lenses, microscope slides, mounting
media and immersion oil, is minimal since otherwise it will not be possible to
distinguish what is often a very weak fluorescence in the specimen. To assist in
this study, it is advisable to work in a darkened room and to utilize a monocular
eyepiece attachment to minimize loss of light by splitting the beam passing
through a binocular eyepiece system. Ideally, for irradiation with ultra-violet
wavelengths shorter than 365 nm, a quartz condenser and slide are necessary,
though epi-illumination systems will help to overcome this need. In the conventional form of fluorescence microscopy dark field condensers may be used to
avoid the cone of focussed light passing directly into the objective and to improving the quality of the image.

   When studying secondary fluorescence in plant tissues, primary fluorescence
can cause problems. These may be overcome in part by a careful choice of
filters. Short-wave pass-interference filters are now available, having a high
(more than 80%) transmittance and eliminating unwanted excitation light towards the longer wavelength. Ploem (1971) has suggested that such filters could
be used in conjunction with long-wave pass glass filters. In this way the long-
wave pass filter is used in the excitation beam to absorb the shorter wavelengths

that cause autofluorescence. This method will also be of value if two fluo-rochromes are being employed at the same time to demonstrate, for example, DNA and protein in the same cell.

Unfortunately, many preparations for fluorescence microscopy are not perma-nent, and indeed on irradiation some compounds fluoresce only for a few seconds.

Recent studies indicate that fluorescence stability involves (a) characteristics of the individual fluorochromes; (b) formation of protective dye–macromolecule complexes with nucleic acids, proteins and other compounds; (c) types of em-bedding or mounting media used; and (d) degree of dye polymerization depend-ing upon the staining conditions (Fukuda *et al.*, 1979).

3. Tissue Preparation

Tissue preparation is important expecially if auto-fluorescence is to be studied since, of necessity, the less the damage from fixation, the better. For this purpose unfixed, frozen sections or razor sections are ideal, since the tissue can be sectioned and used immediately. One difficulty in these procedures is section thickness. Fluorescence is emitted from a restricted source in the specimen and in order to obtain good resolution of these sources, it is of importance to work with very thin (1 μm) sections. It is difficult to obtain serial 1 μm sections by either of the above techniques, though in some studies this can be achieved with frozen-dried material. In the latter case the embedding medium must be checked for fluorescence. Methacrylate seems to be a satisfactory embedding medium. Sec-tion thickness problems may be minimized by using epi-illumination.

Equally, fixatives must be selected with care since formaldehyde, for exam-ple, imparts a strong, bluish-white fluorescence to the tissue. Conversely, fix-atives containing heavy metals will quench any fluorescence; this may be an advantage in studies concerning secondary fluorescence in which it is desired to suppress the primary fluorescence. Finally, where it is important to use a non-fluorescent mounting medium, care should be taken to check the pH of the medium since fluorescence is sensitive to changes of pH.

4. Recording

It is necessary to photograph the preparation if a permanent record is required. When photographing, it is imperative to check that no stray light from the lamp source is passing through the system since this will obviously upset the recorded image of the fluorescent sites. A second difficulty is the low image brightness, especially when working with autofluorescence. The lower the image brightness, the more difficult it is to calculate the exposure time, and exposures of up to 1 h can be required. In addition, some fluorescence fades when subjected to pro-longed exposure of the irradiating source, making it impossible to obtain a photographic record.

5. Quantification

Microfluorometry has the great advantage over microabsorptiometry in that the former is not prone to distributional errors of the type already discussed. Thus, when the fluorescence emitted is proportional to the amount of the stained compound present, which is dependent on the cytochemical method used, the fluorescence of the whole region may be determined by a single measurement within the area delineated by the mask employed. It is not necessary to scan and integrate as happens with micro-absorptiometry. This means that relatively simple microfluometers may be used (Taylor et al., 1971).

Some limits are placed upon the technique and include the fact that the signal-to-noise ratio of the system must be favourable, and, in general, even with low fluorescent signal intensities should be better than 20 : 1 using a measuring period of about 1/100 sec (Ploem, 1977).

Unlike integrating microdensitometry, it is not possible to use the region of the slide adjacent to the specimen as the reference source, and recourse has to be made to a standard fluorescent preparation. Originally, a uranyl glass (GG 17 of Schott & Gen. Mainz, West Germany) was proposed (Rigter, 1966), but this has proved unsatisfactory as an absolute standard since readings are influenced by the position of the collector lens and diameter of the excitation field diaphragm, and also because the fluorescence spectrum of the uranyl glass is not identical with the spectra of all fluorochromes. The possible alternatives have been considered by Ploem (1975), but one particular way is to stained amino-ethyl-Sephadex beads with the fluorochrome and use these as the reference standard (Haaijman and Von Dalen, 1977). In addition to a reference standard, it is also necessary to have a standard preparation against which to calibrate the machine. Thus, if DNA values are being measured, it is essential to establish the diploid values from a standard preparation of known diploid nuclei.

Earlier in this section, it was mentioned that microfluorometry can be used in the absence of scanning facilities. This requires a proportionality between the fluorescence emitted and the amount of compound to be measured. Using epi-illumination Böhm and Sprenger (1968) found the relationship

$$F = I_o \phi_{rel}(1 - e^{-kcd})$$

where F is the intensity of fluorescence, C is the concentration of the fluorescent substance, I_o is the incident light, ϕ_{rel} is the relative quantum efficiency, k is the molar extinction coefficient of the fluorochrome, and d is the object thickness. From a curve derived from the relationship between fluorescence and the concentration of the flurochrome, it can be seen that at high concentration the proportionality will be lost. An approximately linear relationship exists only at low concentrations when low absorbance (0.1–0.2) will obtain. Ploem (1977) indicates that a perfect linear relationship between fluorescence and concentration is not always necessary to achieve reasonable measurements, and, frequently, average absorbances up to 0.4 can be used.

F. Transmission Electron Microscopy

Electron microscopy has been adequately described elsewhere (e.g., Kaye, 1965; Meek, 1976), and recourse is now made to its use in quantitative cytochemistry.

The main advantage of transmission electron microscopy (TEM) is its high resolving power, which is due to the use of electrons of very short wavelength to "illuminate" the specimen. The wavelength of the electron beam is a function of the accelerating voltage to which the beam is subjected, and can be expressed:

$$\lambda = (150)^{1/2}/V$$

where λ is the wavelength and V is the accelerating voltage. Thus acceleration of electrons through a potential of approximately 80,000 V will yield a wavelength of only about 0.004 nm. This allows the possibility of resolving structures 0.3–0.5 nm in size, which is of the order of size of macromolecules.

Basically, the TEM differs from the light microscope by (a) its use of an electron beam and not a light source to illuminate the specimen and (b) the use of electro-magnetic lenses instead of glass optics to focus the electron beam (Fig. 34). Implicit with the use of an electron beam is the need for the whole system, including the specimen, to be under vacuum, since the electron beam cannot function in air. In addition, the specimen must be 10 nm or less in thickness in order that fast electrons may pass through the object.

The procedures for preparing biological tissues for electron microscopy have

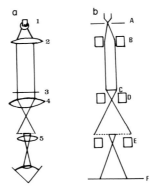

FIG. 34.   Organisation and pathways compared in the light microscope (a) and the electron microscope (b). 1, source of illumination; 2, condenser lens; 3, specimen; 4, objective lens; 5, eye-piece; A, electron source; B, condenser lens; C, specimen; D, objective lens; E, projector lens; F, fluorescent screen.

limited electron microscopy cytochemistry in its application to plants. In addition, the inability to use colour reactions but the need to utilise electron-opaque molecules to visualize the various sites of activity has retarded the development of the subject generally and specifically in plant cytochemistry. Whilst functioning as a qualitative tool, the electron microscope is being developed for quantitative studies. At present, the quantitative methods include high-resolution autoradiography (and stereology) (James, 1977), but work is in progress to produce direct measurements of tissue components through electron diffraction, electron-probe and X-ray microanalysis (see below).

One important development of TEM has been the adaptation of the scanning electron microscope (SEM) to TEM creating a scanning transmission electron microscope (STEM). This has the advantage over SEM of a vastly increased resolution of better than 0.5 nm. General references are available concerning the equipment (Crewe and Wall, 1970; Burge, 1977) and its biological applications (Elder, 1977). From a cytochemical point of view, it is pertinent that STEM permits the detection of individual atoms of heavy elements, especially when present in a low atomic number matrix such as biological tissue. This should open the way to cytochemical analysis of molecular structure by means of heavy metal labelling, and has already been exploited in trying to determine base sequences in molecules of nucleic acids (Crewe, 1971).

The high-voltage electron microscope (HVEM) is a conventional flood-beam TEM operating at an electron accelerating voltage greater than 100 kV [e.g. commercial HVEMs operate between 200 and 1000 kV (1 MV), although research microscopes designed to work at 3 to 10 MV are in use]. This large increase in voltage permits increased specimen penetration, increasing resolving power, and allows use of thicker (0.1–5 μm) sections but reduces contrast (Meek, 1976). This should greatly assist in analysing the three-dimensional distribution of cytochemical reaction products in cells and tissue sections (e.g. acid phosphatase product in the GERL system; Chapter 5).

G. X-Ray Microscopy

A further means of increasing resolution by shortening the wavelength has been achieved by the use of soft X rays instead of visible or ultra-violet light as the means of "illumination".

When X rays pass through material, there is an energy loss that can be due to absorption or scattering. The absorption of X rays is a transformation, the amount of energy taken from the primary X-ray beam reappears as a characteristic secondary radiation, or fluorescent radiation, with the emission of photoelectrons. Scattering involves a change of direction of incident radiation due to the resonance of the electrons in the full X-ray beam. When X rays have a short wavelength, the wavelength of a portion of the scattered radiation is altered. The scattering in which no change of wavelength occurs is known as unmodified or coherent scattering, a portion of such scattered X rays comprising the system of X-ray diffraction. Most of the scattering can be considered unmodified with the wavelength of X rays used in X ray microscopy.

Whilst there is an increased resolution with respect to the light microscope, the initial magnification achieved is normally small, being about 20 times the original. Any further enlargement is achieved by rephotographing the X ray negative through the optical microscope (e.g., 400×) and then enlarging the subsequent negative photographically (e.g., 10×) to yield a final magnification of values up to about 80,000. However, the degree of enlargement depends upon (a) the initial magnification achieved by the X-ray microscope and (b) the grain size of the photographic emulsions used in the subsequent enlargement procedures. The initial enlargement will depend upon the type of X-ray microscope employed since the specimens may be viewed either by the contact or projection methods.

In the case of contact microradiography or microscopy, the specimen is placed as close as possible to the fine grain emulsion, since the resolution obtainable depends upon such factors as the geometry of image formation, the graininess of the emulsion, and the quality of the X rays. The resolution in the microradiograph image increases with decreasing focal spot of the X-ray source (Engström, 1956). Thus, if the focal spot is small enough, the sample and the film can be separated, a "shadow micrograph" being obtained. This is the basis of the idea for the projection X-ray microscope (Sievert, 1936; von Ardenne, 1939; Coslett and Nixon, 1953). In order to obtain any useful information from the shadow microscope, a focal spot of 1 μm or less is essential. This can be achieved by the use of a micro-focus X-ray tube, which results in an initial focal spot of 40 μm or less, the X-ray source finally being reduced at the target level. Because it is extremely difficult to focus X rays, the fine focussing is achieved by focussing the electron beam prior to the formation of X rays. A number of systems were devised for this purpose, but a focal spot of 1 μm or less can be obtained using electron lenses (Coslett and Nixon, 1953). The general principle of this system is outlined in Fig. 35.

A system of focussing X rays by means of reflecting surfaces has been developed (Kirkpatrick and Pattee, 1953). Given that a single mirror can only concentrate X rays in one direction, a true focus can only be achieved by crossing two such mirrors (Fig. 36).

Since this system suffered from coma and spherical aberration, the resolution is limited to 0.2 μm. Consequently, a compound X-ray microscope of four mirrors was suggested. Unfortunately, it seems that the resolving power of the

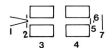

FIG. 35.   X-ray microscope. 1, cathode; 2, anode of electron gun; 3, objective lens; 4, condenser lens; 5, metal foil window; 6, specimen; 7, viewing screen.

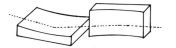

FIG. 36.   Mirror system for focussing X rays.

X-ray microscope cannot easily be varied by more than a factor of 2 from the value given by a simple pair of crossed, circular mirrors (Dyson, 1952).

Whilst this system may not have great value as a microscope, it has a possible use in microdiffraction studies on single cells (Ëngström, 1956).

The greatest potential of this instrument seems to lie in its use for element analysis and mass determination though more recent developments may yield a scanning X-ray microscope (Robinson, 1982).

Recently, it has been superceded by electron-probe analysis and X-ray micro-analysis, which depend upon the elements in the specimen emitting X rays under bombardment with electrons.

H. X-Ray Microanalysis

Whilst not yet fully applied in cytochemistry and although somewhat expensive in terms of equipment costs, this developing field of analysis will have a major part to play in quantitative cytochemistry. It is essentially an extension of elec-tron microscopy that should allow analysis of naturally occurring or foreign (deliberately introduced) elements in tissues and cells, especially ions, as well as the measurement of a number of end-products of cytochemical reactions. The method has now been adopted for the SEM, STEM and TEM.

When an atom is bombarded with electrons, the incident electron beam will cause an electron to be ejected from the outer (K) shell of electrons in the atom. This leaves the atom in an excited or ionised state. Consequently, an electron from a higher energy state (in the adjacent inner shell of electrons in the atom) will fall into the gap, occasioned by the loss of the first electron, to stabilize the atom. The gap left in the second (L) shell will be filled from the next (M) shell and so on. Because of the difference in potential energy levels during each electron transition, the excess energy is emitted as an X-ray photon. In conse-quence, a single ionisation will give rise to a spectrum of X rays that will permit the atom to be identified.

A commonly used X-ray detector is the wavelength dispersive crystal spec-trometer (Fig. 37). The X rays leaving the specimen pass towards a specially curved crystal such that a fraction of the X rays is reflected into a detector. The fraction of the X rays reflected to the detector will be of a particular wavelength, to the exclusion of all other wavelengths. Thus, the crystal acts as a reflection grating for homogeneous X rays, and by moving the crystal through a range of angles the various wavelengths of the X rays can be determined. The process by which the crystal functions is described by the Bragg equation

$n\lambda = 2d \sin \theta$ where n is an integer, λ is the wavelength of the diffracted X ray, d

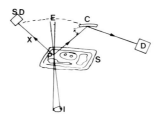

FIG. 37.   Diagram to illustrate X-ray microanalysis of a thin section with TEM. S, specimen; C, crystal; D, detector; I, image; SD, solid state detector; P, electron beam; X, X rays.

is the lattice spacing of the crystal and θ is the angle of incidence (and of reflection) of the X-ray beam at the crystal.

The spectrometer detector then allows identification of the X-ray lines. For a fuller account of this equipment, the reader is referred to Chandler (1977a).

An alternative detector to the crystal is an energy dispersive analyser or solid state detector (SSD), which is capable of providing an energy spectrum of all of the elements analysed simultaneously (Chandler, 1977b). This is not possible with the crystal. The SSD is often the method of choice, since in addition it can accept a wide solid angle of radiation so increasing sensitivity (Fig. 37).

It is clear that specimen preparation is of the utmost importance in order not to allow loss or movement of the elements to be analysed nor to introduce extraneous elements into the specimen. Perhaps the use of frozen-dried, ultra-thin frozen sections will provide one of the best ways of producing material for this form of analysis (Appleton, 1977). Preliminary work has been performed on the application of microanalysis and electron probe analysis to the study of plant material and the results are very encouraging (Sawhney and Zelitch, 1969; Laüchli *et al.*, 1974).

I. Nuclear Magnetic Resonance Spectroscopy

Nuclear magnetic resonance (NMR) spectroscopy has been used extensively in the study of biological macromolecules (Gadian, 1982), and it is only recently that it has been employed in the investigation of whole cells and tissues. As yet, work has been restricted to bacteria, yeast and mammalian tissues, but recent studies using ^{31}P and ^{13}C indicate an interesting potential for determining such things as intracellular pH values, products of metabolic pathways, and fluxes through energy pathways (reviewed in Schulman *et al.*, 1979).

J. Autoradiography

Autoradiography allows the demonstration in intact cells or tissue sections, of the localization of radioactive atoms which may be present in a given component. It is possible, therefore, to follow the uptake, transport and incorporation of radio-active ions into specific compounds or to follow the uptake and sites of incorpo-ration of a radioactive precursor into the end-product of a cellular synthesis. An example may be shown with tritiated thymidine, which can be incorporated *in vivo* into nucleic acids:

(a) [³H]Thymidine $\longrightarrow$ nucleotide $\longrightarrow$ low polymer polynucleotide$\longrightarrow$ DNA
    (water soluble)   (water soluble)   (dilute acid soluble)

(b) [³H]Uridine $\longrightarrow$ nucleotide $\longrightarrow$ low polymer polynucleotide$\longrightarrow$ RNA
    (water soluble)   (water soluble)   (dilute acid soluble)

where (a) is cold acid insoluble, hot acid soluble, DNAse sensitive and (b) is cold acid insoluble, hot acid soluble, RNase sensitive

If a specimen containing radioactive material is placed in contact with a photographic emulsion, the ionizing radiations emitted during the radioactive decay will change the emulsion in such a way that a blackening is produced in the film after development.

There are three main forms of autoradiography, namely, macroautoradiogra-phy, microautoradiography and high-resolution autoradiography. The oldest form is macroautoradiography in which the labelled biological material is placed

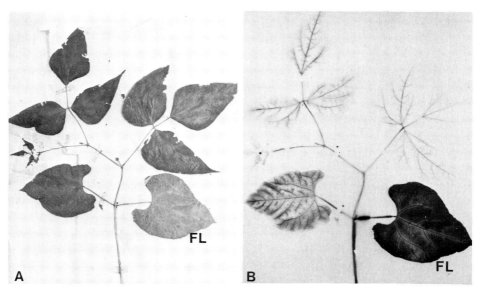

FIG. 38.   Autoradiograph (B) of leaves of *Phaseolus multiflorus* (A). One leaf (FL) was fed with 10 μCi of $^{14}CO_2$ for 2 h and the plant material pressed and dried prior to making an autoradiograph with Kodak No-Screen Film (NS-2T) exposed for 24 h prior to developing and fixing. Note the heavy autoradiograph of the fed leaf, and lighter but significant autoradiographs of the other leaves into which the photosynthates have been translocated.

directly in contact with an emulsion, usually X-ray film. The whole plant organ such as a leaf (Fig. 38) may be used, or thick slices of tissue cut from a large piece of frozen tissue with the aid of a refrigerated microtome. The resolution of this method is not very great, but it does enable the worker to determine the target organs for the particular isotope employed. This will give a guide as to which tissues may be successfully examined by other methods.

Better resolution can be achieved by means of microautoradiography in which histological sections of the material to be examined are left to expose in contact with a nuclear emulsion layer. Nuclear emulsions are constructed to yield greater sensitivity than can be obtained with X-ray film and can be applied either as a liquid coating (liquid emulsion method) or in a prepared layer (stripping film method). The final method is an extension of the liquid emulsion method in which a monolayer of emulsion is applied to an ultra-thin tissue section prepared for examination by electron microscopy. After processing, the whole preparation is viewed in the electron microscope.

1. Photographic Emulsion

These are not genuine emulsions, but are suspensions of silver bromide crystals in gelatin.

During the exposure to light or ionizing radiations, some of the grains are changed in such a way that photographic development reduces them to silver, while only a small number is reduced without previous exposure. Subsequent fixation dissolves the unused silver bromide and hardens the soft gelatin.

2. Sensitivity

Normally, at least 10 quanta of light, i.e. 20–30 eV, are needed to cause the necessary changes within a grain for it to be capable of development. Ionizing particles lose energy at different rates, which is usually expressed as kiloelectron volts per micrometer. On this specific energy loss and specific characteristics of the grains will depend the number of developable grains per unit path length. The larger the grains, the more energy will be absorbed by the grains and the more sensitive will be the emulsion. Thus it has been calculated by Pelc (1958) that since an ion pair is formed in air when approximately 32 eV of ionizing radiation has been absorbed, a higher value may be required to release 1 electron into a silver bromide lattice, and hence grains smaller than 0.1 μm may not be sensitive to radiation from tritium.

However, in practice, Salpeter *et al.* (1969) have found that Kodak NTE emulsion with a grain size of 0.05 μm is still sensitive to tritium.

3. Radiations and Nuclear Emulsions

The radiations emitted from radioactive compounds are of three main types α, β and γ particles.

a. α PARTICLES. α Particles are positively charged particles having a mass of 4 on the conventional atomic weight scale. They move with a high velocity of about 1.4×10^9 to 2.0×10^9 cm/s, the actual value depending upon the source of radiation. They have considerable penetration powers and tend to form tracks in the emulsion. The track of an α particle will be fairly dense with every crystal along its pathlength being activated, and will be quite straight apart from a slight deviation towards its termination if it collides with an atomic nucleus after it has already started to slow down. The track will be very short; in Ilford G5 emulsion, all α particles of initial energies of between 4 and 8 MeV will have ranges between 15 and 40 μm. The track will be fairly wide as the energised electrons resulting from the many collisions along the path of the α particle will themselves travel short distances through the emulsion causing latent images in adjacent crystals (Rogers, 1979).

This high rate of energy loss results in many latent images being formed in every crystal hit, and each latent image has a high probability of containing a large number of atoms of elemental silver. In consequence, an emulsion of low sensitivity will be adequate to record tracks of α particles (Rogers, 1979).

b. β PARTICLES. β Particles are negatively charged particles identical to electrons. Due to their high velocity, which approaches that of light, β particles are able to penetrate matter, but because of their small mass, they are easily deflected from their course. These are the most important particles in micro- and high-resolution autoradiography.

Unfortunately, the β particles emitted by an isotope do not all have the same initial energy, showing a spectrum of energies from a maximum value (E_{max}) down to zero, the maximum being the characteristic value for the isotope. The range of E_{max} values for β particles varies widely from 18 keV for ^{3}H to as high as 3 MeV for other isotopes. Hence, the track length for β particles will vary. Moreover, since the β particle has the same mass and charge as an orbital electron, a collision can deflect the β particle from its course. This mutual repulsion between β particles and the electron near which it passes is one reason for the β particle losing its momentum. The net result is that the β particle has a curved course through the emulsion. Unlike α particles, β particles lose their energy much more slowly and so have a much greater range in the emulsion. Because of the tortuous route normally followed by a β particle it is difficult to make precise measurements of its track length (Fig. 39B).

c. γ PARTICLES. γ Particles are uncharged particles behaving like X rays in magnetic and electrical fields. They are electromagnetic radiations of very short wavelength (10^{-8} to 10^{-10} cm) and possess a high energy.

Normally, they betray their presence only by infrequent secondary electrons. The emulsion used must be highly sensitised, and its crystals should be large to

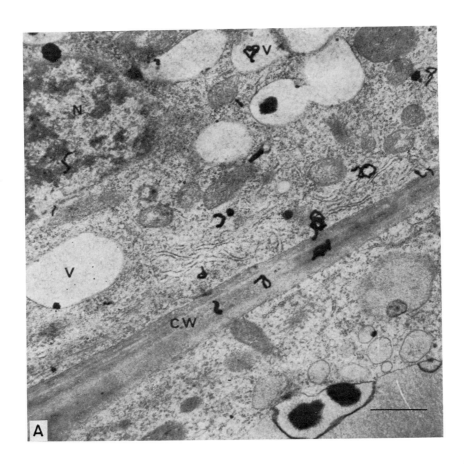

FIG. 39. (A) High-resolution autoradiograph of ³H showing the filaments of silver formed after developing the exposed Ilford L4 emulsion. Section of root apex cells from *Vicia faba*. N, nucleus; V, vacuole; CW, cell wall. Scale, 1 nm. (B) Pathway taken by a β particle through the photographic emulsion. (C) Original silver halide crystal with latent image (q) created by β particle moving along the path pq. Silver filament could form along qr. Thus, although β particle starts at p, the silver grain or filament will be at rq. It will not be possible to know, for example, in (A) whether the latent image formed at r or at q.

give the maximum blackening for the incident radiation. The majority of γ-particle emitters are not of great value in autoradiography.

Some isotopes, such as ^{125}I, emit γ rays of very low energy. These have a certain probability of ejecting from orbit one of the inner electrons around the actual nucleus that is disintegrating. The ejected electron behaves just like a β particle, the principal difference being its mode of origin. The only practical difference is that internal conversion electrons, as they are called, are all of the same energy from a given isotope instead of exhibiting the spectrum of energies of a β emitter. Many internal conversion electrons have a very low energy, which is ideal for autoradiographic purposes (Rogers, 1979).

In general, the data available for the sensitivity of AR 10 stripping film to radiation may be summarized as shown in Table 6. No similar data are available for the liquid emulsion method since the thickness of film varies between preparations and the results are not standard.

4. Photographic Theory

The theory of the photographic process was proposed by Gurney and Mott (1938) and later modified by Mitchell (1949), and although originally proposed for the effect of light upon photographic emulsions, the theory would also seem to hold for ionizing radiations.

Silver bromide crystallizes in a cubic pattern, with the ions of silver and bromide regularly spaced, each silver ion in the centre of six bromide ions, and vice versa. It is thought that the initial effect of light on a silver bromide crystal is to raise the energy of the outermost electron of a bromide ion so that it leaves its orbit. The bromide ion thus becomes an atom of bromine. The electron liberated is mobile when within a perfect silver bromide crystal, but becomes trapped by

TABLE 6.   Sensitivity of AR 10 Stripping Film[a]

Isotope	Particle	Energy (MeV)	Half-life	No. of grains per β particle
^{35}S	β	0.167	87 days	1.8
^{14}C	β	0.155	5760 years	1.8
^{3}H	β	0.018	12.26 years	0.85
^{131}I	β,	0.25–0.81	8.04 days	1.8
^{125}I	I.C. electron[b] X-rays	0.035	60 days	
^{32}P	β	1.71	14.2 days	0.78
^{59}Fe	β,	0.26–0.46	45 days	1.6

[a] From data published by the United Kingdom Atomic Energy Authority, *The Radiochemical Manual*, 2nd ed. (B. J. Wilson, ed.). Radiochemical Centre, Amsterdam, 1966.

[b] I.C. electron, inner conversion electron.

any impurities or fault in the crystal. It is assumed that small accumulations of silver sulphide act as traps, these impurities being known as sensitivity specks. The additional electrons give these specks a negative charge, and positive silver ions are attracted to form a small accumulation of metallic silver, which catalyses the reduction of the silver bromide crystal during the development. A minimal number of silver atoms is required to form an effective catalyst. In autoradiography the change produced by light or radiation of other types within the individual crystal of silver bromide is referred to as the *latent image*.

The creation of a latent image within a crystal of silver halide is a reversible process. If the atoms of silver at the latent image are not too few or too dispersed, they can act as a catalyst for the conversion of the entire crystal to metallic silver in the process of development. However, the silver deposit at the sensitivity specks may become ionized to silver bromide once again before the end of exposure, causing a loss of the latent image. This instability of the latent image is thought to be favoured by high temperatures, the presence of oxidizing agents, such as atomspheric oxygen, or of water in the emulsion (Rogers, 1979).

Latent image fading may be recognized in a thin layer of emulsion where the presence of radioactivity is indicated by an increased density of the silver grains. A series of slides can be given a uniform exposure to either light or radiation and then developed after varying periods of time. If the blackening, measured by grain counting or densitometry, remains constant at all exposure times, then there is no loss of the latent images formed by the initial radiations. If the grain density falls off with increasing time, fading is present. The results of the investigations of Lord (1963) working with liquid emulsions are shown in Table 7 and can be compared with the results using stripping film (Pelc *et al.,* 1965). From these results it is clear that the fading of the latent image is much greater in the liquid emulsions studied than in the stripping film.

TABLE 7.　Loss of the Latent Image in Liquid Emulsions Expressed as a Percentage Loss of the Expected Value without Fading[a]

Emulsion	+ Silica gel[b]		− Silica gel	
	2 weeks[c]	5 weeks[c]	2 weeks[c]	5 weeks[c]
Ilford K5	5	29	19	52
Gevaert 7.15A	7	46	1	29
Gevaert 7.15B	23	44	15	36

[a] After Lord (1963).
[b] Drying agent.
[c] Exposure of the autoradiographs.

5. Development of the Latent Image

Two methods exist for this purpose, namely, the physical and chemical development methods.

a. PHYSICAL DEVELOPMENT. Silver is deposited from the developing solution image. This may be done before fixation with a developer, such as Amidol at an acid pH, and with the addition of silver nitrate or silver sodium sulphite to provide a source of silver. The more usual method is to dissolve out the silver bromide by fixation in sodium thiosulphate before developing in a solution of p-phenylenediamine, sodium sulphate and silver nitrate.

Physical development results in the formation of a very small grain, which, when viewed in the electron microscope, appears spherical or comma-shaped instead of the long coiled filaments produced by conventional chemical developers. This type of development has been suggested by Caro and Van Tubergen (1962) for high-resolution studies, since the small grains are thought to make contact with the presumed site of the latent image and so give better resolution than by the chemical method in which it is not possible to determine the real site of the latent image.

b. CHEMICAL DEVELOPMENT. All chemical developers act in the same general way. They are reducing agents that usually possess the appropriate reducing potential when in slightly alkaline solution. Since the process results in the formation of hypobromic acid, developing systems normally contain some sort of buffering system.

Development proceeds rapidly at the site of the latent image, the silver bromide being converted to metallic silver. Silver deposition results in the formation of elongated, thin ribbons, probably by the deposition of silver at the latent image, and displacement of the ribbon away from it (Fig. 39A). The findings of Bachman and Salpeter (1964) showed that the grain may not necessarily coincide with the position of the parent crystal, although the silver grain always makes contact at the site of the latent image (Fig. 39C). Development will also occur in the absence of the latent image but at a much slower rate.

The optimal development times for autoradiographs can be made by exposing an emulsion to ionizing radiation and then determining the number of grains developed with time in a given developer of fixed dilution and at a fixed temperature (Fig. 40).

From Fig. 40 it is clear that there is a rise in the number of grains developed up to 2 min; between 2 and 5 min the grain increase is in size and not number. Some time after 5 min the number of grains developed increases due to background fog. The optimum period of development therefore is between 3 and 4 min.

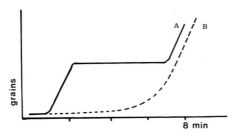

FIG. 40.   Graph of silver grains produced with time of development of an AR 10 stripping film autoradiograph in D19B at 18°C. A, curve of grain production with time of irradiated halide crystals; B, curve of grain production as background. An optimum development time is at 4–6 min. Silver grains at 4 min will be of the same number as, but smaller than, those produced at 6 min.

Almost any agent with the appropriate reducing properties will act as a developer. The commonly used developers generally contain hydroquinone, metol or amidol. There are slight differences between these components in that hydroquinone tends to produce thick filaments of silver, whereas amidol and metol produce finer filaments.

6. Fixation of the Emulsion

After chemical development, fixation usually involves the dissolution of the silver bromide crystals that remain in the emulsion. This is usually performed by placing the emulsion in a solution of sodium thiosulphate. The thiosulphate ion forms a series of complexes with the silver that speed up the process of dissolving the crystals. As with development, the rate of fixation can be speeded up by agitating the solution or by increasing the temperature at which the process is performed. The end-point of fixation is generally taken as twice the period needed for the emulsion to become transparent. The nuclear emulsions tend to contain a higher percentage of silver bromide than do normal photographic emulsions, and the speed of fixation falls off rapidly as the products of fixation accumulate in the solution.

After fixation, the autoradiographs should be washed well in running water to remove any fixer remaining in the emulsion. Although this is normally performed in running water, care must be taken that the emulsion does not move off the slide.

7. Background

During the preparation of emulsions by the manufacturer, some of the silver bromide crystals may be affected in such a way that even though not exposed to light or radiation, on development, they will appear as silver grains in the emulsion. These grains help to form the background fogging of the emulsion. All batches of emulsion should be checked to ensure that the background is not unworkably high. Other ways of increasing the background include the effects of cosmic radiation and handling the emulsion, e.g. light from a luminous watch dial, incorrect or too bright safe-light, electrostatic effects when stripping AR IO film from its glass support, and chemical reaction between the glass slide and the emulsion. Appleton (1967) has found that the background can be kept to a minimum by storing autoradiographs at a low temperature. However, the lower the temperature, the lower the sensitivity of the emulsion to the radiation. A compromise has been reached in which the autoradiographs are stored at $-25°C$.

8. Resolving Power

The highest accuracy of localization of radioactivity is essential if autoradiography is to be of value in cytochemistry. Ionizing particles are emitted in all directions and will tend to cause fogging of the emulsion over an area of film that is wider than the area in which the tracer is concentrated. The spread of the image is obviously not greater than the range of the particles, so that the resolving power of the autoradiograph is much better than would be achieved if the range of the particles were of primary importance. The resolving power tends to be better for the softer emitters such as ^3H, ^{14}C, ^{35}S and ^{125}I.

Basically the factors affecting the resolving power of an autoradiograph are (a) the thickness of the emulsion; (b) the thickness of the section; (c) the separation of the emulsion and the section; (d) the energy of the tracer; and (e) the size of the photographic grains. Obviously the resolving power of the autoradiograph cannot be better than the diameter of the grains in the emulsion. Since the resolving power of $1-2$ μm at the light microscope level can be achieved with a grain size of $2-3$ μm diameter, a reduction in the grain size will not improve the resolution markedly. Nuclear emulsions have a grain diameter of about 1 μm, which would seem to be about the limit for the light microscope since below this size, (a) there is a loss of sensitivity of the emulsion and (b) the grains themselves are much smaller and therefore more difficult to see.

At the level of the electron microscope this is a different proposition, since the increased resolution of the instrument enables one to observe smaller objects. Thus Salpeter et al. (1969) have found emulsions with a grain size of 0.5 μm to be sensitive to tritium and to give an improved resolution. However, even with the electron microscope, there are limits to the reduction of grain size, since ideally the need is to localize the latent image. This can be achieved possibly by using physical development methods. With chemical development, one still has a filament of silver produced, which if produced within the silver halide crystal will be close to the latent image. Generally, it seems that the filament is produced away from the silver halide crystal, and since only the filament is observed, it is difficult to decide at which end of the filament was the latent image (Fig. 39C).

The effect of the gap between the section and the emulsion can be clearly demonstrated (Pelc, 1958), and the closer the contact of the emulsion with the specimen, the better the resolution.

If the maximum energy of the β particle emitted from the isotope is increased there will be silver grains produced at greater distances from the source (Fig. 41). If a plot is made of grain density versus energy of the β particle, then the greater the energy of the particles the broader will be the curve and the lower the resolution (Fig. 42).

The thicker the specimen, the worse the resolution in many cases since the thicker the specimen, the higher the number of radioactive sources in the specimen and hence the larger the amount of fogging. Ideally the section should be 1 μm thick for many light microscope preparations. In the case of tritium, however-er, the situation is slightly different since the range of the β particles emitted is not greater than 1 μm. Thus, any isotope further from the emulsion than 1 μm will not reach the emulsion due to self-absorption by the section and so will not be recorded. In the case of the stronger emitters, self-absorption will not be 100% and hence a more scattered autoradiograph will result (Fig. 41).

A similar argument holds for the use of thick emulsions. The thicker, the emulsion the lower the resolution, since this will enhance the possibility of detecting the scattered particles. In consequence, high-resolution autoradiography requires the use of a monolayer of emulsion to achieve good resolution.

9. Exposure Times

The choice of exposure times is conditioned by a number of factors over and above those discussed in Section II,J,8. The half-life of the isotope employed is of importance for there is no point in exposures that exceed $2\frac{1}{2}$ times the half-life of the isotope when they are short-lived. Frequently, a guide can be taken from the literature, but the time will be influenced by the amount of isotope entering the tissue and cells under study and its distribution within the various cell compartments. Thus, if the isotope will be concentrated at specific sites, e.g. nuclei, causing hot spots to occur, then the exposure time will be shorter than if the same amount of isotope will be distributed evenly throughout the tissues. If no guidance is available, then a series of extra autoradiographs should be set up, one of

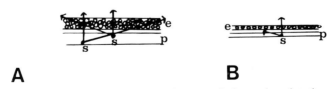

A   **B**

FIG. 41.   (A) High-energy emission from radioactive source in the specimen into the emulsion, and travelling far from the site of origin, e.g. ^{14}C β particle. (B) Low-energy emission yielding short travel in emulsion and better localization, e.g. ^{3}H β particle. s, site of radio-isotope; e, emulsion; p, specimen.

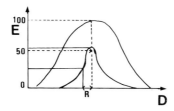

FIG. 42.   Graph of grain density versus energy and showing that the greater the energy of the β particle the worse the resolution. R, mean resolution; E, energy; D, distance from source.

each to be developed at intervals in order to determine the moment at which the first batch of experimental material should be developed. It is useful to run a longer exposure time for some autoradiographs, since a grain density that can be counted frequently is difficult to photograph, and the longer exposure may satisfy the latter need. Often additional and sometimes unexpected information may be obtained from the longer exposure times (e.g., Hurst *et al.,* 1973).

10. Quantification

Most quantitative autoradiographic studies tend to involve micro- and high-resolution autoradiography. Thus, the microscope image presents the investigator with a number of black, silver grains indicating the radioactive sites present in the cell or tissue section. How then can assessment be made? It would be easy to say ''just count the sites over which silver grains occur''. But, firstly, it is necessary to question the meaning of the silver grain, i.e. is it due to the radioactive substance or to some other factor? And if it is due to the radioactive substance, is the labelled atom still attached to the compound you believe it to be associated with?

a. CONTROLS. As has been stressed for all of the methods given in this book, it is essential to run controls (biochemical and cytochemical) to ensure that the radioactive atom remains bound to the molecule presumed to be radioactive. Such controls will vary according to the type of radioactive molecule employed.

b. BACKGROUND. When analyzing an autoradiograph, it is imperative to determine background activity in order to calculate the real level of radioactivity. This can be done in a number of ways depending upon the type of analysis to be performed. In the case of micro-autoradiography, counts may be made upon the emulsion over the slide and away from the biological specimen. Some people prefer to cut a non-radioactive section of the same tissue onto the slide to give a true background derived from the biological material rather than the glass slide. The simple method is then to count silver grains over known areas, e.g. 200 μm^2. This can be done for 20 random fields on each slide, and a mean value calculated. A more mathematically correct value requires a greater effort since the background count over a series of fields will give a Poisson distribution. Hence an observed total count of background (B) plus genuine radioactivity (GR) will consist of estimates of the true values of B and GR each of which could be erroneous. Such errors are additive when $(B + GR) - B$ is used as a measure of GR, and the standard deviation (SD) of GR values made in this way will be given by

$$\{[SD(GR-B)^2] + [SD(B)^2]\}^{1/2}$$

The simple approach will be satisfactory providing the source count is at least five times greater than the background count.

In the case of electron microscope autoradiographs, non-radioactive sections should be employed for the determination of background.

c. MEASURING MICRO-AUTORADIOGRAPHS. In order to determine if an organelle, e.g. a nucleus or nucleolus, is labelled, it is necessary to determine the background count and then the counts over the image to be analysed, the radiation source image being determined by subtracting the background count from the total count. The counts may be made by the investigator counting each grain. All grain counting should be done with a $100\times$ oil immersion objective if any degree of accuracy and repeatability is to occur, and counts should be made on limited fields so that not more than 30–50 grains are present at a time. This avoids confusion in counting. Fields can be limited by producing a series of perspex discs with holes of increasing diameters drilled through them. They can be slipped into the eye-piece and calibrated. The perspex should be opaque so as to minimize the temptation to move to count a "random" field that fits the preconceived idea behind the experiment!

Attempts have been made to automate silver grain counting, and recent developments using photometric measurements of the reflected light image of the silver grains indicate useful potential for such methods (Rogers, 1979).

Comparisons may be made between the degree of label over given structures between treatments or, for example, the percentage of labelled nuclei. More detailed analysis can emerge depending upon the type of experiment involved. This can be a simple comparison of the effects of a treatment on the amount of labelling achieved, or the localization of a compound (Gahan and Hurst, 1977; Hurst et al., 1973; Gahan et al., 1973; Schultze, 1969), or the determination of the cell cycle (see in Cleaver, 1967; Schultze, 1969), or changes during developmental processes (Berjak and Villiers, 1972; Auderset and Greppin, 1976; Jensen, 1957; Clowes, 1961).

Not too many problems are posed if tritum is the β particle source used (Rogers, 1979), but if β particle sources of higher energy are employed, e.g. ^{14}C ^{35}S, then problems of cross-fire labelling occur, and the difficulty of identifying the labelled structures arises. For example, if $[^{14}C]$ethan-2-olamine is incorporporated into root meristem cells, the nuclei and nucleoli are clearly labelled. This could be due to the nuclear membrane being labelled and the cross-fire from the membrane giving the impression that the chromatin and nucleoli are labelled. It could also mean that incorporation has occurred in the chromatin, which results in cross-fire labelling of the nuclear membrane and nucleoli. Clearly, care in interpretation and the setting up of the experiment are important if problems of this type are to be avoided. A fuller discussion of this aspect is given by Rogers (1979).

d. FACTORS AFFECTING QUANTIFICATION. A number of factors will affect the accuracy of the autoradiographic analysis, and these are briefly discussed.

Emulsion thickness is an important factor in quantifying at the light microscope level, since variation in thickness will give variation in the number of fogged silver grains from a variety of given sources. Since it is not possible to have constant thicknesses with liquid emulsions, Kodak AR 10 stripping film is the emulsion of choice. However, liquid emulsions can be used providing that tritium is the energy source and care is taken to ensure that the emulsion is applied in layers thicker than 1 μm in order to maximize fogging over all specimens for comparison.

It is impossible to control photographic processing very precisely, and so comparison of grain counts between different batches of autoradiographs will be unreliable unless the differences are very large. However great the effort to control the temperature and time of development and the degree of agitation during development, it is practically impossible to be exact, and batches of material that should be compared ought, ideally, to be processed together. If such comparisons are necessary, a control may be made by using standard sources of radioactive methacrylate with each experiment for comparison and standardization between experiments.

Latent image fading will occur to differing degrees depending upon the type of emulsion employed and the manner of storing autoradiographs. For long (greater than 6 weeks) exposure times Kodak AR 10 stripping film would seem to be more reliable (Pelc *et al.*, 1965; Hurst *et al.*, 1973), providing it is handled and controlled in a careful manner (Rogers, 1979).

Latent image fading can be checked by exposing slides fogged with light or radiation alongside the test material. Such slides should have very black grains on development. If they have not, there is indication of latent image fading and the source should be tested (Rogers, 1979), e.g. is it due to inadequate drying or storing under humid conditions?

Chemography can affect autoradiographs either by fogging the emulsion in the absence of isotope or by causing latent image fading. It can be detected by setting up control slides of non-radioactive specimens, one autoradiograph being fogged by light, and the other not, prior to exposure. On development, one should be totally black, the other should have no fogging above normal background. Any variation from this will indicate chemography, which will clearly influence the nature of the experimental autoradiographs.

e. MEASURING ELECTRON MICROSCOPIC AUTORADIOGRAPHS. The differences introduced into the analysis of electron microscopic autoradiographs as compared to light microscopic autoradiographs are related to the increased resolving power of the electron microscope. Thus, instead of observing the silver grain as a black dot, it is resolvable into a filament (Fig. 39A). This poses problems of interpretation since, as shown in Fig. 39C, the latent image site is not necessarily at the point of entry into the original silver halide crystal, and there is no knowing which end of the filament of silver is closest to the original site of the latent image. Thus, how can this situation be best exploited in terms of maximum utilization of the extra resolution of the electron microscope, while still accurately localizing the source of origin of the isotope in the section? This can be achieved by introducing two additional definitions of the term resolution which are employed in this form of analysis. The first is HD, the half-distance, which is the distance from a linear source of radioactivity to the lines parallel to it enclosing an area of emulsion containing the centres of half the silver grains produced by the source (Salpeter *et al.*, 1969).

The second definition is HR, or the half-radius, which is the circle around a point source of radioactivity that encloses the area of emulsion containing the centres of half the silver grains produced by the source (Bachman and Salpeter, 1965). The most important of these measurements is HD, since when the grain distributions are normalized in terms of HD units it is found that a universal curve of grain density distribution in relation to a line source can be constructed. Errors due to statistical fluctuation in respect of experimentally determined values for HD have been estimated to be not more than ± 10 nm. Some examples of HDs are 145 nm using Ilford L4 emulsion and sections of 50 nm thickness and 130 nm with sections 50 nm thick. The difference depends on the mode of development, the former occuring with Microdol-X and the latter with *p*-phenylenediamine. An HD of 80 nm was obtained from 50 nm thick sections using Kodak NTE emulsion and Dektol developer (Backman and Salpeter, 1967; Salpeter *et al.*, 1969; Budd, 1972).

These methods work reasonably well if only single structures, e.g. mitochondria, are to become labelled by the particular radioactive precursor employed. However, if a general precursor is employed, e.g. an amino acid or ethanolamine, then many structures are likely to become labelled, and the problem arises as to how to distinguish them. An approach to this problem was proposed by Williams (1969), and is based upon the HR concept. Since the observer is starting with silver grains rather than the original source of isotope, there will be a 50% probability of including the source if a circle of radius HR is placed about the silver grain. This must be done with every silver grain in the series of autoradiographs, after which a compilation is made of the frequency with which each structure appears in the circles. Then, a number of circles of radius HR are scattered randomly over the autoradiographs, and the frequency of appearance of structures occurring in the circles is recorded. If the two sets of data are similar, then the labelling is likely to be genuinely random in the preparation. Structures that are more or less heavily labelled can be calculated by applying a chi-squared test to the data. A problem with this approach arises when considering "junctional items", i.e. when circles fall upon junctions between, for example, a mitochondrion and ribosomes, or when some structures are so small that they never fill the circle completely, e.g. cell membrane. This problem can be resolved by comparing grain frequencies over junctional items with those that would be predicted from frequencies with which grains occur over the component on each side of the junction when occurring as an isolated structure.

10. Soluble Substances and Ions

I. INTRODUCTION

It is very clear from the methods discussed earlier for a variety of compounds that not all of the compounds or molecules are sufficiently tissue bound for them to stay in place for the reaction to be localized, as evidenced by, for example, soluble enzymes. In cytology and plant physiology it is frequently necessary to study the position and routes of translocation of a variety of water-soluble and solvent-soluble molecules, such as sugars, fats and ions. In these circumstances, many of the frequently employed methods of tissue preparation and coloration are of little use.

II. TISSUE PREPARATION

Whether a soluble ion or a soluble molecule is being studied, problems arise in the preparation of the tissue. Thus, in studies on translocation, simply severing a portion of root or shoot for preparation will result in changed tensions in the conducting tissues and hence an altered localization of the molecule or ion under study. One way to overcome this problem is to freeze the whole plant and then to remove frozen pieces of tissue as required (Gahan and Rajan, 1966; Chapter 2). Freeze-sectioning and freeze-drying have tended to form the basis of the methods of preparation for many studies on ions, and there is little to add except to warn that on drying there is likely to be some ion movement as the ice sublimes and a further possible movement of some ions or molecules as the liquid front of the embedding medium passes through the tissue block. The same problem will arise if fixation with a liquid (as opposed to a gaseous) fixative is employed. Even if a precipitating agent is added to the fixative, e.g. iodide to precipitate silver and thallium to precipitate potassium (Van Iren and Van der Spiegel, 1947), or cobaltinitrite to precipitate potassium and silver to precipitate chloride ions (Harvey *et al.*, 1979), there is likely to be some movement as the liquid front passes through the tissue. Such movement may move the ions prior to precipitation, but the cell walls may be a sufficient barrier to result in the movement being contained within a cell. For many studies, this may be a sufficiently good localization. As has been discussed already in Chapter 2, there is no one fixative that may be recommended, and it is a matter of selecting one that will best do the job for a given study. Clearly, though, liquid fixatives ideally should be avoided, not just because they will cause movement, but because there is the risk of introducing additional ions contained in the carrier solution of the fixative.

III. LOCALIZATION OF IONS

There are a number of possible approaches to the *in situ* study of ions.

A. Qualitative Methods

1. Microincineration

Microincineration of frozen-dried or frozen-and-dried sections by heating in a muffle furnace at 650°C provides an approach to localization and identification. All organic material is completely destroyed, leaving deposits only of non-volatile inorganic matter, which can be resolved by means of dark-field illumination. All ashes appear white when viewed in this manner except when iron is present, the colour being yellow to red. The limitations of the method are exposed in this last statement, since although there is little or no change in the localization of organically bound minerals (Scott, 1933, 1937), an analysis of the ash is required to determine its mineral content. If present, and if it has not fused with calcium, silica may be identified by its crystalline appearance, which is doubly refractive in polarized light. Further analysis is made by chemical examination of the ash that yields information on the individual components, but not on their localization (Über, 1940; Glick *et al.*, 1955).

2. Colorimetric Reactions

Colour reactions have been developed for the identification of the various mineral ions *in situ*, but in general have been unsatisfactory since the coloured end-product is soluble, the soluble ions are lost before the reactions are completed, the insoluble or organically bound ions do not always react, or, in attempting to free the insoluble and bound minerals, the sites of localization are destroyed or drastically altered (Jensen, 1962).

Of those tests available, the magnesium method of Broda (1939) is most successful and involves the formation of a blue complex between magnesium and quinalizarin, or a red complex between magnesium and Titan yellow. This method requires a high concentration of magnesium, and Jensen (1962) suggests that the results should only be accepted if the two methods yield parallel results.

Potassium ions have been detected fairly reliably in stomatal cells by the cobaltinitrite method (MacCallum, 1905; Willmer and Pallas, 1973). The method depends upon a rapid penetration of sodium cobaltinitrite to the intracellular sites of potassium ions where potassium cobaltinitrite can be precipitated on cooling to below 2°C. Further treatment with ammonium sulphide solution results in the formation of black cobalt sulphide. Whilst this method has the potential of being quantitative, care should be used in the interpretation of results, since there is no certainty that potassium ions do not move out of the cells and even into the reaction medium during the penetration of the reagents. This is a worry since the technique is thought to work best with a freshly prepared solution that still evolves fumes of nitrogen dioxide, which damages cell membranes and hence organelles. Thus, whilst speeding up the entry of the reagent into the biological material, it could just as easily speed up the loss of potassium ions from the cells.

Calcium in plant cells can be detected by the method of Gomori (1952) in which, if the calcium is present as insoluble calcium phosphate or carbonate, it can be demonstrated by placing the sections in silver nitrate solutions. The calcium is replaced by silver to form silver phosphate or carbonate, which is converted to metallic silver by the routine photographic procedures. Good localization can be achieved, especially if the sections have the soluble phosphate, carbonate or chloride removed beforehand.

3. Autoradiography

Perhaps a more positive approach can be achieved by the use of labelled mineral salts. Thus, if the plants are grown in the presence of radioactive ions, the method for the autoradiography of water-soluble materials can be applied to localize these ions. Such an approach would have the value of demonstrating both soluble and bound ions, yet after suitable extraction procedures, the various proportions and sites of the two fractions can be determined (Gahan and Rajan, 1965, 1966; Gahan, 1972; Rogers, 1979); see Section IV.

B. Quantitative Methods

Whilst some degree of quantification can be achieved with autoradiography, this will not be very adequate due to (a) the limitations of the degree of accuracy of localization and (b) the inadequacies of absolute quantification (Chapter 9).

The various minerals in plant tissues may be readily quantitatively assessed by the many chemical assays available (in Jensen, 1962), and those employing flame photometry provide extremely sensitive assays for many minerals, including potassium, sodium, calcium, boron and lithium. However, whilst all of these methods yield information as to the quantity of mineral, none of them yield information on the localizations of the mineral.

Whilst electron microanalysis (Hall, *et al.,* 1963) and X-ray microanalysis (Chapter 9) have been employed for a number of studies in the localization of ions (Harvey *et al.*, 1976, 1979; Laüchli *et al.*, 1974), perhaps the more adequate approach concerns the use of unfixed, ultra-thin frozen sections (Pallaghy, 1973, Van Steveninck *et al.*, 1978; Van Steveninck and Van Steveninck, 1978). A variety of ions can be detected by this method, but some caution must be given in terms of the possible achievements. Until further improvements can be obtained in the handling of the plant material prior to examination by X-ray microanalysis, the results must be treated with caution, and experiments designed to exploit the method within the limitations imposed by the shortcomings of the preparative methods.

IV. LOCALIZATION OF MOLECULES

The most generally used method for the localization of compounds that are usually soluble in water or in organic solvents normally employed in tissue preparation methods is soluble-compound autoradiography (Gahan, 1972; Rogers, 1979), a method also of value for the localization of ions. It will enable much more detailed studies to be made on the incorporation of precursors into various compounds, since not only the transport and final distribution of the precursor can be studied, but also the availability of the precursor in a given tissue or cell. Essentially the material must be treated by a freezing process (for further discussion of the available methods see Chapter 2). The two main approaches involve the use of either unfixed, frozen material or of frozen-dried material.

Early attempts to localize water-soluble materials involved the use of freeze-drying (Branton and Jacobson, 1962; Lüttge and Weigl, 1962; Perkins *et al.*, 1959). In this way, after feeding either the intact plant or isolated portions, such as root tips, the tissues were freeze-dried and infiltrated with an embedding medium. The sections obtained in this way were autoradiographed by placing them in contact with the photographic emulsion either before or after dewaxing the sections. A disadvantage of this approach is that the pieces of tissue are removed from the treated plants prior to freezing and so they are prone to bleeding from the cut. This results in the loss of material or the redistribution of material within the piece of tissue. A second possible hazard is that the pieces of tissue may be immersed in a liquid phase at some stage of the proceedings, perhaps resulting in the redistribution of the soluble material within the tissue.

The more obvious approach of employing frozen sections was neglected until relatively recently, presumably due to the lack of a suitable freeze-sectioning method for plant tissues. The method was initially developed for use with animal tissues. The mere placing of frozen sections on to emulsion at room temperature is unsatisfactory since the section thaws and the soluble material is redistributed. Fitzgerald (1959) tried the alternative approach of stripping AR 10 film from its support and applying it dry to the frozen section with the aid of a rubber roller, but this still did not overcome the possibility of thawing. Miller *et al.* (1964) and Caro (1964) then applied the liquid emulsion method in which a large wire loop was dipped into the emulsion and the subsequent layer trapped across the loop allowed to dry. Cryostat sections were dried at low temperature, and the dried film of emulsion applied to the section.

An alternative approach was provided by Appleton (1964) and was successfully applied to the study of plant tissues by Gahan and Rajan (1966). In this method the plants are fed, and the whole plant is frozen in a large tube that has been precooled to $-70°C$ with crushed solid CO_2. The frozen portions of tissue are removed from the plant and mounted for sectioning in the cryostat without allowing the tissue to thaw. AR 10 stripping film is mounted onto a cover slip supported by a slide with the emulsion facing outwards (Fig. 43). The dried autoradiographs are then precooled to $-5°C$ (Appleton, 1968). Frozen sections are cut in a room illuminated only with a red safe light, and the sections are picked from the knife directly on to the photographic emulsion in the absence of any thawing. The autoradiographs are then stored at $-25°C$ in light-proof boxes, and ultimately processed in the normal way. It has been found that some tissues do not stay on the emulsion during development, fixation and staining, and after exposure, the sections can be coated by immersing the whole autoradiograph in 0.25% formvar in ethylene dichloride. After drying, the tissue is fixed by immersing the autoradiograph in either 4% formaldehyde for 10 min, or 5% acetic alcohol for 1 min, or absolute alcohol for 10 min. The preparations are then developed, fixed and washed in the normal way prior to staining and mounting.

High-resolution water-soluble compound autoradiography is not such an easy process, and there is little published work on the subject. The most widely attempted method is to freeze-dry the tissue and to infiltrate with an epoxy resin. Whilst this may be satisfactory for compounds that link to tissue components and so may be retained, there is no evidence as yet that it can be successfully applied to studies on ions.

The light microscope method would seem to allow the localization of both water-soluble compounds and ions (Appleton, 1967; Gahan and Rajan, 1966). One difficulty encountered is that with prolonged exposures some plant tissue on

FIG. 43.   (A) Section is picked up and exposed on emulsion backed by a cover slip on a slide. (B) Emulsion plus section (+ coverslip) removed from slide, inverted and mounted, specimen down, onto slide + euparal. 1, slide; 2, cover slip; 3, gelatin, 4, emulsion layer of Kodak AR10 stripping film; 5, specimen; 6, euparal.

drying lose close contact with the photographic emulsion so resulting in a weak or no autoradiograph. However, the method offered as a substitute provides no guarantee against diffusion.

Alternative methods for trapping molecules have been devised, most of them offering doubtful results. One such method that has been used to effect concerns the localization of ascorbic acid. The total ascorbic acid in a tissue section can be extracted in 10% acetic acid and determined spectrophotometrically by measurement of ultra-violet light absorption resulting from the presence of a double bond in the reduced state (Chayen, 1953). The absorption of reduced ascorbic acid is compared to that of the oxidized form in order to avoid confusion with that resulting from the presence of other compounds, such as nucleic acids. Oxidation can be achieved by the addition of copper sulphate (Chayen, 1953). It is possible to determine the localization of ascorbic acid in tissue sections because of the high reducing capacity of the compound. Tissues are placed in acidified silver nitrate in the dark, and black deposits of metallic silver indicate the sites of ascorbic acid. No other plant components normally reduce silver nitrate under these conditions.

The histochemical method for ascorbic acid is relatively specific (Chayen, 1953; Jensen and Kavaljian, 1956), but is unsatisfactory because the high water solubility of ascorbic acid makes localization studies difficult either through a loss from, or a redistribution throughout, the sections. Although Chayen (1953) suggested that tissues fixed in Clarke's solution or absolute ethanol and embedded in paraffin wax could be used satisfactorily, Jensen and Kavaljian (1956) recommended the use of frozen-dried material since this avoids the use of aqueous solutions during tissue preparation. These workers performed the assay for ascorbic acid without dewaxing the sections. The presence of paraffin wax increases the time taken for the reagents to penetrate, and whilst there is a tendency to lose sections that float off the slide, it was considered that the more reliable localization of the end-product and the reduction of artefacts more than compensated for these difficulties. The use of unfixed frozen sections has been found to be unsatisfactory due to ascorbic acid movement within the section when placed in contact with the reaction medium (P. B. Gahan, unpublished).

Practical Appendices

Appendix 1. Qualitative Analysis

Essentially, it is possible to approach the analysis of a cell as one considers the analysis of a pure organic or inorganic compound in classic analytical chemistry. The following approach offers one possibility of analysis based upon the main groups of compounds present in the cell. Although it is not possible to analyse a cell completely by direct cytochemistry, an attempt is made to offer some guide-lines for the future development of this approach.

GROUP 1. NUCLEIC ACIDS

I 1. Stain with methyl green–pyronin mixture at pH 4.2.

2. If positive, extract sections with 5% aqueous trichloroacetic acid at 95°C for 15 min. Repeat staining.

3. If now negative, RNA and highly polymerized DNA are likely to be present.

II 1. If positive to pyronin (pink colour) then prior to staining, digest sections using a fully controlled ribonuclease method.

or 2. Extract section with 1 *N* HCl for 3–6 min (after fixation in Clarke's fixative) at 60°C.

3. If no reaction on staining, then original pyronin reacting sites were due to the presence of RNA.

III 1. If positive with methyl green, then prior to staining,

2. Digest using the fully controlled deoxyribonuclease reaction.

or 3. Extract the section with 1 *N* HCl at 60°C for 90 min (Clarke's fixative).

4. If no reaction, then original reaction with methyl green due to the presence of DNA.

5. Confirm DNA with the Feulgen reaction, when positive sites indicate DNA.

IV 1. If the material is positive for methyl green–pyronin, but which is not indicative of either DNA or RNA, then:

2. Test with toluidine blue at pH 4, 2, and 1.

a. If positive below pH 4, mucopolysaccharide or acidic polysaccharide is present (Group IV).

b. If positive below pH 2, then unlikely to be acidic polysaccharide only.
Test for polyphosphate. If negative, then reaction is probably due to sulphated or
sulphonated compounds, since sulphate is the most likely group to be ionized at
pH2.

GROUP 2. PROTEINS

I 1. Stain with the dinitrofluorobenzene *or* tetra-azotized dianisidine *or* Biuret
reactions.

2. If no response, protein is likely to be absent.

3. If positive, protein is present.

II 1. Stain with fast green at pH8, 6, or 4.

2. Strong reaction indicates presence of basic protein. Confirm.

3. Diazotize sections and restain. No stain confirms presence of basic
proteins.

or 4. Test for arginine with modified Sakaguchi reaction.

or 5. Test for —SH groups by method of Chévremont and Frédéric or by the
method of Bennett.

or 6. Test for lysine by blocking arginine with α-naphthol and staining with
fast green at pH 8.

III 1. If basic proteins are absent and only a weak reaction is obtained at pH 6 or
pH 4, *either* basic protein is present, but is masked by another tissue component,
or neutral or acidic proteins are present.

2. Extract sections with an unmasking agent, e.g. 5% aqueous trichloroacetic
acid at 95°C for 15 min. Restain as II.1.

a. If positive, masked basic proteins are present.

b. If negative, then

3. Stain with 0.1% aqueous toluidine blue solution at pH 2, 4 and 6.

a. If positive, acid protein likely to be present, the degrees of staining
indicating the relative availability of acidic groups.

b. If negative, neutral protein likely to be present. Confirm.

4. Test for tryptophan by the method of Bruemmer *et al.* (1957) or the
xanthoprotein test.

or 5. Test for tyrosine by the modified dinitrofluorobenzene reaction, or the
xanthoprotein test or Millon's test.

or 6. Test for individual proteins by immuno-assay methods.

IV 1. Reactions are available for a number of enzymic proteins (Chapter 5).

GROUP 3. LIPIDS

I 1. Test sections with 3,4-benzpyrene or Sudan black B.

2. If no reaction, no lipid is available to react.

3. Use unmasking procedure (Chapter 6), and restain. If still negative, lipid is probably absent.

4. If positive, lipid is present.

II 1. Test with Sudan III.

a. If positive, unsaturated triglycerides, sterol esters and fatty acids are present.

b. Confirm by reacting with Nile blue sulphate. Red sites confirm presence of these compounds.

2. Test with the acid haematein reaction.

a. If positive, phospholipids are present.

b. Confirm presence of phospholipids with the OTAN reaction.

3. Test with the PARS reaction. If positive at sites reacting as in I or II, may indicate presence of phosphoglycerides, glycerosphingosides, steroids or fatty acids.

4. Plasmal reaction. If positive, may indicate the presence of plasmalogens.

III 1. Test with auramine O. If positive, may indicate acidic waxes and precursors.

2. a. Irradiate specimen with UV light. Suberin will fluoresce yellow if mounted in 0.02 M phosphate buffer at pH 9.1.

b. Confirm by staining with Sudan blue and resistance to digestion with concentrated H_2SO_4.

GROUP 4. CARBOHYDRATES

I 1. React sections by the aqueous or alcoholic PARS test.

a. If negative, carbohydrates are unlikely to be present.

b. If positive, carbohydrate or oxidizable bonds are present. Confirm presence of carbohydrates:

2. Acetylate or benzoylate sections prior to performing the PARS reaction.

a. If negative, then PARS reaction due to vic-glycol groups and carbohydrates.

b. If 2a positive, block free aldehydes with dimedone (saturated solution) in 5% acetic acid at 60°C for 18 h, and react by the PARS test. If positive, confirms presence of carbohydrate.

or 3. Digest the section with a specific enzyme, e.g. diastase, and stain by PARS reaction. If negative, but 1 is positive, then indicates the presence of a specific form of carbohydrate.

or 4. a. Extract sections with 0.5% ammonium oxalate at 70°–80°C to remove pectin and water-soluble polysaccharides. Stain with PARS. No reaction indicates presence of pectins and water-soluble carbohydrates in I.2. Confirm by reacting with alkaline hydroxylamine hydrochloride reaction. If positive, pectic compounds present.

b. If 4a is positive, then extract sections as per 4a followed by extraction with 4% NaOH at 25°C to remove hemicelluloses. Stain with PARS. If 4a is positive and 4b is negative, PARS reaction due to hemicelluloses.

c. If 4b is still positive, extract as in 4b followed by extraction with 17.5% NaOH at 25°C to leave only cellulose. Stain with PARS. If positive, indicates cellulose.

II 1. Stain with iodine. Blue colour indicates short chain starch molecules.

2. Observe structures stained in II1 and determine birefringence pattern for confirmation of starch.

3. Digest sections with diastase and restain with iodine. If negative, starch is present.

III   React with the alkaline hydroxylamic acid test. Red complex with ferric ions indicates presence of esterified pectins.

IV 1. Stain with aniline blue. If positive may indicate callose.

2. Confirm by staining with decolorized aniline blue and viewing by fluorescence microscopy.

V 1. Autoclave specimen in 23% potassium hydroxide, and stain with potassium iodide in 1% sulphuric acid. Violet colour indicates chitin.

2. Lack of colour after autoclaving in 2% acetic acid confirms chitin.

VI 1. Stain with phloroglucinol-HCl. Red stain indicates cinnamaldehyde groups of lignin.

2. Confirm lignin by

a. Reacting with chlorine-sulphite test indicating syringyl groups of lignin and

b. Viewing by UV absorption microscopy when lignin strongly absorbs UV light.

VII 1. Treat sections with ferric salts. Blue-black colour indicative of tannins.

VIII 1. Immerse sections in 10% aqueous sodium nitrate; urea; acetic acid; 1:1:1 (v/v) for a few minutes. Add 2 N sodium hydroxide. Yellow to red colour indicative of polyphenols.

2. Confirm by

a. Reacting sections with diazotized sulphanilic acid at pH 4.7 for a few minutes. Yellow-orange colour indicative of polyphenols *or*

b. React sections with Fast blue BB at pH 6.5 for 15 min. Red to brown colour indicative of polyphenols.

GROUP 5. SOLUBLE SUBSTANCES

I 1. Micro-incinerate sections.

a. Examine by dark-ground illumination. White ash indicates presence of Na, K, Ca, Mg, P. Confirm by flame photometry. Yellow to deep red ash indicates presence of Fe.

b. Examine by polarized light. Birefringent crystals indicate presence of silicon.

2. Confirm presence of Mg with quinalizarin method.

3. Confirm presence of Ca by silver method of Gomori.

II 1. Examine by X-ray microprobe analysis to localize C, N, O, P, S, Ca, Si, K, Na, Cl, and other ions.

III 1. React sections by the silver nitrate method of Chayen or Jensen and Kavaljian. Deposit of silver indicates site of ascorbic acid.

IV 1. Examine section by fluorescence microscopy using light of different wavelengths.

a. Brick-red autofluorescence indicates porphyrins, e.g. chlorophyll.

b. Transient white-green fluorescence indicates vitamin A.

Appendix 2. Fixatives, Dehydration and Embedding

FIXATIVES

The following list gives the composition of some of the fixatives that have been found of use in plant cytochemistry and that are referred to in this text.

Formal–Calcium (Baker, 1946)

Calcium chloride 1% in 4% neutral formaldehyde (which has stood over marble chips). Useful general fixative and recommended by Baker for phospholipids.

Acetic acid : Alcohol (Clarke, 1851)

Glacial acetic acid	1 part
Absolute ethanol	3 parts

Prepare immediately prior to use. Good for chromosomes.

Acetic acid : Alcohol : Chloroform

Glacial acetic acid	1 part
Absolute ethanol	6 parts
Chloroform	3 parts

Good for chromosomes.

Chromium-Formal (Lewitsky, 1931)

Formaldehyde, 4%	1 part
Chromium trioxide, 1%	1 part

Prepare immediately prior to use. Useful in preserving phospholipids.

Formal–Calcium–Reinecke (Gahan, 1965b)

A saturated solution of Reinecke's salt namely, $NH_4[CR(NH_3)_2(SCN)_4] H_2O$ in standard formal–calcium (above). A useful fixative for the preservation of phospholipids.

Weak Bouin Fixative (Baker, 1946)

Saturated aqueous picric acid solution	50 ml
Formaldehyde (35–40%)	10 ml
Glacial acetic acid	5 ml
Distilled water	35 ml

Glutaraldehyde

This fixative is useful in the electron microscope studies of acid hydrolases and has also been used as a standard fixative for morphological studies. The concentration of the solution employed and duration of time of fixation varies between workers, but 2.5% glutaraldehyde in 0.1 M cacodylate buffer or phosphate buffer at pH 7.2 for $\frac{1}{2}$ to 2 h at 4°C has proved effective in many instances. After fixation, the tissue should be washed in buffer for at least 18 h at 4°C.

N.B. Although purified glutaraldehye can be purchased, many commercial glutaraldehydes are frequently contaminated with a variety of substances that inhibit enzyme activity. In this case, it is good practice to purify the glutaraldehyde prior to use, e.g. by vacuum distillation or by treatment with activated charcoal.

Osmium Tetroxide

Frequently used as a 2% solution in 0.1 M veronal–acetate buffer at pH 7.4 (Caulfield, 1957), for the post-fixation of material for electron microscopy when fixation for a period of 30 min at 4°C will suffice. Sucrose (1.5%) may be added as an osmo-protectant.

II. DEHYDRATION AND EMBEDDING

If the material has been fixed in an aqueous fixative and washed in water, then dehydrate:

a. Aqueous ethanol, 40%	1 h
b. Aqueous ethanol, 70%	1 h
c. Aqueous ethanol, 90%	1 h
d. Absolute ethanol	1 h
e. Absolute ethanol	2 h

If the material has been fixed in an alcoholic fixative, then dehydrate:

a. Aqueous ethanol, 90%	1 h
b. Absolute ethanol	1 h
c. Absolute ethanol	2 h

It is possible that with some tissues that contain air, e.g. leaves, infiltration and hence dehydration will be incomplete (seen by the fact that the pieces of tissue float in the dehydration fluid). In this case, it is advisable to dehydrate under a vacuum to ensure good penetration of the media. If it is necessary to leave the tissues for prolonged periods during dehydration, hardening of the tissue will be reduced if it is stored in 70% ethanol.

After dehydration, the tissues may be embedded by the following procedure (under vacuum if the tissue warrants):

a. Absolute *n*-butanol : chloroform, 3 : 1
b. Absolute *n*-butanol : chloroform, 1 : 1
c. Absolute *n*-butanol : chloroform, 1 : 3
d. Chloroform, just enough to cover the tissue. Add small chips of wax to the chloroform to obtain a saturated solution. Leave overnight at room temperature in a stoppered tube. Transfer the tube (minus stopper) to a 60°C oven and leave for 3 h allowing evaporation of the chloroform. (It may be necessary to add additional wax so that the loss of chloroform does not leave the tissue exposed.)

Transfer the material to fresh molten wax for 30 min and embed.

Acetone–Ester Wax (Chayen and Gahan, 1958)

After fixation in an aqueous solution, the tissues are dehydrated:

a. Aqueous acetone, 50%   1 h
b. Aqueous acetone, 70%   2 h
c. Aqueous acetone, 90%   2 h
d. Absolute acetone   1 h

The tissues are transferred directly to fresh absolute acetone and small pieces of tropical ester wax are added, and the whole (in a stoppered tube) is left overnight at room temperature. The stoppered tube is then placed in a 50°C oven, with the addition of more solid wax, for 30 min with occasional shaking to ensure good mixing of the wax and acetone. The stopper is removed and the acetone allowed to evaporate (2 h). Transfer the material to fresh molten wax (at 50°C) for 10 min and embed.

N.B. If the material has been fixed in acetone, dehydration is unnecessary and after placing the tissue in fresh acetone, the embedding procedure can occur directly.

Aquax Embedding Procedure

After fixation and washing well in running water, the material is transferred to distilled water (e.g. 5 ml for 10 root apices). Small pieces of Aquax–glycerol* are added to the tissue in the water until the solution approaches saturation (and usually takes about 2 days). Transfer the material to a 60°C oven and leave 1–2 h. Place the tissue in fresh, molten aquax–glycerol at 60°C and leave for 1 h.

*Aquax–glycerol is a mixture of 9 parts aquax with 1 part glycerol (w/w).

Change the tissue to fresh aquax–glycerol and embed in this mixture. Cool on an ice-tray and place at 4°C until solid, i.e. 5–10 min. Store blocks in a desiccator.

Embedding in Resin

This processing will aid the production of semi- and ultra-thin sections.

DEHYDRATION

a. Aqueous ethanol, 30%	30 min
b. Aqueous ethanol, 50%	30 min
c. Aqueous ethanol, 70%	30 min
d. Aqueous ethanol, 90%	1 h
e. Absolute ethanol*	1 h
f. Absolute ethanol	1 h

EMBEDDING PROCEDURE (AFTER LUFT, 1961). At room temperature

a. Absolute ethanol:1,2-epoxypropane, 1:1(v/v)	1 h
b. 1,2-Epoxypropane	30 min
c. 1,2-Epoxypropane	30 min
d. 1,2-Epoxypropane : araldite I† 1 : 1 (v/v)	1 h
e. 1,2-Epoxypropane : araldite I, 1 : 3 (v/v)	18 h
f. Fresh aralidite II**	24 h

g. Embed in fresh araldite II mixture in B.E.E.M. capsules. Harden at room temperature for 24 h and then at 48°C for 18–24 h.

Water-Miscible Resin (after Livingstone et al. 1969)

DEHYDRATION

a. Durcupan †† 50% in water	1–2 h
b. Durcupan, 70% in water	1–2 h
c. Durcupan, 90% in water	1–2 h
d. Durcupan	1–2 h
e. Durcupan	1–2 h

EMBEDDING (AT 50°C)

a. Araldite I, 30% in Durcupan	12 h
b. Araldite I, 50% in Durcupan	12 h

*Absolute ethanol should be stored over silica gel to ensure total removal of water from the alcohol.

†Araldite I: 14.0 ml epoxy resin, 16.0 ml Hardener 964, 0.75 ml dibutyl phthalate.

**Araldite II: 30.75 ml Araldite I, 0.6 ml accelerator.

††Water-soluble Durcupan (Fluka Ltd). Care should be taken not to allow this compound to touch the skin, and work should be performed in a well-ventilated fume-cupboard.

c. Araldite I, 70% in Durcupan   12 h
d. Araldite I   18 h
e. Araldite II   24 h
f. Embed in fresh Araldite II

Glycol–Methacrylate (after Ashford et al., 1972)

DEHYDRATION. GMA monomer mixture is composed of
Glycol methacrylate 95% (v/v)
Polyethylene glycol 5% (v/v)
Azo-bis-isobutyronitrile 0.05-0.15% (v/v)
Water to make up an aqueous GMA monomer mixture at the following concentrations:
1. 5%, 0°C   3 h
2. 10%, 0°C   3 h
3. 20%, 0°C   3 h
4. 40%, 0°C   3 h
5. 60%, 0°C   3–18 h
6. 80%, 0°C   3 h
7. 90%, −25°C   3 h
8. 95%, −25°C   3 h
9. 100% for infiltration, −25° or 35°C   variable*

POLYMERIZATION. This is achieved with light from a Philips Actinic Blue 15 W fluorescent lamp (maximal energy at 370 nm) at a distance of 7–14 cm from the GMA. The GMA and specimens are contained in aluminium weighing dishes refrigerated by an insulated bath 56% (v/v) aqueous ethylene glycol, the temperature of which is maintained at −45°C to achieve −35°C for the GMA. In order to eliminate oxygen, which inhibits polymerization, dry nitrogen gas is allowed to flow over the samples.

*Root apices of *Zea mays* required 2 weeks.

Appendix 3. Nucleic Acids

METHYL GREEN–PYRONIN REACTION FOR RNA AND DNA

Fixation

Fresh frozen sections; Clarke's 3 : 1; Ca-formaldehyde.

Solutions

SOLUTION A

0.5 M Acetate buffer pH 4.2	100 ml
Methyl green	1.0 g

SOLUTION B

0.5 M Acetate buffer pH 4.2	100 ml
Pyronin G	1.0 g

Solution A is repeatedly shaken with $CHCl_3$ until all methyl violet has been removed (normally three extractions, each of 30 min). The final staining mixture is composed of 3 parts purified solution A and 7 parts of solution B.

Procedure

1. Take sections to water.
2. Stain for 30 min in the methyl green–pyronin mixture.
3. Rinse briefly in distilled water.
4. Gently blot dry with filter paper.
5. Leave in n-butanol or tertiary butanol for 1–2 min.
6. Mount in Euparal.

Result

RNA stains with the pyronin (pink), and the DNA with the methyl green (green).

ACRIDINE ORANGE FOR RNA AND DNA

Tissue

Fresh or unfixed cryostat sections, formaldehyde-calcium fixed or tissues fixed in Clarke's solution, e.g., root or shoot apices of *Vicia faba*, *Pisum sativum*, are used.

Solutions

1. HCl-acetate buffer pH 2.1.
2. 0.05% acridine orange solution (colour index 788) in buffer at pH 2.1.

Procedure

1. Hydrate sections if necessary.
2. Immerse sections in buffer at pH 2.1.
3. Transfer to acridine orange solution for 30 min.
4. Wash sections in veronal–acetate buffer for 15 min.
5. Mount in buffer solution. Ring coverslip with wax to prevent desiccation of specimen.
6. Examine by blue or ultra-violet light.
7. Examine adjacent section subject to treatments 1–6 except that 3 is replaced by 30 min in buffer alone. Examine for autofluorescence.

Result

DNA fluoresces bright yellow. RNA fluoresces flame red.

Controls

See pp. 198–199.

METHYL GREEN FOR DNA

Tissue

Fresh or unfixed cryostat sections are used; Clarke's solution; 45% acetic acid. Root tips.

Solutions

1. 0.2 M Acetate buffer pH 4.2.
2. Methyl green solution: methyl green, 0.5 g; buffer, 100 ml.
Extract repeatedly with chloroform to remove methyl violet, and keep in a dark bottle at 4°C.

Procedure

1. Hydrate sections if necessary.
2. Rinse sections in buffer.
3. Stain 18 h in purified methyl green solution pH 4.2 at 4°C.
4. Wash sections in 0.05 M buffer pH 4.2, two washes each of 10 min.
5. Blot sections gently with filter paper and transfer to absolute ethanol for 2 min.
6. Mount in Euparal.

N.B. It may be advisable, between steps 1 and 2, to immerse the sections in 0.1 *N* NCl for 15 min at room temperature, to release the DNA from its binding with basic protein.

Result

Sites of DNA stain green.

Controls

See pp. 198–199.

THE FEULGEN REACTION FOR DNA

Tissues

Fresh or unfixed cryostat sections are used; almost any fixation and any tissues can be used.

Solutions

1. Fuchsin solution: Dissolve 1 g basic fuchsin by the addition of 200 ml boiling distilled water, with constant stirring. Allow the solution to cool to 50°C and filter. Add 30 ml *N* HCl to the filtrate, followed by 3 g $K_2S_2O_5$. Stand the solution for 24 h in the dark, in a well-stoppered bottle, to allow it to bleach. Then add 0.5 g decolourizing carbon and shake the solution well for 1 min, and then rapidly filter the solution through a coarse filter paper. The filtrate, now ready for use, must be stored in a dark, tightly stoppered bottle (Darlington and La Cour, 1976).

2. SO_2 water: 1 *N* HCl, 5 ml; 10% $K_2S_2O_5$, 5 ml; distilled water, 100 ml. This solution should be mixed fresh as required.

Procedure

1. Hydrate sections as necessary.
2. Leave sections in 1 *N* HCl for 15 min at room temperature.*
3. Transfer to 1 *N* HCl at 60°C for hydrolysis.
4. Remove immediately and wash in 1 *N* HCl at room temperature.
5. Transfer to the Fuchsin solution and leave in the dark for $1\frac{1}{2}$ h.
6. Wash in SO_2 water for 5–10 min.
7. Repeat 6.
8. Repeat 6.
9. Rinse well in distilled water to remove all traces of SO_2.
10. Dehydrate through an alcohol series to absolute ethanol.
11. Mount in Euparal.

*For quantitative assays, replace steps 2 and 3 by hydrolysis (step 3) at 20°C in 5 *N* HCl.

Hydrolysis Times

A. 1 *N* HCl AT 60°C

Fixative	Time (min)
Clarke	6
Carnoy	8
Helly	8
Lewitsky (1931)	12
Unfixed	2

B. 5 *N* HCl AT 20°C

Fixative	Time (min)
Clarke	45
Formal-calcium	120

N.B. When using a new fixative or tissue, it is advisable to determine the hydrolysis time that yields the most intense colour reaction. Chromic and osmic fixed tissues may require up to 20 min hydrolysis at 60°C in 1 *N* HCl.

Result

DNA is coloured reddish purple.

Controls

See below. An additional control that should be treated as for the full method except that stage three should be performed at room temperature, should be colourless on reacting with Schiff reagent.

CONTROLS FOR NUCLEIC ACID

Prior to staining, tissue sections should be subjected to one or more of the following procedures:

RNA

I   1. Fixation in Clarke's solution for 3 h.
    2. Extraction by hydrolysis for 3–6 min in 1 *N* HCl at 60°C.

or II 1. Extract sections in 5% aqueous trichloroacetic acid at 95°C for 15 min.

2. Three washes in 70% aqueous ethanol, each of 5 min.

3. Place in 50% aqueous ethanol for 2 min.

4. Transfer to distilled water.

or III 1. Digest in ribonuclease solution for 1 h at 37°C (1 mg ribonuclease per 1 ml veronal acetate buffer at pH 7.7).

2. Parallel extraction in buffer alone of a serial section for 1 h at 37°C as a control to the digestion.

3. Wash sections thoroughly in distilled water.

DNA

I 1. Fixation in Clarke's solution for 3 h.

2. Extraction for 1.5 h in 1 N HCl at 60°C.

or II 1. Extract section in 5% trichloroacetic acid* at 95°C for 15 min.

2. Three washes in 70% aqueous ethanol for 5 min each.

3. Transfer to 50% aqueous ethanol for 2 min.

4. Wash in distilled water.

or III 1. Dissolve 0.05 M cysteine hydrochloride in 0.05 M sodium acetate solution. Adjust the pH to 7.0 by the addition of a little NaOH.

2. Add 0.2% of $MgCl_2$ to solution in (1)—a later dilution makes this a 0.1% solution.

3. When this solution is ready, add 1.7 mg deoxyribonuclease per 1 ml of solution in (2). Shake well and leave to stand at room temperature for 10 min.

4. To 1 ml of the deoxyribonuclease solution (3), after standing, add 1 ml of HCl–veronal buffer at pH 7.0.

5. Incubate sections for 1–2 h at 37°C.

6. Control sections should be prepared by incubating in the above solution (4) which lacks deoxyribonuclease.

7. Wash in distilled water.

TOLUIDINE BLUE

Fixation

Sections should be used preferably unfixed since coagulation of the cytoplasm may affect metachromasia. Most fixatives can be used if necessary.

---

*N.B. In view of the ease of loss of sections from the slide during extraction in 5% trichloroacetic acid, slides may be subbed as for autoradiography (Chapter 9) with gelatin, or sections should be handled as free-floating during the extraction procedure and subsequent washes.

Solution

Aqueous toluidine blue (0.1%) at the appropriate pH.

Method

1. Bring sections to water.
2. Stain in toluidine blue solution for 30 min.
3. Rinse in buffer of same pH as the dye solution.
4. Blot section dry.
5. Place section in absolute *n*-butanol for 2 min.
6. Mount in Euparal.

Result

Nucleic acids stain orthochromatically at pH 4.2, the ability to bind the dye diminishing with pH. Sulphated compounds and polyphosphate will stain metachromatically even down to pH 1.0. If polyphosphate is suspected, this can be tested by the method of Ebel.

EBEL TEST FOR POLYPHOSPHATE (after Chayen *et al.,* 1973)

Fixation

Use unfixed tissues.

Solution

1. Lead nitrate (10%) in 0.05 M acetate buffer at pH 4.5
2. H_2S water (freshly prepared).

Method

1. Immerse the sections in the lead nitrate solution for 5 min.
2. Wash well in 0.05 *M* acetate buffer at pH 4.5.
3. Place sections in H_2S water for 5 min.
4. Wash well in distilled water.
5. Mount in Farrants' medium.

Result

Sites of polyphosphates stain brown-black.

Appendix 4. Proteins

DINITROFLUOROBENZENE METHOD FOR TYROSINE AND HISTIDINE, AND NH$_2$ AND SH GROUPS

Tissues

Root and shoot apices. Fresh or frozen sections. Ca-formal-fixed tissues.

Solutions

1. 1-Fluoro-2,4-dinitrobenzene (DNFB), 0.5ml (excess), in 30 ml of 65% ethanol saturated with NaHCO$_3$.
2. Dithionite (Na$_2$S$_2$O$_4$), 20%, solution. Prepare by warming distilled water to 45°C and then stir in the dithionite, which dissolves more readily.
3. Sodium nitrite, 2%, solution.
4. K acid (8-amino-1-naphthol-4,6-disulphonic acid), 0.5%, in 1% NaHCO$_3$ solution. H acid may replace K acid.

Method

1. Place sections in solution 1 for 2 h. Stir occasionally, since the DNFB is sparingly soluble and needs to be continually brought into solution.
2. Wash three times in 60% ethanol, each of 2 min.
3. Place in solution 2 for 10 min at 40°C.
4. Wash well in distilled water.
TRANSFER TO AN ICE-BATH
5. Leave sections in an equal volume of 2% sodium nitrite and 0.1 N HCl for 5 min.
6. Wash 3 times, each for 1 min, in ice-cold water to 30 ml of which has been added one drop of 0.1 N HCl to keep the solution acid.
7. Transfer to solution 4 for 15 min.
8. Wash in distilled water.
REMOVE FROM ICE-BATH
9. Dehydrate via alcohol.
10. Mount in Euparal.

Result

Tyrosine and histidine and —SH and —NH$_2$ groups stain deep magenta, if K acid is used and red with H acid.

Controls

The various reactive groups may be selectively blocked: (a) —NH$_2$ groups by treating the sections with HNO$_2$ (freshly prepared) in the cold for 6 min; (b) —SH groups by treating sections with saturated aqueous HgCl$_2$ solution for 48 h.

TETRA-AZOTIZED *o*-DIANISIDINE METHOD FOR HISTIDINE, TRYPTOPHAN AND PHENOLS

Tissues

Shoot and root apices. Fresh or frozen sections from tissues fixed overnight in formal–calcium.

Solutions

1. Aqueous 2% sodium veronal solution.
2. H or K acid, 0.5%, in 1% aqueous sodium bicarbonate.

Methods

1. Hydrate sections.
PERFORM PROCEDURE IN ICE-BATH
2. Cool pestle and mortar in an ice-bath.
3. Place 2% sodium veronal in ice-bath to cool.
4. Grind some tetra-azotized *o*-dianisidine powder in the mortar with some of the veronal solution until it dissolves.
5. Pour into cooled container for stirring and add more cold veronal solution to yield final concentration of 0.15 g % in 100 ml veronal solution. *N.B.* This solution remains active for 6 min.
6. Stain sections for 6 min.
7. Make up fresh solution (2–5).
8. Stain for a further 6 min.
9. Wash twice in solution 1.
10. Wash in cold, distilled water.
11. Stain for 15 min in solution 2.
12. Wash in distilled water.
REMOVE FROM ICE-BATH
13. Dehydrate and mount in Euparal.

Result

Histidine, tryptophan and phenols stain red.

BUIRET REACTION

Tissues

Root and shoot apices. Razor or frozen sections; absolute ethanol or formal-calcium fixation.

Solutions

1. Aqueous 10% KOH solution.
2. $CuSO_4$ 1% solution.

Method

1. Hydrate sections, if necessary.
2. Warm sections on a slide in 10% aqueous KOH solution(1).
3. Add 1 drop of 1% $CuSO_4$ solution.
4. Mount in water.

Result

Violet colour indicates peptide linkages in higher proteins. Red colour indicates peptide linkages in lower protein forms.

FAST GREEN FCF (Alfert and Geschwind, 1953)

Tissues

Root or shoot apices. Razor or frozen sections, or sections from tissues fixed in 10% neutral formalin for 3–6 h.

Solutions

1. Aqueous 5% solution of trichloroacetic acid (TCA).
2. Aqueous 0.1% solution of fast green FCF adjusted to pH 8.0–8.1 with a minimum of NaOH.

Method

1. Fix tissues and wash them in running water overnight. Dehydrate and embed in paraffin wax. Section.
2. De-wax sections and rehydrate if necessary.
3. Immerse in solution 1 in a boiling water-bath for 15 min to remove nucleic acids.
4. Wash sections in three changes of 70% aqueous ethanol each of 10 min, and rehydrate the sections.
5. Stain for 30 min in solution 2 at room temperature.

6. Wash sections for 5 min in distilled water followed by 95% ethanol and absolute ethanol.

7. Mount sections in Euparal.

Result

Sites of basic proteins such as histones and protamines stain green.

N.B. Fixation in Zenker's or Clarke's solutions does not allow the reaction to occur, nor will it occur if the nucleic acids are not removed; nucleases have been found to be unsatisfactory for this purpose. Sections may detach themselves from the slide whilst in the hot TCA solution. This loss can be minimized by emplying subbed slides (see Chapter 9).

COOMASSIE BRILLIANT BLUE R250 (Cawood *et al.,* 1978)

Tissues

Anthers. Unfixed frozen sections or sections from tissues fixed in 2.5% glutaraldehyde.

Solutions

1. Coomassie brilliant blue R 250 0.02% (C.I. 42660) in Clarke's solution (pH 2.0).

2. Clarke's (1851) solution.

Method

1. Stain sections for 24 h.
2. Rinse in Clarke's solution.
3. Destain in fresh Clarke's solution for 20 min.
4. Dehydrate in 98% and absolute ethanol each for 5 min.
5. Mount in Euparal.

Result

Proteins stain blue.

NAPHTHOL YELLOW S (Tas *et al.,* 1974)

Tissues

Anthers, apices. Unfixed frozen sections; fixation for 2 h in absolute ethanol: glacial acetic acid (5 : 1) or in absolute methanol–40% formaldehyde–glacial acetic acid (17 : 2 : 1).

Solutions

1. Naphthol yellow S, 0.1%, in 1% aqueous acetic acid (pH 2.8).
2. 1% aqueous acetic acid.

Method

1. Stain slides in solution 1 for 30 min.
2. Rinse in solution 2 (with constant agitation) for 30 min, changing the bath at 0.5, 5 and 15 min, respectively.
3. Air-dry preparations.
4. Rinse briefly in *tert*-butanol, three times, and mount in Euparal.

Result

Sites of basic protein (arginine) stain yellow.

SAKAGUCHI REACTION FOR ARGININE (McLeish *et al.,* 1957)

Tissue

Root and shoot apices. Fresh or frozen sections or tissues fixed in Ca-formal for 18 h, or Lewitsky's fluid for 6 h, or 10% neutral formalin for 18 h. Smears and squashes may also be used.

Solutions

1. Aqueous 1% NaOH solution.
2. 2,4-Dichloro-α-naphthol, 1%, in 70% ethanol.
3. Sodium hypochlorite (NaOCl, Hopkins and Williams reagent containing 10–14% (w/w) available chlorine) diluted $\times 10$ with distilled water.
4. Glycerol–10% NaOH (9:1).

Procedure

1. Coat smears and squashes with celloidin. Air-dry and rehydrate.
2. To 47 ml 1% NaOH solution add 1 ml of solution 2 and shake vigourously. Rapidly blow 2 ml NaOCl solution in from a fine pipette. The mixture is again shaken vigourously and *must* be used immediately.
3. Immerse preparations for 6 min at 20°C.
4. Drain and rinse in a large volume of 1% NaOH for 10 min.
5. Mount in alkaline glycerol at pH 11.3.

Results

Arginine stains orange-red. Absorption maximum of the end-product is at 517 nm.

SULPHYDRYL GROUPS (Bennett and Watts, 1958)

Tissues

Root and shoot apices. Razor or frozen sections.

Solution

1. Toluene-saturated solution of 1-(4-chloromercuriphenylazo)naphthol-2 (mercury orange).

Method

1. Celloidin-coated sections.
2. Place sections in solution 1 for 30 min at room temperature.
3. Rinse sections in toluene and mount in clarite.

Result

Sulphydryl groups appear as pink to red.

SULPHYDRYL GROUPS (Chévrement and Frédéric, 1943)

Tissues

Root and shoot apices. Razor or frozen sections are recommended. Fixation in formal-calcium for 18 h or Lewitsky's fluid for 6 h.

Solutions

1. Ferric sulphate solution, 1%.
2. Potassium ferricyanide solution, 0.1%, freshly prepared. Mix 3 parts of solution 1 with 1 part of solution 2 prior to use. Adjust to pH 2.4.

Method

1. Hydrate sections if necessary.
2. Immerse sections for 10–20 min in each of three changes of the mixture (frozen sections). If paraffin sections are employed, immersion should be for 20–25 min.
3. Wash sections in distilled water.
4. Mount in Farrants' medium (fresh or frozen sections) or dehydrate and mount in Euparal (paraffin sections).

Result

Sulphydryl group sites stain blue.

Controls

Immerse sections in a saturated aqueous solution of $HgCl_2$ for 48 h prior to staining. Alternatively, saturated phenylmercuric chloride in *n*-butanol for 2–3 days may be used. Lack of blue colour after blocking confirms the presence of —SH sites.

Reduction of S—S Bonds to —SH for Reacting

1. Treat the sections with 20% sodium dithionite solution at 40°C for 10 min. Follow with repeated washing in distilled water to remove all traces of the dithionite *or*

2. Immerse collodion-coated sections in a freshly prepared solution of 0.2– 0.5 M thioglycollic acid titrated to pH 8.0 with 1 N HCl, at 50°C for 1–2 h *or*

3. Immerse collodion-coated sections over-night at room temperature or at 37°C, or for 1–2 h at 50°C, in 40 ml of distilled water containing 3 ml thioglycerol and 10 ml of 0.5 M borate buffer at pH 8.5–9.1.

Resultant —SH groups can be demonstrated by either the mercury orange or the ferricyanide methods. In this case, blocking of free —SH groups in the sections should occur prior to reduction of the S—S bonds.

PROTEIN CONTAINING TRYPTOPHAN (Bruemmer *et al.*, 1957)

Tissues

Root and shoot apices fixed in Carnoy's fixative or formaldehyde–acetic acid.

Solutions

1. Nitrous acid [8% sodium nitrate–6 N HCl (1 : 1)] in the cold.
2. Equal volumes of
   a. 1 N HCl.
   b. Freshly prepared 2% N-(1-naphthyl)ethylenediamine dihydrochloride in 95% ethanol.

Method

1. Take sections to 50% ethanol.
PERFORM REACTION IN ICE-BATH
2. Place sections in solution 1 for 15 min.
3. Wash for 5 min in each of two changes of distilled water.
4. Place sections in solution 2 for 15 min.
5. Place sections in 70% *tert*-butanol.
REMOVE FROM ICE-BATH

6. Two changes of absolute *tert*-butanol containing a few drops of H_2SO_4.
7. Two changes of xylene–glacial acetic acid (5 : 1), and mount sections.

Result

Purple colour indicates proteins that contain tryptophan.

Control

Repeat using either 1,6-dihydroxynaphthalene or 1-amino-8-hydroxynaphthalene-3,6-disulphonic acid instead of *N*-(1-naphthyl)ethylenediamine, to determine the sites of other compounds which will undergo diazotization. A colour developed with these compounds is not indicative of tryptophan.

XANTHOPROTEIC REACTION FOR TYROSINE, TRYPTOPHAN AND PHENYLALANINE

Tissues

Root and shoot apices. Razor or frozen sections; absolute ethanol or formal–calcium fixation.

Method

1. Hydrate sections if necessary.
2. Warm sections on slide in the presence of concentrated HNO_3.
3. Cool and add strong ammonia solution.
4. Mount in glycerol.

Result

Yellow colour turning red in the presence of ammonia indicates the tyrosine, tryptophan and phenylalanine in the protein.

MILLON'S REACTION FOR TYROSINE-CONTAINING PROTEINS (Rasch and Swift, 1960)

Tissues

Root and shoot apices. Razor or frozen sections; fixation in formal–calcium for 18 h or Clarke's solution for 3 h.

Solution

1. Mercuric acetate, 5%, in 30% trichloroacetic acid.
2. Aqueous 0.05% sodium nitrite.

Method

1. Coat sections with celloidin.
2. Place in solution 1 for 10 min at 40°C.
3. Transfer to solution 2 for 1 h at 30°C.
4. Place sections directly in 70% ethanol for 10 min.
5. Each of 2 changes of 70% ethanol for 10 min.
6. Dehydrate and mount in Euparal.

Result

Tyrosine-containing proteins are stained red or pink.

Appendix 5. Enzymes

Unless stated specifically for a given enzyme, unfixed razor or frozen sections of tissues from *Vicia faba, Pisum sativum* may be used as test materials.

TETRAZOLE REDUCTASE

Incubation Media

1. TEST SOLUTION. Glycylglycine, 0.05 M, buffer at pH 7.8 containing 4 mg/ml NBT, 2.5mg/ml $NADH_2$ or $NADPH_2$, and 22% polyvinyl alcohol (BO5/140).

2. CONTROL SOLUTION. As solution 1 but with the omission of $NADH_2$ or $NADPH_2$.

Incubation Period

This will vary according to the tissue. Sections should be tested for periods of time, e.g. 5, 10, 20, 40, 80 min, and may be reacted at room temperature or at 37°C using microcells (Jones, 1964).

Result

Sites of the tetrazole reductase activity are revealed by the deposition of formazan, which should be absent from control sections when incubated in the absence of $NAD(P)H_2$.

GLUCOSE-6-PHOSPHATE DEHYDROGENASE. METHOD I

Incubation Media

1. TEST SOLUTION. Glycylglycine 50 mM, buffer pH 7.8 containing 22% (w/v) polyvinyl alcohol (BO5/140), 4.6 mM glucose 6-phosphate, 3.2 mM NADP and 3.7mM NBT or 4.5 mM NT. Oxygen-free nitrogen gas is bubbled through the solution prior to use.

CONTROL. Test solution lacking either glucose 6-phosphate, or NADP, or both glucose-6-phosphate and NADP.

Method

1. Incubate sections in plastic rings at room temperature in the dark.
2. Rinse sections in warm water.
3. Mount in Farrants' medium.

Result

Purple-blue formazan (NBT) at sites of enzyme activity, which should be assessed before removing incubation medium. Controls should normally be negative.

METHOD II

Incubation Media

TEST MIXTURE (after Kalina and Gahan, 1968). Equal volumes of 10% gelatin in 0.05 M glycylglycine buffer pH 7.8 and the same buffer containing 0.007 M NADP, 0.014 M glucose 6-phosphate, 0.0024 M NBT and 0.02 M potassium cyanide.

CONTROL. Similar mixture but lacking either glucose 6-phosphate or NADP.

Method

1. Evenly spread 2ml of the incubation mixture on a piece of polythene sheet 0.13 mm thick stretched over a staining jar to give a flat surface (7 × 9 cm). Allow to set in the dark at room temperature (about 30 min).
2. The solidified medium and support is cut into strips.
3. Frozen sections are brought to room temperature by placing in a precooled vacuum desiccator ($-20°$C) evacuating, and bringing to room temperature.
4. A strip of reaction mixture is placed onto the section carefully avoiding air-bubbles. Even contact is achieved by gentle pressure.
5. Incubate for 20–40 min at room temperature.
6. Remove film by floating off in distilled water at 45°C.
7. Mount in Farrants' medium.

Result

Formazan at sites of dehydrogenase activity. Controls should normally be negative.

SUCCINIC DEHYDROGENASE ACTIVITY

Incubation Media

1. TEST SOLUTION. 0.05 M phosphate buffer at pH 7.8 containing 40 mM sodium succinate, 0.5 mg/ml of NBT and 22% polyvinyl alcohol (BO5/140).

2. CONTROL MEDIA. a. As (1) but containing 0.01 M sodium malonate to inhibit succinic dehydrogenase. Check that the pH of the solution is at pH 7.8.

b. As (1) but with the omission of the sodium succinate.

Oxygen-free nitrogen should be bubbled through the solution for 10 min to create anaerobic conditions.

Incubation Period

This will vary according to the tissue. Sections should be tested for periods of time such as 5, 15, 30, 45, 60 and 90 min. Incubations should be performed at 37°C in micro-cells (Jones, 1964).

Results

Sites of succinic dehydrogenase activity are revealed by the deposition of formazan, whereas in the presence of malonate there will be no formazan produced. Any formazan produced in the absence of substrate will be due to endogenous dehydrogenase activities.

For Electron Microscopy

TEST SOLUTION (after Ekés, 1971). 0.8 ml of 0.1 M Sorensen's phosphate buffer at pH 7.6 containing 0.7 ml of 1 M aqueous sodium succinate solution, 0.15 ml of 50 mM aqueous potassium ferricyanide solution, 0.35 ml of 0.3 M aqueous copper sulphate solution, and 3 ml of 0.5 M sodium/potassium tartrate in phosphate buffer at pH 7.6

CONTROLS. Incubation of the unfixed tissues in the test solution lacking sodium succinate or containing 140 mM sodium malonate.

Method

1. Incubate unfixed tissues for 20–30 min at room temperature.

2. Fix tissues in 2% glutaraldehyde in 0.5 M cacodylate buffer pH 7.2 for 2 h at 4°C.

3. Post-fix in OsO_4 and embed by standard methods for electron microscopy.

Result

Electron-opaque deposits in mitochondria at sites of succinic dehydrogenase activity which should be absent from controls.

6-PHOSPHOGLUCONATE DEHYDROGENASE

Similar to the method for glucose-6-phosphate dehydrogenase, but substituting 6-phosphogluconate for glucose 6-phosphate.

ISOCITRATE DEHYDROGENASE

Incubation Media

TEST SOLUTION. Ten milliliters of 0.05 M Tris-HCl buffer pH 7.4 containing 40 mg NBT, 2.2 g polyvinyl alcohol (BO5/140), 25 mg NAD (or NADP), and 30.3 mg of trisodium DL-isocitrate. Adjust pH to 7.4 with sodium hydroxide. Bubble oxygen-free nitrogen through the solution prior to use.

CONTROL. Test solution lacking substrate or NAD(P).

Method

1. Incubate sections in rings for 15–60 min at room temperature in the dark.
2. Wash in warm water.
3. Mount in Farrants' medium.

Result

Formazan deposit indicates enzyme activity. Controls normally should be negative.

MALATE DEHYDROGENASE

As for isocitrate dehydrogenase but substituting sodium malate for trisodium DL-isocitrate as substrate.

PHOSPHOFRUCTOKINASE

Incubation Media

TEST SOLUTION. Dissolve 31.2 mg sodium arsenate in 10 ml of water and add 40 mg NBT, 2 g polyvinyl alcohol (BO5/140), 5.5 mg ATP, 7.4 mg NAD, 0.1 ml of 0.1 M Mg^{2+} and 6 mg fructose 6-phosphate. Adjust to pH 7.0 and add 1 drop (25 μl) of glyceraldehyde-3-phosphate dehydrogenase.

CONTROLS. Test solution lacking NAD or fructose-6-phosphate or glyceraldehyde-3-phosphate dehydrogenase, or test solution containing 8.6 mg of fructose 1,6-diphosphate instead of fructose 6-phosphate or 20 mM phosphoenol pyruvate.

Method

1. Incubate sections for 5–30 min at 30°C in the dark.
2. Wash gently in warm water.
3. Mount in Farrants' medium.

Result

Sites of enzyme activity indicated by formazan. No substrate or NAD controls should be negative. Absence of added enzyme should yield low level reaction, whilst use of fructose 1,6-diphosphate as substrate should enhance reaction. Phosphoenol pyruvate will inhibit the enzyme.

HEXOKINASE

Incubation Media

TEST SOLUTION (after Meijer, 1967). 2 ml of 0.04 M imidazole buffer at pH 7.5 containing 30 mg of D-glucose, 2.5 mg NADP, 5.5 mg ATP, 20 mg magnesium chloride, 2.5 mg NBT, 0.1 ml of 0.6 M aqueous potassium cyanide solution, 0.005 ml glucose-6-phosphate dehydrogenase enzyme (Böhringer, 1 mg/ml), and 0.44 g polyvinyl alcohol. Adjust pH to 7.5.

CONTROLS. Full test solution lacking either D-glucose or ATP or glucose-6-phosphate dehydrogenase.

Method

1. Incubate sections for various periods of time 10–60 min at 30°C and in the dark.
2. Rinse in warm water.
3. Mount in Farrants' medium.

N.B. It is more accurate to examine the sections prior to removal of the incubation medium.

Result

Formazan deposit in the test medium which is absent from the no D-glucose, no ATP controls is due to hexokinase activity. Some activity may occur in the absence of added enzyme due to endogenous glucose-6-phosphate dehydrogenase.

CYTOCHROME OXIDASE

Tissues

These may be fixed for 2 h at 4°C in buffered 2–4% depolymerized paraformaldehyde or 0.1–0.2% glutaraldehyde. Tissues should be washed for several hours in the buffer at 4°C.

Incubation Media

TEST SOLUTION. Nine milliliters of 0.05 M phosphate buffer (pH 7.4) containing 4 mg DAB, 20 μg cytochrome c (type II, Sigma) and 750 mg sucrose.

CONTROL SOLUTIONS. Full incubation medium omitting cytochrome c, or including sodium azide or potassium cyanide.

Result

Deposits of brown-black (electron-dense) material at sites of cytochrome oxidase activity. Controls should lead to no such deposition.

PEROXIDASE

Incubation Media I

TEST SOLUTION (after Graham and Karnovsky, 1966). 10 ml of 0.05 M Tris-HCl buffer at pH 7.6 containing 5 mg DAB and 0.2 ml of freshly diluted 1% H_2O_2 (from 30% stock just prior to use). It may be necessary to warm the solution in order to increase the solubility of the DAB. This should be cooled and filtered prior to the addition of the H_2O_2.

CONTROL SOLUTIONS. The test solution without H_2O_2 may be used with or without the addition of 0.01% catalase to eliminate any endogenous H_2O_2. Heat-treated sections (15 min in boiling water) may be reacted in the test solution.

Results

Brown-black (electron-opaque) deposit at sites of peroxidase activity which should be absent from the controls. Control for the adsorption of DAB may be made by incubation of sections in the test solution lacking H_2O_2, washing, and treating with the buffer containing $2 \times 10^{-3}\,M$ potassium ferricyanide to oxidize the DAB.

Incubation Media II

TEST SOLUTION (after Hanker et al., 1977). Twenty milliliters of 0.1 M Tris-HCl buffer at pH 7.6 containing 10 mg p-phenylenediamine, 20 mg pyrocatechol, and 0.2 ml of a freshly diluted 1% H_2O_2.

CONTROLS. As for method I.

Result

Black (electron-opaque) deposit at sites of peroxidase activity, which are absent from test sections.

Incubation Media III

TEST SOLUTION (after Papadimitriou et al., 1976). Ten milliliters of 0.2 M acetate buffer at pH 6.0 containing 51 mg homovanillic acid (and 1 mg rhodamine B if fluorescence method is used). Readjust pH to 6.0 with 0.2 M NaOH. To another

10 ml of acetate buffer, add 132–134 mg lead nitrate. Slowly add the lead nitrate solution to the homovanillic acid solution with stirring. Finally, add 0.2 ml of a freshly prepared 1% H_2O_2.

CONTROL SOLUTIONS. Incubate heat-inactivated sections in the full reaction mixture, or react sections in the full reaction mixture without H_2O_2 (with or without catalase).

Method

1. Incubate for up to 10 min at room temperature.
2. Wash well in buffer.
3. Immerse in saturated H_2S water for 2 min.
4. Wash well in distilled water.
5. Mount in Farrants' medium.
or if rhodamine B is employed, then proceed
2. Wash for 10 min in three changes of 50% ethanol to remove uncoupled rhodamine B.
3. Hydrate and mount in Farrants' medium, or dehydrate and mount in Euparal.
4. Examine by fluorescence microscopy.

Results

Brown-black (electron-opaque) deposits at the sites of peroxidase activity, which are lacking from control sections. If rhodamine B is used, there is a reddish white fluorescence at the sites of peroxidase activity, which should be lacking from the control sections.

CATALASE

Incubation Media

TEST SOLUTION (after Frederick and Newcombe, 1969). Five milliliters of 2-amino-2-methyl-1,3-propanediol buffer at pH 10.0 containing 10 mg DAB and 0.1ml of 3% freshly diluted H_2O_2. The medium should be prepared just before use and the pH adjusted to 9.0. Filter before use and incubate at 37°C in the dark for periods of up to 1 h.

CONTROLS. Incubate sections in the test solution lacking H_2O_2, or heat-inactivated sections (15 min at 98°C) in the test solution. Sections may also be preincubated for 1–2 h in the buffer solution containing 0.02 M aminotriazole prior to incubating in the test solution containing a final concentration of 0.02 M aminotriazole.

POLYPHENOL OXIDASE

Incubation Media

TEST SOLUTION. Ten milliliters of 0.067 *M* Sorensen's phosphate buffer at pH 7.0 containing 50 mg D-1,3,4-dihydroxydiphenylalanine.

CONTROL SOLUTION. Test solution containing 0.02 *M* sodium diethyldithiocarbamate.

Method

Incubate sections at 37°C for periods of time up to 1 h.

Result

Pigment visible at sites of polyphenol oxidase activity, but lacking in controls.

ACID PHOSPHATASE (after Gomori, 1952)

Tissues

Unfixed, razor cut or cryostat sections of any tissue.

Solutions

1. Acetate buffer pH 5.0 (0.05 M)
   a. 2.85 ml glacial acetic acid in 500 ml distilled water.
   b. 6.85 g sodium acetate in 500 ml distilled water.
2. 3% aqueous solution of sodium β-glycerophosphate (0.1 M).
3. To 100 ml solution 1, add 0.12 g lead nitrate (0.003 *M*) and 10 ml solution 2. Leave this solution at 37°C for 3–4 h, filter and use immediately.
4. Aqueous 1% acetic acid.
5. Bubble H_2S through distilled water for 5–10 min.

Method

1. Incubate sections in solution 3 at 37°C. The length of time of incubation will depend upon the particular tissue and each tissue from each organism must be assessed individually, e.g. liver from August rats need 20 min, liver from Glaxo Piebald need 10 min, meristem cells from lateral root tips of *Vicia faba* need 10–20 min.
2. Briefly rinse in distilled water.
3. Place in solution 4 for 10 sec.
4. Briefly rinse in distilled water.
5. Immerse slides in solution 5 for 2 min.
6. Wash in distilled water and mount in Farrants' medium.

Controls

1. At stage 1, use solution 3 with the omission of sodium β-glycerophosphate.
2. At stage 1, use solution 3 with the addition of 0.42 g/litre NaF.
3. Incubate boiled sections as per schedule.

Result

Brown-black deposit of PbS in test sections, but no reaction in all of the controls indicates sites of enzyme activity.

N.B. Sections should be examined immediately since under certain conditions the end-product colour fades.

ACID PHOSPHATASE (after Burstone, 1958)

Tissue

Any plant tissues. Unfixed, frozen sections.

Solutions

1. Dissolve 6 mg naphthol AS BI phosphate (Sigma Ltd) in 1 ml dimethylformamide (or acetone), and add to 50 ml 0.2 M phosphate or Tris-maleate buffer at pH 5.0. Shake well and add 50 mg fast blue BB (Sigma, Ltd). Shake well and filter.

Method

1. Incubate sections at 37°C in solution 1. *N.B.* The length of incubation time needed will depend upon the particular tissues employed and hence a range of time from 1 to 30 min should be tried.
2. Rinse in distilled water.
3. Mount in Farrants' medium.

Controls

1. Incubate sections in solution 1 from which the substrate has been omitted.
2. Incubate sections in solution 1 to which 0.01 M sodium fluoride or 0.001 M sodium molybdate has been added.
3. Incubate boiled sections in solution 1.

Result

Blue deposits in test sections which are absent from control sections indicate the site of enzyme activity.

ACID PHOSPHATASE FOR ELECTRON MICROSCOPY

Tissue

Microdissected meristematic region from roots of *Vicia faba*. Fix pieces (not larger than 10 × 5 × 2 mm) 2–4 hours in 2.5% glutaraldelyde solution buffered to pH 7.2 with 0.1 *M* cacodylate buffer. Wash well in cacodylate buffer overnight at 4°C.

Solutions

1. As for Gomori reaction solution 3.
2. Aqueous 10% acetic acid.

Method

1. Incubate tissue blocks for 8–20 min in solution 1.
2. Rinse in distilled water.
3. Rinse blocks in solution 2 for 20 sec.
4. Rinse in distilled water.
5. Dehydrate and embed in araldite (see Appendix 2).
6. Section material and view in electron microscope.

Controls

1. Incubate blocks in solution 1 lacking substrate.
2. Incubate blocks in solution 1 containing 0.01 *M* NaF.

Result

Sites of enzyme activity indicated by electron-dense deposits in test material which are absent from controls.

ALKALINE PHOSPHATASE (after Burstone, 1962)

Tissue

Any plant tissue. Unfixed frozen sections, or frozen sections fixed briefly in acetone.

Solutions

1. Dissolve 5 mg naphthol AS B1 phosphate in 0.25ml *N,N*-dimethylformamide. Add 25 ml distilled water followed by 25 ml 0.2 *M* Tris buffer pH 8.3–9.3. Add 30 mg Fast Red Violet LB shake well and filter.

Method

1. Incubate sections at 37°C in solution 1
N.B. The length of time of incubation will depend upon the particular tissues.
2. Rinse in water.
3. Mount in Farrants' medium.

Controls

1. Incubate sections in solution containing 0.1 M cysteine hydrochloride.
2. Incubate boiled sections in solution 1.
3. Incubate sections in solution 1 without naphthol AS BI phosphate.

Result

Red deposits in test sections that are unstained in the controls indicate the presence of enzyme activity.

GENERAL ESTERASE (after Burstone, 1958)

Tissues

Stele of roots and embryos of *Vicia faba*. Unfixed, frozen sections.

Solutions

1. Dissolve 5 mg naphthol AS D acetate (Sigma, Ltd) in 0.5 ml dimethylformamide and add 25 ml of 0.2 M Tris buffer at pH 6.5 and 25 ml distilled water. Add 20–40 mg fast blue BB (Sigma, Ltd). Shake well and filter.

Method

1. Incubate sections at room temperature or at 37°C in solution 1 for 5, 10 or 15 min.
2. Rinse in distilled water.
3. Mount in Farrants' medium.

Controls

1. Incubate boiled sections in solution 1.
2. Incubate sections in solution 1 from which the substrate has been omitted.

Result

Blue deposits on test sections that are absent from control sections indicate the sites of enzyme activity.

GENERAL ESTERASES (after Holt, 1958)

Tissues

Any plant tissue that has been fixed within 1–2 min of the removal from the living plant.

Solutions

1. Formaldehyde, 4%, containing 1% $CaCl_2$. Make up fresh and cool to 0°–2°C.
2. Gum acacia, 1%, containing 0.88 M sucrose. Add 0.1 g thymol per litre of gum–sucrose and store at 0°–2°C.
3. Oxidant: 0.05 M potassium ferrocyanide solution. Store at 0°–2°C and do not keep for longer than 1 week.
4. Dissolve 1.5 mg 5-bromo-4-chloroindoxyl acetate in 0.1 ml absolute ethanol. Add the following mixture rapidly and with shaking:

Oxidant, 1.0 ml
2 M NaCl, 5.0 ml
1 M $CaCl_2$, 1.0 ml
0.1 M Tris buffer pH 8.5, 2.0 ml
Make up to 10 ml with distilled water.

Method

1. Fix pieces of tissue not larger than $10 \times 5 \times 2$ mm in ice-cold solution 1 for 24–36 h at 0°–2°C using about 100 ml fixative per 1 g of tissue. After fixation, blot tissue gently and transfer to solution 2 for storage at 0°–2°C for not less than 24 h.
2. Cut frozen sections.
3. Incubate in solution 4 at 37°C for a period of time depending upon the particular tissue employed.

Result

Blue deposit at site of enzyme activity.

ATPase

Incubation Media

TEST SOLUTION. Tris-maleate buffer, 0.048 M, at pH 7.0 containing 2 mM ATP, 2 mM calcium nitrate or magnesium nitrate and 3.6 mM lead nitrate.

CONTROL SOLUTION. Test medium lacking ATP.

Method

1. Incubate sections at room temperature for varying periods of time up to 30 min.
2. Rinse in buffer and place in freshly prepared H_2S water for 2 min.
3. Wash in distilled water.
4. Mount in Farrants' medium.

For electron microscopy:
1. Incubate for 2 h at room temperature.
2. Rinse well in buffer.
3. Proceed for normal embedding procedures (Appendix 2).

Result

Brown-black (electron-opaque) deposits of lead sulphide at sites of enzyme activity, but lacking from the control material.

NUCLEOTIDE PYROPHOSPHATASE

Incubation Media

TEST SOLUTION (after Sierakowska *et al.*, 1978). One-fourth volume of 0.4 *M* acetate buffer pH 5.2 containing 0.5 volume 0.4 g % Fast Garnet GBC in distilled water (filtered) and 0.1 volume of 25 m*M* thymidine-5'-monophospho-naphthol AS-BI ester. Distilled water is added to make 1 volume.

CONTROLS. Heat inactivated sections (95°C for 15 min) reacted in full test solution or normal sections incubated in the test solution lacking substrate.

Method

1. Incubate sections for 2–30 min at 37°C.
2. Rinse in distilled water.
3. Mount in Farrants' medium.

Results

Brown reaction product at sites of nucleotide pyrophosphatase activity. Heat-inactivated sections or no substrate controls are negative.

GLUCOSE-6-PHOSPHATASE

Incubation Media

TEST SOLUTIONS. To 20 ml of 0.2 *M* Tris buffer, pH 6.7, add 20 ml of 125 mg % solution of potassium glucose 6-phosphate, 3 ml of a 2% aqueous lead nitrate solution, and 7 ml distilled water.

CONTROLS. Test solution containing 1,5-sorbitan 6-phosphate or lacking glucose 6-phosphate, or incubation in test solution of sections heated at 37°C for 15 min.

Method

1. Incubate sections from 5 to 30 min at 37°C.
2. Wash in distilled water.
3. Place in saturated H_2S water for 2 min.
4. Wash in distilled water.
5. Mount in Farrants' medium.

Result

Brown-black (electron-opaque) product at sites of enzyme activity, but absent from controls. For electron microscopy, material is incubated for up to 60 min at 25°C in 35 mM acetate buffer at pH 5.7 containing 1 mM potassium glucose 6-phosphate and 4 mM lead nitrate. The material is post-fixed in glutaraldehyde and embedded in resin.

NUCLEOTIDE PHOSPHATASE

Incubation Media

TEST SOLUTION (after Goff, 1973). Two milliliters of 0.2 M Tris–maleate buffer at pH 7.35 containing 1 ml of aqueous 75 mM IDP solution, 1 ml of 25 mM aqueous manganese chloride solution, 0.6 ml of 1% aqueous lead nitrate solution and 0.4 ml of distilled water.

CONTROLS. Heat-inactivated material incubated in the test solution, or material reacted in the test solution lacking IDP.

Method

1. Incubate sections for periods of time up to 2 h at 37°C.
2. Rinse in buffer.
3. Place in ammonium sulphide water for 2 min.
4. Rinse well in distilled water.
5. Mount in Farrants' medium.
6. For electron microscopy, dehydrate and embed after step 2.

Result

Black-brown, electron-opaque deposits indicate sites of nucleoside phosphatase activity.

ADENYL CYCLASE

Incubation Media

TEST SOLUTION. Tris-maleate buffer, 80 mM, pH 7.2, containing 0.5 mM AMP-PNP (Boehringer), 2 mM magnesium sulphate, 4 mM lead nitrate, 8% dextran, and 5 mM theophylline.

CONTROLS. React heat-inactivated sections in the full reaction medium, or ordinary sections in the test solution lacking AMP-PNP, or containing 10 mM alloxan as inhibitor.

Method

1. Incubate sections for 10–30 min at 37°C.
2. Wash in Tris-maleate buffer at pH 7.2.
3. Immerse in saturated hydrogen sulphide water for 2 min.
4. Wash well in distilled water.
5. Mount in Farrants' medium.
6. For electron microscopy, material fixed for 2 h at 4°C in 1% glutaraldehyde in 0.5 M cacodylate buffer at pH 7.4 containing 4.5% glucose is incubated for 30 min at 30°C. This is then processed by the standard methods for electron microscopy (Appendix 2).

Result

Deposits of electron-opaque, brown-black deposits indicate sites of adenyl cyclase activity. They should be absent from the controls.

MYROSINASE

Tissues

Root tips of *Sinapis alba*. For electron microscopy fix in 3% glutaraldehyde in 0.1 M cacodylate buffer at pH 7.2 for 2 h at 4°C.

Incubation Medium

(after Iverson, 1970, 1973)

TEST SOLUTION. To 8 ml of 0.1 M cacodylate buffer at pH 7.2, add 4 ml of 0.1 M sinigrin (potassium myronate) in distilled water, 3 ml of 0.005 M lead nitrate in distilled water and 0.225 g of sucrose. The pH should be adjusted to 7.2.

CONTROLS. Use heat-inactivated material in the full test solution or react sections in the incubation medium lacking either sinigrin or lead nitrate.

Method

1. Incubate for 30–60 min at 30°C.
2. For light microscopy, rinse sections in buffer for 5 min.
3. Place in freshly prepared saturated ammonium sulphide water.
4. Wash well in distilled water and mount in Farrants' medium.
  5. For electron microscopy, proceed from 2 to normal methods for embedding (Appendix 2).

Result

Sites of myrosinase activity shown as brown-black (electron opaque) sites of lead sulphide (lead sulphate).

β-GLUCURONIDASE

Incubation Media

TEST SOLUTION

1. Stock solution of 11.4 mg naphthol AS-B1-β-D-glucuronide in 1 ml of dimethylformamide added to 49 ml of 0.2 M acetate buffer pH 4.5. Dilute 0.8 ml of stock solution with 3.2 ml of 0.2 M acetate buffer pH 4.5 and 4.0 ml distilled water.

2. Post-coupling solution of 1 mg fast blue B in 5 ml of 0.1 M phosphate buffer pH 7.5.

CONTROL. Test solution lacking substrate.

Method

1. Incubate sections for 15–120 min at 37°C.
2. Rinse in distilled water.
3. Post-couple for 5 min at 4°C.
4. Wash sections.
5. Mount in Farrants' medium.

Result

Blue product at sites of enzyme activity, which should be absent from "no substrate" control.

LEUCYL NAPHTHYLAMIDASE

Incubation Media

TEST SOLUTION

1. Stock solution of either 10 mg/ml of L-leucyl-4-methoxy-2-naphthylamide HCl or 8 mg/ml of L-leucyl-β-naphthylamide in distilled water, which will keep for several months at 0°–4°C.

2. One milliliter of stock solution is added to 10 ml of 0.1 M acetate buffer pH 6.5 containing 8 ml of 0.85% aqueous sodium chloride solution, 20 mM potassium cyanide and 10 mg fast blue B salt.

CONTROL. Omit substrate from the test solution.

Method

1. Incubate sections for 15–120 min at 37°C.
2. Rinse sections in 0.85% aqueous sodium chloride solution.
3. Immerse sections in 0.1 M aqueous cupric sulphate solution for 2 min.
4. Rinse sections in saline.
5. Mount sections in Farrants' medium.

Result

Bright red (4-methoxy derivative) or purplish blue colour indicates sites of leucyl naphthylamidase activity.

DEOXYRIBONUCLEASE/RIBONUCLEASE

Incubation Media

TEST SOLUTION. Acetate buffer (12.5 ml of 0.2 M) pH 5.0 containing 10 mg DNA, 5 mg acid phosphatase, 0.25 ml of 0.4 M aqueous lead nitrate solution and distilled water to make 50 ml final volume.

CONTROLS. Test medium lacking DNA or acid phosphatase, or the full reaction medium containing 0.01 M sodium fluoride.

Method

1. Incubate sections for 0.5–2 h at 37°C.
2. Rinse in distilled water.
3. Place in saturated hydrogen sulphide water for 2 min.
4. Wash in distilled water.
5. Mount in Farrants' medium.

Result

Sites of deoxyribonuclease activity are brown-black. Controls of ''no DNA'' and sodium fluoride should be negative, whilst the ''no added enzyme'' should be low activity-negative.

This may be used for electron microscopy by reacting small pieces of tissues fixed in 2% glutaraldehyde; stage 2 should be followed by dehydration and embedding in resin.

Appendix 6. Lipids

3,4-BENZPYRENE REACTION

Tissues

Unfixed, frozen sections of roots of *Vicia faba* or *Allium cepa*, or fixation in formal-calcium for 24 h at 4°C or in Lewitsky's fluid at room temperature for 6 h.

Solutions

Prepare a saturated solution of caffeine in water (about 1.5%). To 100 ml of filtered solution add 0.002 g of 3,4-benzpyrene and incubate at 37°C for 2 days. Filter off excess 3,4-benzpyrene and dilute with an equal volume of distilled water. Allow to stand for 2 h and refilter. This solution contains about 0.00075 g/100 ml, and it can be used for some months if stored in a dark well-stoppered bottle.

Method

1. Hydrate the material.
2. Stain for 20 min in the 3,4-benzpyrene solution.
3. Wash in distilled water and mount the sections in water.
4. Ring the coverslips to prevent the preparations from drying out.
5. Examine the material by fluorescence microscopy using ultra-violet light.

Result

Lipids give a blue or bluish-white fluorescence that fades relatively rapidly.

SUDAN BLACK B

Tissues

Roots of *Allium cepa* or other fatty tissue, e.g. *Helianthus annuus* cotyledons. Unfixed frozen sections.

Procedures (after Bayliss and Adams, 1972)

1. Place sections overnight in freshly prepared bromine water (0.1%) and

wash well with distilled water.

2. Stain the material in a saturated solution of Sudan black B in 70% aqueous ethanol at room temperature for 30 min. Filter before use.

3. Briefly rinse the sections in 50% aqueous ethanol.

4. Hydrate the sections and mount in Farrants' medium.

N.B. As an alternative to steps 3 and 4, wash in running water and mount in glycerine jelly (Pearse, 1968).

Results

Lipids stain black or blue, though occasionally some phospholipids may appear brownish black.

Control

Extraction of the sections with a lipid solvent prior to staining may be employed (e.g. ethanol, methanol–chloroform).

SUDAN 111

Tissues

Most tissues, e.g. onion scale epidermis. Unfixed or fixed frozen sections.

Solution

A saturated solution of Sudan 111 in 70% aqueous ethanol. This solution should be filtered before use.

Method

1. Take sections to 50% aqueous ethanol.
2. Stain in Sudan 111 solution for 30 min.
3. Rinse sections in 50% aqueous ethanol.
4. Mount in Farrants' medium or glycerine jelly.

N.B. Avoid the use of absolute ethanol since the lipids will be soluble in this solvent.

Result

Neutral fats and fatty acids stain red.

RHODAMINE B

Tissues

Any tissues, e.g. roots of *Allium cepa*. Unfixed frozen section.

Solution

Rhodamine B, 0.1%, in distilled water.

Method

  1. Stain for 30 min in the Rhodamine B solution.
  2. Mount the sections with distilled water and ring the coverslip to prevent drying out.
  3. Examine the preparation by ultra-violet light fluorescence microscopy.

Result

Lipids fluoresce white-pink.
  N.B. This dye may be used also as a vital dye either in isolated tissues or by injection directly into the vascular system of the plant followed by cutting razor or frozen sections.

NILE BLUE SULPHATE

Tissue

Any tissue, e.g. root or shoot apices. Unfixed or Lewitsky-fixed frozen sections.

Solutions

  1. Nile Blue sulphate, 1%, in distilled water.
  2. Aqueous, 1% acetic acid.

Method

  1. Stain in the Nile Blue sulphate solution at 37°C for 30 s.
  2. Differentiate in 1% acetic acid at 37°C for 30 s.
  3. Wash in distilled water.
  4. Mount in Farrants' medium or glycerine jelly.

Result

Neutral lipids stain red; acidic lipids stain blue (i.e. free fatty acids and phospho-lipids).
  N.B. (a) The blue component is also a basic dye and so will stain other than lipid sites. (b) If only the blue dye is required, then use a 0.02% solution of Nile blue sulphate.

ACID HAEMATEIN METHOD

Tissues

Root or shoot apices. Fresh tissue sections or unfixed frozen sections are well fixed by the mordanting solution. Fixation may be achieved with formal-calcium for 18 h at 4°C; Bouin's fluid for 20 h; Lewitsky's fluid for 6 h or formal–calcium saturated with Reinecke's salt for 6 h.

Solutions

1. Mordant
   Potassium dichromate, 5.0 g
   Calcium chloride, 1.0 g
   Distilled water to 100 ml

2. Haematoxylin solution: Dissolve 0.1 g of haematoxylin (B.D.H. SS brand) in 96 ml of distilled water. Add 2 ml of 1% potassium iodate solution. Heat until the solution just boils. Cool and add 2 ml of glacial acetic acid.

N.B. This solution must be prepared fresh on each occasion, and should be heated until really boiling, but not kept boiling. Many batches of haematoxylin dye are unsuitable for the acid haematein test. Whilst the B.D.H. samples have been reliable for many years, Sigma samples are proving better.

3. Differentiating solution
   Sodium tetraborate, 0.25 g
   Potassium ferricyanide, 0.25 g
   Distilled water, 100 ml

N.B. This solution should be stored in the dark, but preferably for not longer than 1 week.

Procedure

1. Mordant the sections for 18 h at room temperature. Transfer unfixed sections directly to this solution.
2. Transfer the sections to fresh mordant at 60°C for 24 h.
3. Wash well in distilled water.
4. Stain in the freshly prepared haematoxylin solution for 5 h at 37°C.
5. Wash well in distilled water.
6. Transfer the sections to the differentiating bath at 37°C for 18 h.
7. Wash well in distilled water, dehydrate through a graded alcohol series and mount in Euparal.

N.B. If the material has been fixed in a chromium-containing fixative, the duration of stage 1 should be adjusted to compensate for the length of fixation.

Result

Phospholipid sites stain blue-black or black.

Control I

1. Pretreat unfixed sections with bromine water at room temperature for 18 h.
2. Wash the sections well in distilled water.
3. Procede from step 1 for the complete reaction.

This should prevent the reaction for phospholipids.

Control II

1. Fix material in weak Bouin's solution for 20 h.
2. Wash in alcohol to remove the picric acid.
3. Immerse in pyridine at room temperature for 30 min.
4. Transfer to fresh pyridine at 60°C for 18 h.
5. Wash in running water for 2 h.
6. Procede as from stage 1 of the acid haematein test.

Result

A positive acid haematein reaction and a lack of stain after the pyridine extraction is indicative of phospholipid.

Control III

A more efficient way of extracting lipids is through the use of acidified methanol chloroform (HCl–methanol–chloroform, 1 : 33 : 66) though this severely distorts the sections.

OSMIUM TETROXIDE–α-NAPHTHYLAMINE (OTAN) REACTION

Tissues

Preferably use frozen sections of tissues that have been fixed in formal–calcium.

Solutions

1. OsO_4–$KClO_3$: 1% osmium tetroxide–1% potassium chloride (1:3).
2. A saturated solution of α-naphthylamine (made by adding α-naphthylamine to water warmed to 40°C). Filter.
   N.B. Care must be taken in handling α-naphthylamine in case that there should be slight contamination with β-naphthylamine, which is highly carcinogenic.

Method

1. Treat free-floating sections for 18 h in the OsO_4–$KClO_3$ solution in a tightly stoppered vessel to prevent volatilization of the OsO_4.
2. Wash the sections in distilled water for 10 min and mount them on a slide.
3. Treat the sections with α-naphthylamine solution at 37°C for 20 min (10–15 min for sections 15 μm thick).
4. Wash in distilled water for 5 min.
5. Mount the sections in glycerine jelly.

Result

Unsaturated phospholipids stain orange-red; cholesterol esters and triglycerate esters stain black.

Controls

Sections may be extracted with lipid solvents prior to staining.

PLASMAL REACTION (after Hayes, 1949)

Tissues

Root and shoot apices unfixed or fixed briefly (3–6 h) in formal–calcium. Cut frozen sections and mount onto slides.

Solutions

1. Aqueous 1% mercury chloride.
2. Schiff reagent.
3. Sulphur dioxide water (see Feulgen reaction).

Method

1. Immerse the sections in mercury chloride solution for 10 min.
2. Wash the sections in three changes of distilled water.
3. Stain with Schiff reagent for 20 min.
4. Rinse the sections in three changes of freshly prepared SO_2 water, each of 10 min.
5. Wash the sections well in distilled water.
6. Mount in Farrants' medium or glycerine jelly.

Result

Plasmalogen sites will colour magenta.

Control

The presence of pseudo-plasmal aldehydes, due to the atmospheric oxidation of lipid ethylene bonds, can be detected by omitting stage 1 of the method. Usually, most reaction in a section is due to pseudo-plasmal reaction unless the material is very fresh.

PRESENCE OF MASKED LIPID (after Berenbaum, 1958)

Tissues

Razor or frozen sections of shoot or root apices, unfixed or fixed at 4°C for 18 h in formal–calcium.

Solution

Saturated Sudan black B in 70% aqueous ethanol.

Method

1. Rinse the sections in absolute acetone.
2. Stain sections in the Sudan black B reagent in a sealed container at 60°C for 1 h.
3. Wash the sections in 70% ethanol (briefly).
4. Hydrate the sections and mount in Farrants' medium.

Result

Bound or masked lipids stain black.

SUBERIN

Tissues

Unfixed, razor cut or cryostat sections of woody stem, e.g. *Tilia* or *Ribes*.

Solution

Phosphate buffer, 0.02 *M*, at pH 9.1.

Method

Mount sections in the buffer and view by fluorescence microscopy using UV light for excitation.

Result

Yellow fluorescence indicates suberin.

Control

Mount sections in concentrated sulphuric acid. Resistance to this treatment is indicative of suberin.

AURAMINE O

Tissues

Unfixed, razor cut or cryostat sections of leaves of *Dianthus, Brassica* spp. or *Agave* spp.

Solution

Auramine O, 0.01%, solution in 0.05 *M* Tris-HCl buffer at pH 7.2.

Method

Mount sections in auramine O solution for 10 min and view by fluorescence microscopy with blue light excitation.

Result

Unsaturated acidic waxes fluorescence bright greenish yellow.

Appendix 7. Carbohydrates

PARS REACTION (after Hotchkiss, 1948)

Tissues

Any plant tissue. Unfixed cryostat or razor cut sections. Fix in 4% formaldehyde for 18 h or in Lewitsky's fluid for 6 h.

Solution I

Periodic acid	0.4 g
Absolute ethanol	35 ml
0.2 M sodium acetate solution	5 ml
Distilled water	10 ml

Solution II

Reducing bath: Dissolve 1 g potassium iodide and 1 g sodium thiosulphate in 30 ml absolute ethanol and 20 ml distilled water. Add 0.5 ml 2 N HCl ignoring any deposit of sulphur.

N.B. This should be made up fresh on each occasion.

Solution III

Schiff reagent (see Appendix 3).

Solution IV

Freshly prepared SO_2 water (see Appendix 3).

Method

1. Take sections to 70% aqueous ethanol.
2. Place the sections in solution I for 10 min.
3. Rinse the sections in 70% aqueous ethanol.
4. Transfer the sections to solution II for 3 min.
5. Rinse the sections in 70% aqueous ethanol.
6. Stain the sections in Schiff reagent for 20 min.
7. Wash the sections in three changes of solution IV, each for 10 min.
8. Dehydrate the sections through a graded series of ethanol and mount in Euparal.

Result

Aldehyde groups formed by the splitting of the 1,2-diglycol linkages are stained pink.

Control I

Acetylation to confirm the presence of the 1,2-diglycol linkage.
   1. Transfer the section to a mixture of 16 ml acetic anhydride and 24 ml anhydrous pyridine at 58°C for 6 h.
   2. Wash the section well with 70% aqueous ethanol.
   3. Continue from stage 2 of the PARS reaction.

Control II: Free Aldehydes

Omit the periodic acid oxidation and react the section as from stage 6 of the PARS reaction.

Control III

Reaction is due to the presence of free aldehydes.
   1. Treat the section with a saturated solution of dimedone in 5% aqueous acetic acid at 60°C for 18 h.
   2. Continue as for the PARS reaction from stage 6.

Control IV

Reaction is due to aldehydes formed by oxidation.
   1. Treat the sections with dimedone (Control III, step 1, above).
   2. Proceed with steps (1–5) of the PARS reaction.
   3. Repeat step 1 to block any created aldehyde groups.
   4. Continue with the PARS reaction as from step 6.

Control V

To control that the oxidation step does not remove the dimedone blockade.
   1. Perform the dimedone blockade.
   2. Treat the sections with 0.05 M alcoholic HCl for 10 min.
   3. Continue with the PARS reaction from step 6.
Blockade should result in the abolition of the PARS reaction.

SILVER–METHENAMINE REACTION FOR CARBOHYDRATES

Tissues

Any plant tissue fixed in 2.5% glutaraldehyde.

Solutions

1. To 45 ml of freshly prepared 3% aqueous methenamine add 5 ml of freshly prepared 5% aqueous silver nitrate. Shake well and add 5 ml of freshly prepared 2% aqueous sodium borate. Filter through two sheets of Whatman No. 42 filter paper prior to use.

2. Aqueous 1% periodic acid.

3. Aqueous 5% sodium thiosulphate.

N.B. Glassware for the above solutions should be used new and kept for these solutions, being washed only with soap and water and rinsed well in water.

Method

1. Cut sections and float on distilled water.

2. Float sections onto solution 2 for 20 min.

3. Wash the sections three times with distilled water, and leave overnight in distilled water to remove all of the periodic acid.

4. Stain the sections with solution 1 for 30 min at 60°C.

5. Rinse the sections well in distilled water.

6. Stain the sections in solution 1 at 60°C for 30 min.

7. Wash the sections well in distilled water.

8. Float the sections on solution 3 for 5–10 min.

9. Wash the sections three times in distilled water.

10. Mount the sections on formavar-covered grids.

N.B. Sections may be transferred from solution to solution with a fine platinum wire loop.

Result

Aldehyde groups are indicated by silver deposits.

THE PA–TSC–SP (PERIODIC ACID–THIOSEMICARBOHYDRAZIDE–SILVER PROTEINATE) METHOD (Thiéry, 1967)

Tissues

Root apices fixed in 2.5% glutaraldehyde and embedded in Epon or methacrylate.

Solutions

1. Aqueous 1% periodic acid solution.

2. Thiosemicarbohydrazide, 1%, in 5% aqueous acetic acid.

3. Aqueous 5% acetic acid.

4. Aqueous 1% solution of silver proteinate (pH 6.4), or brought to pH 4.4 with acetic acid, or brought to pH 9.2 with borate buffer.

Method

1. Cut ultra-thin sections and float on distilled water.
2. Treat with solution 1 for 1 h at 22°C.
3. Wash sections with three changes of distilled water, 10 min for each.
4. Immerse sections in solution 2 for 90 min at 60°C.
5. Wash sections in solution 3 for 2–5 min at 40°C.
6. Rinse sections in distilled water for 10 min.
7. Immerse section in one of solutions 4 for 45 min in the dark.
8. Rinse sections in three changes of distilled water, 10 min each change.
9. Mount on grids for examination.

Result

Aldehyde groups are identified by silver deposits.

PECTINS (after Reeve, 1959)

Tissues

Any plant tissue. Relatively thick razor cut or cryostat sections.

Solutions

1. A freshly prepared mixture of equal volumes of (a) Sodium hydroxide, 14 g, in 100 ml 60% aqueous ethanol and (b) Hydroxylamine hydrochloride, 14 g, in 100 ml 60% aqueous ethanol.
2. Concentrated HCl–95% aqueous ethanol, 1 : 2 (v/v).
3. Ferric chloride, 10%, in 60% aqueous ethanol containing 1% HCl (0.1 N).

Method

1. Place the sections in 5–10 drops of solution 1 for at least 5 min.
2. Add an equal volume of solution 2 to acidify the reaction mixture.
3. Remove the excess solution from the sections and flood them with solution 3.

Result

Esterified pectins stain red, a colour that is intensified by methylation of the sections in a hot solution of absolute methanol containing 0.5 N HCl.

STARCH

Tissues

Razor cut sections or cryostat sections of any starch-containing tissue, e.g. potato tuber.

Solution

Iodine (0.5%) in 5% aqueous potassium iodide solution. Store in the dark.

Method

1. Place the sections in the iodine solution for 2 min.
2. Rinse the sections in distilled water and observe directly.

N.B. It may be necessary to dilute the iodine solution for use with a number of tissues.

Result

Short chain starch molecules stain red-brown; long-chain starch molecules stain deep blue.

CELLULOSE

Tissues

Any plant tissue. Razor cut or cryostat sections or sections of tissue fixed in absolute ethanol.

Solution

Zinc chloride, 30 g
Potassium iodide, 5 g
Iodine, 1 g
Distilled water, 14 ml
    Keep the solution in the dark.

Method

1. Hydrate the sections.
2. Mount and examine in the chloride–iodide solution.

Result

Cellulose swells slightly and colours blue after a few minutes.

LIGNIN

1. Aniline Sulphate

Tissues

Razor cut or cryostat sections or sections of ethanol-fixed material. Any lignified plant tissue.

Solution

Aniline sulphate, 1 g
Sulphuric acid (0.1 N), 10 ml
Aqueous 70% ethanol, 89 ml

Method

1. Hydrate the sections.
2. Mount and examine the sections directly in the aniline sulphate solution.

Result

Lignin is coloured bright yellow. This is not a permanent preparation.

2. Phloroglucin

Tissue

Stem or root material fixed in absolute ethanol, or razor cut or cryostat sections of unfixed material.

Solutions

1. Phloroglucin, 10 g
   Absolute ethanol, 95 ml
2. Concentrated hydrochloric acid.

Method

1. Soak the sections in solution 1 for 3 min.
2. Drain well and add a few drops of solution 2.
3. Mount in 75% glycerine.

Result

Lignin stains red. Temporary preparation only.

3. Chlorine–Sulphite (after Faulkner and Kimmins, 1976)

Tissues

Any lignified plant material.

Solutions

1. Freshly prepared saturated solution of calcium hypochlorite acidfied with 11 N HCl.
2. Aqueous 1% solution of sodium sulphite.

Method

Flood sections with solution 1 followed by solution 2.

Result

Lignin stains bright red. Colour fades to a brown hue after 30–45 min.

POLYPHENOLS

Tissues

Unfixed, razor cut or cryostat sections of leaves, roots or stems of *Pinus* sp., *Tilia, Salix, Rubus.*

Ferric Chloride Test

SOLUTION. Ferric chloride, 2%, in 95% ethanol.

METHOD
  1. Stain for 5 min in the ferric chloride solution.
  2. Rinse in 95% ethanol, hydrate and mount in Euparal or examine directly.

RESULT. Phenols yield a green colour.

Gibb's Reagent

SOLUTIONS
  1. 2,6-Dichloroquinone-4-chloroimine, 0.5% solution.
  2. Borate buffer, 0.2 M, at pH 9.5.
  3. Freshly mix 0.5 ml of solution 1 with 10 ml of solution 2.
  4. Aqueous 5% ammonium hydroxide.

METHOD
  1. React sections for 30 min in solution 3.
  2. Transfer to solution 4 for 10 min.

RESULT

Blue colour (ammonium salt of indophenol) indicates sites of polyphenols.

DIAZOTIZED SULPHANILIC ACID

Solutions

  1. Diazotized sulphanilic acid is freshly prepared by dissolving 0.3 g of sulphanilic acid in 2 ml of 10% aqueous Na_2CO_3 solution. Cool in ice and add

2–3 drops of 20% sodium nitrite solution and 1 ml of cold 1 N HCl. Shake well and leave for 2–3 min.

  2. Acetate buffer, 0.2 M, at pH 4.8.

  3. Mix 5 ml of solution 1 with 50 ml of solution 2 (final pH 4.7).

Method

1. React sections for 10 min.

Result

Yellow (to light orange) colour indicates phenols.

FAST BLUE BB

Solution

Fast Blue BB, 0.08%, in acetate buffer at pH 6.5.

Method

1. Incubate sections for 15–30 min at room temperature.

Result

Red to dark brown colour indicates phenols.

NITROUS ACID TEST

Solutions

  1. Aqueous 10% sodium nitrate
  2. Aqueous 10% acetic acid.
  3. Aqueous 10% urea.
  4. 2 N NaOH.

Method

  1. React sections for 3 min in a freshly mixed solution of equal volumes of solutions 1–3.

  2. Add a few drops of 2 N NaOH.

Result

Phenol sites are indicated by a yellow-red colour.

TANNINS

Tissues

Unfixed razor cut or cryostat sections of stems of *Rubus*.

Ferric Salt Solution

Ferric chloride, 1%, in 0.1 N HCl.

Method

React sections for 15 min.

Result

Tannin sites show blue-black colour.

Appendix 8. Vital Dyes

JANUS GREEN B

Tissues

Unfixed, razor cut or cryostat sections of any tissue—but root apices of *Vicia faba* are a good reference.

Solution

0.001% Janus green B in distilled water.

Method

1. Mount sections in a few drops of the dye solution and place a coverslip on the preparation.
2. Leave to react for 20 min at room temperature, and view directly by light microscopy.

Result

Mitochondria stain blue in living cells only. Dead cells are completely stained.

EVANS BLUE

Tissues

Unfixed, whole cells or razor cut or cryostat sections of any tissues.

Solution

0.1% Aqueous solution of Evans blue.

Method

Bathe cells for 5 min at room temperature and examine by light microscopy.

Result

Dead cells stain blue. Living cells remain unstained.

NEUTRAL RED

Tissues

Unfixed whole cells, or razor cut or cryostat sections of any tissue.

Solution

1. 0.1% neutral red in 20 mM phosphate buffer at pH 7.5 containing 600 mM potassium nitrate and 1 mM calcium chloride.
2. As 1 but omitting the dye.

Method

1. Stain in the dye solution for 20 min at room temperature.
2. Rinse sections in solution 2, mount in fresh rinsing solution and view by light microscopy.

Result

Living cells accumulate the dye only in the vacuolar system.

FLUORESCEIN DIACETATE

Tissues

Cell cultures or unfixed razor cut or cryostat sections of any tissue.

Solutions

1. Dissolve fluorescein diacetate in acetone at a concentration of 5 mg/ml.
2. Dilute this solution to a final concentration of 0.01% by the addition of 0.05 M phosphate buffer at pH 5.8

Method

1. Stain the material in the buffered dye solution for 5 min at room temperature.
2. View by fluorescence microscopy using ultra-violet light for excitation.

Result

Only living cells fluoresce, dead cells do not.

PHENOSAFRANIN

Tissues

Unfixed razor cut or cryostat sections, or whole cell preparations.

Solution

1. 0.05 *M* phosphate buffer at pH 5.8.
2. 1% phenosafranin in 0.05 *M* phosphate buffer at pH 5.8.

Method

1. Stain the preparations for 5 min in solution 2.
2. Rinse in solution 1, and view by fluoresence microscopy using blue light excitation.

Result

Dead cells fluoresce. Living cells exclude the dye.

CALCOFLUOR M2R NEW

Tissues

Cell cultures or unfixed razor cut or cryostat sections of root apical meristems of *Vicia faba*.

Solution

0.1% aqueous solution of Calcofluor M2R New. Stain material for 30 sec and examine by fluorescence microscopy using ultra-violet light excitation.

Result

Sites of cellulose fluoresce.

Appendix 9. Quantification

AUTORADIOGRAPHY

The Stripping-Film Technique

Preparation of Material

For autoradiography involving the use of water-insoluble materials, the tissue may be fixed in absolute ethanol, Clarke's fixative or formaldehyde-calcium, paraffin embedded and sectioned at 5 μm. Alternatively, frozen sections may be used. This technique is also applicable to squash preparations or cell cultures.

Before placing the specimen on the slide, the slide should be coated (subbed) with either (a) egg-albumin or (b) a solution of gelatin, 0.5 g, chrome alum, 0.05 g, distilled water, 100 ml and dried for at least 2 days. This is necessary to retain the section on the slide and to assist in good adherence of the emulsion to the slide.

After mounting the sections, dewax them and take to water through an alcohol series. Wash for at least 1 h with distilled water. Keep the slides in distilled water. Squash preparations should be made straight onto the subbed slides and taken to water.

Preparation of the Autoradiographs

1. The stripping-film is handled in a darkroom and a red safelight, Wratten Series No. 1 may be used. It is best to keep illumination to a minimum.

2. During the process, care should be taken not to scratch the film with the cuff of any clothing.

3. The plate of Kodak ARIO stripping-film should be placed on the bench and with the aid of a sharp scalpel or razor blade cut through the film, 1 cm from the edge of the plate along the four sides. Then make one median longitudinal cut and three equidistant lateral cuts resulting in the production of 8 pieces of film, each about $1\frac{1}{2} \times 2$ inches (Fig. 44). The plate being cut should be placed on dark paper on the bench, as should the glass dishes used for floating out, in order to facilitate ease in observing the film.

4. With a scalpel, raise the corner of one piece of the film, and holding it

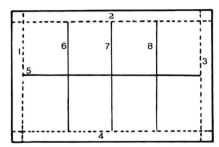

FIG. 44.   Lines of cutting with a razor blade to prepare AR10 stripping film. First cut as per dashed lines 1–4 so as to exclude emulsion of uneven thickness at the peripheral 1 cm. Then cut lines 5–8 so producing 8 pieces of stripping film per plate.

between the thumb and forefinger of the left hand, *slowly* strip the piece of film from the plate.

N.B. Do not strip the film rapidly, since this will produce flashes of light which will fog the film. If, owing to high temperatures or humidity, stripping is difficult, dry the plates in a desiccator.

5. The film is mounted on the glass plate emulsion side uppermost. Therefore, as the film is stripped it should be turned over and placed emulsion side down on the surface of the floating out solution containing 50 mg KBr per litre of distilled water, which should be maintained at 25°C.

N.B. The dishes used to contain the floating out solution (30 × 15 m) should be kept specifically for this purpose and must be rigorously clean. The solution must be kept at 25°C to allow for maximum expansion of the stripping film.

6. Leave the film to float for $2\frac{1}{2}$ min to allow for expansion. (During this time the next plate can be prepared as per stage 3.)

7. Place a slide, specimen upwards, in the dish and beneath the floating film. Lift the slide and film together out of the bath. As the slide is being raised, it should be tilted slightly so that no air bubble is trapped between the slide and the film.

8. Hang the slide from a rack and dry in front of a current of cold air. An electric fan can be used for this purpose, and this should be done, preferably in a dust-free room.

9. When dry, store the slides for exposure in a light-tight box and store at −25°C. For safety against fogging it is suggested that the slides be placed in a black wooden slide-box which can be placed in another light-tight box. A sac of silica gel placed in the box will ensure that the preparations remain dry.

10. After a suitable exposure period, the slides are removed from the light-tight box and developed in D19b developer for 6 min at 17°–18°C. The slides are then rinsed in distilled water at 17°–18°C and fixed in dilute fixer at 17°–18°C for 10 min, i.e. fix until the slides are clear the then for half that time again. The

fixer (Johnson's Fix-Sol) is diluted 1 : 9 with distilled water. It is also recommended that the D19b be prepared from Analar reagents where possible to avoid contamination from small particles of dirt. All developing and fixing solutions should be discarded after one use because of radioactive contamination. In making the D19b solution, components should be dissolved completely before the addition of the next.

D19b	
Elon or metol	2.2 g
Anhydrous sodium sulphite	72.0 g
Hydroquinone	8.0 g
Anhydrous sodium carbonate	48.0 g
Potassium bromide	4.0 g
Distilled water	1000.0 ml

This solution should be filtered before use.

WARNING. *All* solutions used in the process of developing, fixing and staining must always be maintained at a constant temperature of 17°–18°C for good results (see text).

11. Wash the developed slides in running water or frequent changes of distilled water for 30 min–1 h. Since tap-water is often dirty, a filter should be fitted to the tap. Washing should be carried out at 17°–18°C.

12. Hang the slides from a rack to dry. It is normal to leave the autoradiographs to dry for 24 h prior to staining in order to minimise movement of the film through continuous exposure to solutions.

Liquid Emulsion Method (after Rogers, 1979)

Materials

Ilford K2 or L4 emulsion; Ilford "S" or Wratten "OC" safelight. Waterbath at 43°C. Cold metal drying plate.

Method

1. Mark 25 ml measuring cylinder with a wax pencil at the 24 ml mark.

2. Place 11.7 ml distilled water and 0.24 ml glycerol into a dipping jar.

3. Place measuring cylinder, dipping jar and emulsion in the water-bath for 15 min.

4. While the emulsion settles, stir gently with a glass rod being careful not to create air bubbles.

5. Pour the emulsion gently into the 25 ml cylinder until the level reaches the 24 ml mark.

6. Transfer the contents of the cylinder to the dipping jar and stir gently to ensure good mixing of the contents.

7. Leave for 2 min to allow air bubbles to rise to the surface.

8. Dip a clean slide and move gently across the emulsion to pick up any air bubble. Examine slide for air bubbles.

9. Repeat step 8 until there are no more air bubbles.

10. When ready, dip experimental slides, keeping slide vertical, dip and withdraw slowly and steadily. Hold the slide vertically for a fixed number of seconds, e.g. 2 or 5, allowing excess emulsion to drain into paper tissue. Wipe the back of the slide and lay flat on a cold metal plate to dry for 45–60 min. Store for exposure in the dark at $-25°C$.

11. After exposure process slides in the normal manner.

N.B. The extension of the use of liquid emulsion for electron microscope autoradiography is dealt with in Gahan (1972) and Rogers (1979), and below.

STAINING OF SECTIONS WITH AUTORADIOGRAPHS

A. Ehrlich's Haematoxylin and Eosin

1. If dry, soak the autoradiographs for 30 min in water.
2. Stain in Ehrlich's haematoxylin* for 30 min.
3. Wash in running water for 15 min.
4. Differentiate in 0.2% aqueous HCl 30–60 s.
5. Blue in running tap water for at least 30 min.
6. Stain with 1% eosin for 3–5 min.
7. Wash until the film has lost most of its eosin.
8. Air dry and mount in Euparal.

B. Harris' Haematoxylin

1. If dry, soak the autoradiographs in water for 30 min.
2. Stain in Harris' haematoxylin for 20 min.
3. Wash in running tap water for 30 min.
4. Air dry and mount in Euparal.

C. Methyl Green–Pyronin

1. If dry, soak the autoradiographs in water for 30 min.
2. Stain for 30 min in methyl green–pyronin mixture.

*The standard Ehrlich's haematoxylin should be diluted by half with distilled water for the purposes of this method.

3. Rinse in distilled water.

4. Air dry rapidly and mount in Euparal.

D. Feulgen Staining

The normal Feulgen reaction must be carried out on the preparation prior to mounting the emulsion and exposure.

N.B. It is advisable to centrifuge or filter all stain solutions before use in order to exclude any particles of dust or stain that may be present and that would interfere with the autoradiographs. All solutions in procedures A–C *must* be maintained at a temperature of 17°–18°C.

PREPARATION OF ELECTRON MICROSCOPE AUTORADIOGRAPHS

Method I (after Pelc *et al.*, 1961)

Preparation of Membranes

Glass slides (7.5 × 3.75 cm) are cleaned by immersing in chloroform and polishing with a clean cloth. Only slides that have no surface scratches should be used.

a. FORMVAR MEMBRANES. Dip the clean slides into a fresh 0.3–0.4% solution of polyvinyl formvar in ethylene dichloride (w/v). The slides are allowed to dry in a dust-free atmosphere in a vertical position.

b. PARLODION MEMBRANES. These produce slightly tougher membranes. Two to 3 drops of 0.5% solution of Parlodion in amyl acetate (w/v) are pipetted onto one surface of the clean slide. This solution is then spread evenly over the surface by means of a filter paper used in a "whipping motion". The slides are then allowed to dry in the same manner as for formvar. When the slide is dry a line is scored around the edge about 2 mm inwards, using the points of fine forceps.

Immerse the slide slowly at an angle of 45° into a bowl of clean water (preferably distilled). The surface of the water must be kept free of dust. This can be facilitated by means of a cover, and also by whipping the surface with special Velin tissues.

The fine film of plastic will float on the water surface. Its thickness and uniformity may be judged by observation of the colour of the interference patterns. Usually pale gold and silver are the most suitable, but gold membranes are also usable. The floating film is picked up on the Perspex slide pierced with holes, and the preparation is allowed to dry in a dust-free atmosphere.

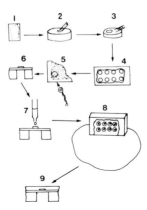

FIG. 45. Preparation of electron microscopic autoradiographs. A clean slide is dipped into 0.3% formvar in ethylene dichloride, air-dried and scored around the edge (1). The formvar film is floated onto a water bath (2) and is picked up onto a plastic slide in which 6 or 8 holes have been drilled (3). This yields the set of holes covered by the membrane (4) and ultra-thin sections are placed on the film over the holes (5) yielding the side-view (6). A drop of emulsion is pipetted onto the preparation (7) and is drained across the sections and onto filter paper (8) so yielding a section on the film over the hole and coated with emulsion (9), which is dried flat.

Slide dimensions 7.5 cm × 3 cm × 3 mm with six holes of approximately 6–7 mm in diameter (Fig. 45).

Preparation of Sections

Ultra-thin sections (50–100 nm) cut on an ultramicrotome from plastic-embedded specimens are transferred onto each membrane-covered hole using a fine wire loop.

Preparation of Autoradiographs

Autoradiographs are prepared in a darkroom using a red Safelight (Wratten Series no. 1). Prepare in a water bath at 45°C a solution of freshly obtained Ilford L4 photographic emulsion (store at 0°–4°C and order new batch every 6–8 weeks). With 8 ml of distilled water in a graduated centrifuge tube, top up to 10 ml by addition of pellicles of the emulsion. Allow 5–10 minutes for the pellicles to mix with the water. *Gentle* pipetting with a wide bore pipette will hasten this process. Make sure no air bubbles are blown through the mixture.

A drop of this emulsion is pipetted onto each membrane containing sections. Run emulsion across the section and off the membranes under gravity, draining onto filter paper, and, after a standard time interval (2–3 seconds), place the preparations on a horizontal surface warmed to 45°C. Rocking the slide up and down traps air behind the membranes and spreads the emulsion in a characteristic pattern before it dries. Allow 15–20 min for drying (Fig. 45). Store the preparations in light-tight boxes at 0°–4°C.

Developing Autoradiographs after Suitable Exposure Period

Develop in slide dishes in D19b (Kodak) developer at 20°C for 2 min. Wash gently for 15 s in distilled water. Fix in 20% sodium thiosulphate for 5 min. Wash in several changes of distilled water for 15 min. Dry in dust-free air and store in slide boxes if required later.

Note: All solutions should be filtered, and transfers and washings should be executed gently.

Preparation of Autoradiographs for Electron Microscope (Fig. 46)

Invert the autoradiograph and drop one spot of water onto each membrane. Place an EM grid, shiny surface down, onto the water. Carefully drain away the water under the grid, until the latter rests on the membrane immediately above the sections. Correct positioning of the grid in relation to the section may be checked with phase-contrast microscopy. Carefully perforate the membrane around the grid, remove the grid (+ membrane + section + processed photographic emulsion) with fine forceps (*watchmaker's*).

Method II (after Salpeter and Bachman, 1964)

Preparation of Ultra-thin Sections

1. Coat a normal microscope slide by drawing it at a uniform rate through 0.5% collodion in amyl acetate. Stand the slide on one end and allow to dry.

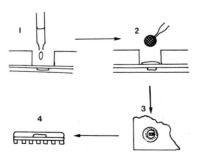

FIG. 46 After exposing and processing, electron microscopic autoradiographs are mounted for viewing by turning the Perspex slide upside down and placing a drop of clean distilled water into the hole on the film (1). A grid is then placed on the water (2) which is then drained with a piece of tissue so letting the grid lay flat on the film. With a fine needle, prick a circle of holes in the film around the specimen [from the specimen/emulsion side (3)] and lift out the grid bearing the formvar film, specimen and emulsion with the autoradiograph (4).

2. Ultra-thin sections of the radioactive specimen are cut and placed onto the collodion-coated slide, with the help of a wire loop or toothpick, about 1–2 cm from one end of the slide.

3. Dry the preparation and stain with a drop of uranyl acetate (2% aqueous) for 3–4 h to improve specimen contrast.

4. Evaporate a thin (5 nm thick) carbon layer onto the washed and dried sections.

5. Spare slides, without sections, are prepared by coating with collodion and carbon.

Preparation of Emulsion

1. Under safelight conditions add 4 g of Kodak NTE emulsion gel to 40 ml of distilled water.

2. Emulsify the gel in a water-bath at 60°C for a few minutes and stir *very gently*.

3. Place the dilute emulsion into centrifuge tubes and spin in a centrifuge that has been warmed to 60°C until the supernatant is clear.

4. Decant and discard the supernatant from each tube.

5. Resuspend the pellet in 1–4 ml of distilled water. The exact amount of water must be determined empirically. With the aid of a broad fronted pipette apply a drop of emulsion to a clean, uncoated microscope slide and allow to dry. Take the slide out of the dark room and observe by daylight, when a colour spectrum will be seen from the reverse side of the slide (interference effect). Look for a region on the slide which is coloured silver to pale gold in white light. This will indicate the closest-packed monolayer of silver halide crystals. If this is not achieved dilute further and repeat, dilutions being done stepwise with 0.5 ml of water at a time until a large enough area of silver to pale gold is present to cover the region of the sections on the slides. A final volume of 3–4 ml should be adequate for the coating of 20–30 experimental slides. Final testing is then performed on coated slides without sections.

Storing of Slides

When the emulsion is dry, store the preparations in a light-tight box at 4°C for an adequate period of time (2–8 weeks). To stabilize the emulsion it is advisable to store the sections in an atmosphere of inert gas, e.g. helium, and in the presence of silica gel.

Photographic Processing

1. Develop the autoradiographs in Dektol for 2 min at 24°C.

2. Place in a stopbath of 3% aqueous acetic acid for 10–30 s followed by a brief rinse in water.

3. Fix for $1\frac{1}{2}$ min in fixer (20% sodium thiosulphate or a commercial non-hardening fixer) at 18°C.

4. Wash in distilled water at 18°C for 3 min or more.

Mounting the Specimens

Score round the edges of the section and emulsion and float from slide onto the surface of a distilled water bath. The preparation can then be picked up directly onto a grid and dried on filter paper when it is ready for viewing.

Appendix 10. Soluble Compounds

ASCORBIC ACID

System 1 (after Chayen, 1953)

Tissues

Vicia faba root or shoot apices. Fix in Clarke's solution or absolute ethanol for 3–24 h.

Solution

Silver nitrate, 10%, in 10% acetic acid.

Method A (Whole Tissues)

1. Hydrate the fixed material through a graded series of alcohol.
2. Stain for 4 h in the silver nitrate solution *in the dark*.
3. Gently dehydrate the material and embed.
4. Section the material at 7μm, dewax gently in xylene and mount in Depex.

N.B. Any counter-staining should be made with alcoholic staining solutions prior to dewaxing the sections. Blot the sections dry, dewax in xylene and mount in Depex.

Method B (for Sections)

1. Embed and section the material.
2. The wax-embedded sections are placed flat in the silver nitrate solution for 4–7 h *in the dark*.
3. Gently blot dry.
4. Rinse briefly with absolute ethanol.
5. Dewax in xylene and mount in Depex.

Result

Blackened silver grains or red-brown colloidal silver occur at the sites of ascorbic acid. It is unlikely that this method will demonstrate free ascorbic acid, which diffuses rapidly from the sections.

System 2 (after Jensen and Kavaljian, 1956)

Tissues

Frozen-dried root or shoot apices of, for example, *Vicia faba.*

Solutions

1. Silver nitrate, 10%, solution in 3% acetic acid.
2. Crystal violet, 1%, in absolute ethanol.

Method

1. Sections (10 μm) are mounted on slides lightly coated with Haupt's adhesive by pressing them onto the slide with a rubbing motion of the finger. Leave the slides overnight on a warming plate at 40°C.
2. Place the slides in an atmosphere of H_2S for 15 min to reduce dehydroascorbic acid to ascorbic acid.
3. Pass highly purified nitrogen over the section to remove the H_2S.
4. Place the sections in solution 1 for 4–24 h *in the dark.*
5. Wash the sections rapidly in distilled water.
6. Dehydrate through a graded ethanol series.
7. Dewax in xylene to which solution 2 is added thereby staining the sections.
8. Mount in Depex.

Result

As for system 1.

Controls

1. Place the sections only in 3% acetic acid in step 4.
2. Sections are pretreated with 10% aqueous copper sulphate solution prior to step 4 in order to oxidise all of the ascorbic acid to dehydroascorbic acid.

Any silver deposits in the controls are not due to the presence of ascorbic acid.

PLANT STUDIES

Microincineration of Plant Tissues (Scott, 1937)

Tissues

Any tissue. Frozen-dried tissues should be embedded in paraffin wax of the highest purity. Unfixed, frozen and dried sections.

Method

1. Mount sections without adhesives. Keep sections dry. Do not dewax paraffin sections.

2. Place slide bearing sections on a quartz slide or slab since ordinary microscope slides become plastic at high temperatures.

3. Place in any clean muffle furnace and increase temperature slowly to about 200°C within 10–15 min. This period is critical since most shrinkage of tissue occurs at this time.

4. Increase temperature to 650°C during the next 30 min.

5. Shut off furnace and allow to cool.

6. Carefully remove slide from furnace and carefully place a cover slip over the ash. Seal the edges of the cover slip.

Results

Examine the preparation by dark-ground illumination. If the ash appears brownish or black, the preparation is not good since the carbon has not been fully removed. White ash can contain sodium, potassium, calcium, magnesium and phosphorus. Yellow to deep red colour indicates presence of iron, but does not exclude the above ions. The silicon may be present as crystals that are doubly refractive in polarized light.

MAGNESIUM (Broda, 1939)

Tissues

Root or shoot apices, leaves. Chemically fixed, frozen or frozen-dried sections.

Solutions

1. Quinalizarin, 100 mg
   Sodium acetate, 500 mg
   5% NaOH solution, 120 ml
2. Aqueous 10% NaOH solution

Method A

1. Add 1 or 2 drops of solution 1 to the section.
2. Add 1 or 2 drops of solution 2.

Result

Magnesium will develop a blue colour after several hours.

Method B

1. Add 1 or 2 drops Titian yellow solution to the section.
2. Add 1 or 2 drops of solution 2.

Result

Magnesium sites appear brick red.

CALCIUM (Gomori, 1952)

Tissue

Any tissue. Frozen-dried or frozen sections.

Solutions

1. Aqueous 0.5% $AgNO_3$ solution.
2. Aqueous 0.5% Amidol solution.
3. Aqueous 1.0% sodium thiosulphate.

Method

1. Immerse sections in solution 1 for 10 min.
2. Wash well in distilled water.
3. Place sections in solution 2 for 2 min.
4. Rinse in distilled water.
5. Immerse sections in solution 3 for several minutes.
6. Wash well in distilled water and mount.

Result

Deposits of silver indicate the sites of calcium carbonate or calcium phosphate.

Control

If the presence of uric acid is suspected, place sections at 37°C in a solution of 5 ml of 5% aqueous $AgNO_3$ solution in 100 ml of 3% methenamine solution, the whole buffered to pH 9, for 30 min. Wash sections in distilled water and transfer to solution 3. Metallic silver will be present at sites of uric acid.

COPPER-CONTAINING PROTEINS (after Lake and Smith, 1980)

Tissues

Any tissues from plants growing on copper mine spoils.

Solutions

1. Potassium ferricyanide, 0.1 M.
2. Diaminobenzidine, 0.05%, in 0.05 M phosphate buffer pH 6.8.

3. Aqueous 1% osmium tetroxide.
4. Potassium ferrocyanide, 0.1 M.

Method

1. Incubate sections in solution 1 for 10 min at room temperature.
2. Transfer sections to solution 2 for 45 min at room temperature.
3. Treat sections in solution 3 for 10 min.
4. Dehydrate sections and mount in Euparal from absolute ethanol.

Result

Sites of copper-containing proteins stain brown-black (electron-dense). Inorganic copper only will be shown if sections are reacted in solution 4 for 10 min.

SOLUBLE COMPOUND AUTORADIOGRAPHY

Tissue Preparation

Where possible, it is preferable to freeze the whole plant, the relevant portions being removed in the frozen state. This may be achieved by freezing in a large stoppered glass tube precooled in solid CO_2. Alternatively pieces of tissue should be frozen directly on the specimen holder of the microtome.

Autoradiographs

ARIO stripping-film autoradiographs are prepared, but unlike the conventional method, they are picked up onto a slide and long coverslip with the emulsion facing outwards (Fig. 43). These are air-dried, stored in a light-tight box and maintained at $-5°C$.

Mounting of Sections

Frozen sections are prepared in the normal way, except that the cryostat should be housed in a darkroom, illuminated by a safelight (Wratten Red No. 1). The sections are then picked straight from the knife onto the photographic emulsion side of the film mounted on the slide and coverslip at $-5°C$. The preparations are immediately stored in a light-tight box at $-25°C$ for exposure. Great care must be taken to avoid thawing of the sections at all stages until the moment for photographic processing.

Histological Fixation

After exposing for an adequate length of time, the sections are fixed. To achieve this and not lose the section (very dry) from the film, it is helpful to take the box of autoradiographs from the $-25°C$ chamber and allow it to warm to room temperature. Rapidly coat the section by dipping the whole preparation for a few seconds into 0.5% polyvinyl formvar in ethylene dichloride and dry rapidly in front of a fan. Then, briefly fix the sections by placing the whole preparation in 5% acetic ethanol (1 min) or 4% formaldehyde (10 min) or methanol (10 min) at 17°C. In this way the sections will be protected against the action of the photographic processing.

Photographic Processing

Develop the autoradiographs for 6 min at 17°C in D19B developer (Kodak), rinse briefly in distilled water (17°C) and fix for 12 min at 17°C in Johnson's Fix-Sol diluted 1 : 9 with distilled water. Gently wash the autoradiographs in running filtered water for 30 min (17°C). Frequent changes of distilled water (CO_2-free) at 17°C may be used if the temperature of the tap water is too high or too low.

Staining

Since the section is on the outer surface, most stains can be used as long as they do not damage or colour the emulsion too much. Staining should be performed at 17°C. After staining and washing, the preparations should be air-dried.

Mounting

A drop of Euparal should be placed on a slide. The coverslip, bearing the section, should be cut free of the support slide with a razor blade and mounted section first onto the Euparal covered slide. This will give an autoradiograph preparation with the film above the section as in a standard preparation.

Bibliography

Adams, C. W. M. (1959). A histochemical method for the simultaneous demonstration of normal and degenerating myelin. *J. Pathol. Bacteriol.* **77**, 648–654.

Adams, C. W. M. (1965). "Neurohistochemistry." Elsevier, Amsterdam.

Adams, C. W. M. and Bayliss, O. B. (1975). Lipid Histochemistry. *Tech. Biochem. Biophys. Morphol.* **2**, 99–156.

Adams, C. W. M. and Tuquan, N. A. (1961). The histochemical demonstration of protease by a gelatin–silver film substrate. *J. Histochem. Cytochem.* **9**, 496–472.

Adams, C. W. M., Abdulla, Y. H. and Bayliss, O. B. (1967). Osmium tetroxide as a histochemical and histological reagent. *Histochemistry* **9**, 68–77.

Al-Azzawi, M. J. and Hall, J. L. (1976). Cytochemical localization of adenyl cyclase activity in maize root tips. *Plant Sci. Lett.* **6**, 285–289.

Al-Azzawi, M. J. and Hall, J. L. (1977). Effects of aldehyde fixation on adenosine triphosphatase and peroxidase activities in maize root tips. *Ann. Bot.* **41**, 431–435.

Albersheim, P., Mühlethaler, K. and Frey-Wyssling, A. (1960). Stained pectin as seen in the electron microscope. *J. Biophys. Biochem. Cytol.* **8**, 501–506.

Alfert, M. (1954). Composition and structure of giant chromosomes. *Int. Rev. Cytol.* **3**, 131–176.

Alfert, M. and Geschwind, I. I. (1953). A selective staining method for the basic proteins of cell nuclei. *Proc. Natl. Acad. Sci. U.S.A.* **39**, 991–999.

Allison, A. C. and Malucci, L. (1964). Uptake of hydrocarbon carcinogens by lysosomes. *Nature (London)* **203**, 1024–1027.

Altman, F. P. (1972). Quantitative dehydrogenase histochemistry with special reference to the pentose shunt dehydrogenases. *Prog. Histochem. Cytochem.* **4**, 225–273.

Altman, F. P. (1976). Tetrazolium salts and formazans. *Prog. Histochem. Cytochem.* **9**, 1–56.

Altman, F. P. (1980). Tissue stabilizer methods in histochemistry. *Ciba Found. Symp.* No. 73, pp. 81–120.

Altman, F. P. and Chayen, J. (1965). Retention of nitrogenous material in unfixed sections during incubation for histochemical demonstration of enzymes. *Nature (London)* **207**, 1205–1206.

Altmann, R. (1889). "Die Elementarorganismen und ihre Bezeihungen zur Zellen." Leipzig.

Amhrein, N. (1977). The current status of cyclic AMP in higher plants. *Annu. Rev. Plant Physiol.* **28**, 123–132.

Anderson, P. J. (1967). Purification and quantitation of gluteraldehyde and its effects on several enzyme activities in skeletal muscle. *J. Histochem. Cytochem.* **15**, 652–658.

Anderson, W. A., Bara, G. and Seligman, A. M. (1975). The ultrastructural localization of cytochrome oxidase via cytochrome *c*. *J. Histochem.* **23**, 13–20.

Appleton, T. C. (1964). Autoradiography of soluble labelled compounds. *J. R. Micros. Soc.* **83**, 277–281.

Appleton, T. C. (1967). Storage of frozen materials for cryostat sectioning and soluble – compound autoradiography. *J. R. Micros. Soc.* **87**, 489–492.

Appleton, T. C. (1968). Ultra-thin frozen sections for X-ray microanalysis of diffusible elements. L.K.B. Instruments publication.

Appleton, T. C. (1977). The use of ultrathin frozen sections for X ray microanalysis of diffusible elements. *Semin. Ser. Soc. Exp. Biol.* **3**, 247–268.

Aronson, J., Hempelmann, L. H. and Okada, S. (1958). Preliminary studies on the histological demonstration of DNAse (II) by adaptations of the Gomori acid phosphatase method. *J. Histochem. Cytochem.* **6**, 255–259.

Asahina, E. (1956). The freezing process in plant cells. *Contrib. Inst. Low Temp. Sci., Hokkaido Univ., Ser. A* No. 10, pp. 83–126.

Asahina, E. (1958). On a probable freezing process of molluscan cells enabling them to survive at super-low temperature. *Low Temp. Sci., Ser. B* **16**, 72–93.

Ashford, A. E. (1970). Histochemical localization of β-glucosidases in roots of *Zea mays*. I. A simultaneous coupling azo-dye technique for the localization of β-glucosidase and β-galactosidase. *Protoplasma* **71**, 281–293.

Ashford, A. E. and Jacobsen, J. V. (1974). Cytochemical localization of acid phosphatase in barley aleurone cells. The pathway of gibberellic acid-induced enzyme release. *Planta* **120**, 81–105.

Ashford, A. E. and McCully, M. E. (1973). Histochemical localization of β-glycosidase activity in the meristems of lateral roots. *Protoplasma* **77**, 411–425.

Ashford, A. E., Allaway, W. G. and McCully, M. E. (1972). Low temperature embedding in glycol methacrylate for enzyme histochemistry in plant and animal tissues. *J. Histochem. Cytochem.* **20**, 986–990.

Ashraful, H. (1963). Differential labelling of *Trillium* chromosomes by ^{3}H-thymidine at low temperature. *Heredity* **18**, 129–133.

Auderset, G. and Greppin, H. (1976). Étude de l'apex caulinaire de l'épinard avant et après l'induction florale. *Saussurea* **7**, 73–103.

Avers, C. J. (1958). Histochemical localization of enzyme activity in the root epidermis of *Phleum pratense. Am. J. Bot.* **45**, 609–612.

Avers, C. J. (1961). Histochemical localization of enzyme activities in root meristem cells. *Am. J. Bot.* **48**, 137–142.

Avers, C. J. and Grimm, R. B. (1959). Comparative enzyme differentiation in grass roots. *J. Exp. Bot.* **10**, 341–344.

Avrameus, S. (1969). Coupling of enzymes to proteins with gluteraldehyde. Use of the conjugates for the detection of antigens and antibodies. *Immunocytochemistry* **6**, 43–47.

Bachmann, L. and Salpeter, M. M. (1965). Autoradiography with electron microscopy. A quantitative evaluation. *Lab. Invest.* **14**, 1041–1053.

Bachmann, L. and Salpeter, M. M. (1967). Absolute sensitivity of electron microscope autoradiography. *J. Cell Biol.* **33**, 299–305.

Bahr, G. F. (1954). Osmium tetroxide and ruthenium red and their reactions with biologically important substances. *Exp. Cell Res.* **7**, 457–479.

Baker, J. R. (1933). "Cytological Technique," 1st ed. Methuen, London.

Baker, J. R. (1944). The structure and chemical composition of the Golgi element. *Q. J. Microsc. Sci.* **85**, 1–71.

Baker, J. R. (1946). The histochemical recognition of lipine. *Q. J. Microsc. Sci.* **87**, 441–471.

Baker, J. R. (1947). Further remarks on the histochemical recognition of lipine. Q. J. Microsc. Sci. **88**, 463–465.

Baker, J. R. (1948). The cell theory—A restatement, history and critique I. *Q. J. Microsc. Sci.* **89**, 103–125.

Baker, J. R. (1949). The cell theory—A restatement history and critique II. *Q. J. Microsc. Sci.* **90**, 87–108.

Baker, J. R. (1952). The cell theory—A restatement, history and critique III. *Q. J. Microsc. Sci.* **93**, 157–190.

Baker, J. R. (1958). "Principles of Biological Microtechnique." Methuen, London.

Baker, J. R. (1960). "Cytological Technique," 4th ed. Methuen, London.

Baker, J. R., Kempson, D. A. and Brunet, P. C. J. (1949). A simple method for phase-contrast microscopy: Improvements in technique. *Q. J. Microsc. Sci.* **90**, 323–329.

Bal, A. K. (1974). Cellulase. *In* "Electron Microscopy of Enzymes" M. A. Hayat, ed. Vol. 3, pp. 68–76. Van Nostrand-Reinhold, Princeton, New Jersey.

Bal, A. K., Verma, D. P. S., Bryne, H. and MacLachlan, G. A. (1976). Subcellular localization of cellulases in auxin-treated pea. *J. Cell Biol.* **69**, 97–105.

Balogh, K. (1965). A method for the histochemical demonstration of triphosphopyridine nucleotide-linked L-hexonate dehydrogenase activity in kidneys of several species. *J. Histochem. Cytochem.* **13**, 533–540.

Barer, R. (1952). *In* "Contraste de Phase et Contraste par Interférences" (M. Francon, ed.), p. 56. Revue d'Optique, Paris.

Barer, R. (1956a). Interference microscopy. *In* "Physical Techniques in Biological Research" (G. Oster and A. W. Pollister, eds.), Vol. 3, pp. 30. Academic Press, New York.

Barer, R. (1956b). The interference microscope in quantitative cytology. *In* "Supplement to the Baker Interference Microscope," 2nd ed. C. Baker of Holborn Ltd., London.

Barlow, P. W. (1971). Properties of cells in the root apex. *Rev. Fac. Agron., Univ. Nac. La Plata* **47**, 275–301.

Barron, A. L. E. (1966). "Using The Microscope." Chapman and Hall, London.

Barter, R., Danielli, J. F. and Davies, H. G. (1955). A quantitative cytochemical method for estimating alkaline phosphatase activity. *Proc. R. Soc. London, Ser. B* **144**, 412–426.

Barton, D. (1976). Application of cryo-ultra-microtomy techniques to microtubules of bracken (*Pteridium aquilinum* L.) sperm cells. *Planta* **132**, 9–12.

Basham, H. G. and Bateman, D. F. (1975). Relationship of cell death in plant tissue treated with a homogenous endopectate lyase to cell wall degradation. *Physiol. Plant Pathol.* **5**, 249–262.

Bayliss-High, O. B. (1977). Lipids. *In* "The Theory and Practice of Histological Techniques" (J. D. Bancroft and A. Stevens, eds.), pp. 168–185. Churchill, London.

Bayliss, O. B. and Adams, C. W. M. (1972). Bromine-Sudan black (BSB). A general stain for tissue lipids including free cholesterol. *Histochem. J.* **4**, 505–514.

Bayliss, O. B. and Adams, C. W. M. (1976). Resistance of aldehyde blockades to periodic acid. *Histochem. J.* **8**, 71–75.

Beadle, D. J., Dawson, A. L., James, D. J., Fisher, S. W. and Livingstone, D. C. (1974). The avidity of heavy metal diazotates for animal lysosomes and plant vacuoles during the ultra-structural localization of acid hydrolases. *In* "Electron Microscopy and Cytochemistry" (E. Wisse, W. T. Daems, I. Molenar and P. Van Duijn, eds.), pp. 85–88. Elsevier/North-Holland, New York.

Beaufey, H. (1972). Methods for the isolation of lysosomes. *In* "Lysosomes, a Laboratory Handbook" (J. T. Dingle, ed.), pp. 1–45. North-Holland Publ., Amsterdam.

Becker, W. A. (1929). Influence des colorants vitaux sur le caratère de la cinèse somatique. *Acta Soc. Bot. Pol.* **6**, 214–229.

Bélanger, L. F. and Leblond, C. P. (1946). A method for locating radioactive elements in tissue by covering histological sections with photographic emulsions. *Endocrinology (Baltimore)* **39**, 8–13.

Bell, L. G. E. (1952). The application of freeze-drying techniques in cytology *Int. Rev. Cytol.* **1**, 35–62.

Bell, L. G. E. (1959). The combination of a portion of the cytoplasmic ribonucleic acid compounds with mercury. *Exp. Cell Res.* **16**, 615–663.

Bell, P. R. (1963). The cytochemical and ultrastructural peculiarities of the fern egg. *J. Linn. Soc. Bot.* **58**, 353–359.

Bell, P. R. and Mühletahler, K. (1964). Evidence for the presence of deoxyribonucleic acid in the organelles of the eggs of *Pteridium aquilinum J. Mol. Biol.* **8**, 853–862.

Belyaeva, E. S. and Volkova, L. V. (1964). O formirovanii yadryshka v rastitch'nykh kietkakh. *Tsitologia* **6**, 286–290.

Beneš, K. (1964). Detection of lipids in the plant meristematic cell with the aid of Sudan black B. *Biol. Plant.* **6**, 142–151.

Beneš, K. (1968). On the stainability of plant cell walls with alcian blue. *Biol. Plant.* **10**, 334–336.

Beneš, K. (1974). The use of derivatives of 2-naphthol as substrates for the demonstration of carboxylesterases *in situ* and the enhancement of the reaction with DMSO. *Histochemistry* **42**, 193–197.

Beneš, K. and Uhlířová, S. (1966). Staining plant tissues with alcian blue (The affinity of alcian blue to polysaccharides). *Comm. Czech. Soc. Histochem. Cytochem.* **12**, 858–859.

Beneš, K., Lojda, Z. and Horavka, B. (1961). A contribution to the histochemical demonstration of some hydrolytic and oxidative enzymes in plants. *Histochemie* **2**, 313–321.

Beneš, K., Georgieva, Y. D. and Poláčková, D. (1973). The presence and distribution of α- and β-glucosidase in root tip. *Biol. Plant.* **15**, 88–94.

Benitez, L. and Fischer, R. (1964). A modification to the "incubation mixture film method" for the histochemical localization of lactic dehydrogenase. *J. Histochem. Cytochem.* **12**, 858–859.

Bennett, H. S. and Watts, R. M. (1958). The Cytochemical demonstration and measurement of sulphydryl groups by azo-aryl mercaptide coupling, with special reference to mercury orange. *In* "General Cytochemical Methods" (J. F. Danielli, ed.), Vol. 1, pp. 318–374. Academic Press, New York.

Berenbaum, M. C. (1958). Histochemistry of bound lipids. *Q. J. Microsc. Sci.* **99**, 231–242.

Berg, N. O. (1951). A histological study of masked lipids. Stainability, distribution and functional variations. *Acta Pathol. Microbiol. Scand., Suppl.* **90**, 1–192.

Berjak, P. (1968). A lysosome-like organelle in the root cap of *Zea mays. J. Ultrastruct. Res.* **23**, 233–242.

Berjak, P. (1972). Lysosomal compartmentalization, ultrastructural aspects of the origin, development and function of vacuoles in roots of *Lepidium sativum. Ann. Bot.* **36**, 73–81.

Berjak, P. and Lawton, J. R. (1973). Prostelar autolysis: A further example of a programmed senescence. *New Phytol.* **72**, 625–637.

Berjak, P. and Villiers, T. A. (1972a). Ageing in plant embryos, II. Age-induced damage and its repair during early germination. *New Phytol.* **71**, 135–144.

Berjak, P. and Villiers, T. A. (1972b). Ageing in plant embryos. IV. Loss of regulatory control in aged embryos. *New Phytol.* **71**, 1069–1074.

Bernard, W. (1965). Ultramicrotomie à basse temperature. *Ann. Biol.* **4**, 5–19.

Bernard, W. and Nancy, M. T. (1964). Coupes à congélation ultrafines de tissu inclus dans la gelatine. *J. Microsc. (Paris)* **3**, 579–588.

Bernier, G. and Jensen, W. A. (1966). Pattern of DNA synthesis in the meristematic cells of *Sinapis. Histochemie* **6**, 85–92.

Bisulpatra, T. and Bisulpatra, A. A. (1967). The occurrence of DNA fibrils in chloroplasts of *Laurencia spectabilis. J. Ultrastruct. Res.* **17**, 14–22.

Bitensky, L. (1962). The reversible activation of lysosomes in normal cells and the effects of pathological conditions. *Ciba Found. Symp. Lysosomes* pp. 362–375.

Bitensky, L. (1963). Modifications to the Gomori acid phosphatase technique for controlled temperature frozen sections. *Q. J. Microsc. Sci.* **104**, 193–196.

Bloch, D. P. and Goodman, G. C. (1955a). A microphotometric study of the synthesis of desoxyribonucleic acid and nuclear histone. *J. Biophys. Biochem. Cytol.* **1**, 17–28.

Bloch, D. P. and Goodman, G. C. (1955b). Evidence of differences in the deoxyribonucleoprotein complex of rapidly proliferating and non-dividing cells. *J. Biophys. Biochem. Cytol.* **1**, 531–550.

Bloor, W. R. (1943). "Biochemistry of the Fatty Acids and their Compounds, the Lipids." Van Nostrand-Reinhold, Princeton, New Jersey.

Böhm, N. and Sprenger, E. (1968). Fluorescence cytophotometry: A valuable method for the quantitative determination of nuclear Feulgen–DNA *Histochemie* **16**, 100–118.

Bottelier, H. P., Holter, H. and Linderstrøm-Lang, K. (1943). Studies on enzymatic histochemistry. XXXVI. Determination of peptidase activity, nitrogen content, and reduced weight in roots of barley, *Hordeum vulgare*. *C. R. Trav. Lab. Carlsberg, Ser. Chim.* **24**, 289–313.

Bourgeois, C. and Hack, M. H. (1962). Concerning the specificity of the dichromate–haematoxylin, dichromate–Sudan black techniques for the histochemical detection of phospholipids. *Acta Histochem.* **14**, 297–307.

Bowen, I. D. (1973). Glycosidases, β- glucosidases, β-glucuronidase. *In* "Electron Microscopy of Enzymes" (M. A. Hayat, ed.), Vol. 1, pp. 77–103. Van Nostrand-Reinhold, Princeton, New Jersey.

Bowen, I. D. and Evans, W. A. L. (1966). Localization of β-glucosidases in the digestive caeca of the locust, *Schistocerca gregaria*. *Proc. R. Microsc. Soc.* **1**, 215.

Brachet, J. (1940a). La detection histochimique des acides pentosenucléiques. *C. R. Soc. Biol. Paris* **133**, 88–90.

Brachet, J. (1940b). La localization des acides pentosenucléiques pendant le devéloppement des amphibiens. *C. R. Soc. Biol. Paris* **133**, 90–91.

Brachet, J. (1941). La localisation des acides pentosenucléiques dans les tissus animaux et les oeufs d'amphibions en voie de devéloppement. *Arch. Biol.* **53**, 207–257.

Brachet, J. (1945). "Embryologie Chimique," 2nd ed. Desoer, Liège.

Brachet, J. (1957). "Biochemical Cytology." Academic Press, New York.

Brante, G. (1949). Studies on lipids in the nervous system. *Acta Physiol. Scand., Suppl. 63* **18**, 1–189.

Branton, D. and Jacobson, L. (1962). Dry high resolution autoradiography. *Stain Technol.* **37**, 239–342.

Brawerman, G. and Chargaff, E. (1955). Distribution and biological significance of the nucleoside phosphotransferases. *Biochim. Biophys. Acta* **16**, 524–532.

Brisson, J. D., Robb, J. and Peterson, R. L. (1976). Phenolic localization by ferric chloride and other iron compounds. *Proc. Microsc. Soc. Can.* **3**, 174–175.

Brisson, J. D., Peterson, R. L., Robb, J., Rauser, W. E. and Ellis, B. E. (1977). Correlated phenolic histochemistry using light, transmission and scanning electron microscopy, with examples taken from phytopathological problems. *Ill. Ind. Technol. Res. Inst./SEM* **2**, 667–676.

Broda, B. (1939). Uber die Verwendbarkeit von Chinalizatin, Titangelb und Azublau zum mikro-und histo-chemischen Magnesiumnachweis in Pflanzengeweben. *Mikrokosmas* **32**, 184–189.

Brown, R. (1831). On the organs and mode of fecundation in Orchideae and Asclepideae. *Trans. Linn. Soc.* **16**, 685–721.

Brown, R. and Broadbent, D. (1950). The development of cells in the growing zones of the root. *J. Exp. Bot.* **1**, 249–263.

Brown, R. and Rickless, P. (1949). A new method for the study of cell division and cell extension with some preliminary observations on the effect of temperature and nutrients. *Proc. R. Soc. London, Ser. B* **136**, 110–125.

Bruemmer, N. C., Carver, M. J. and Thomas, L. E. (1957). A tryptrophan histochemical method. *J. Histochem. Cytochem.* **5**, 140–144.

Brunschwig, A., Schmitz, R. L. and Jennings, S. (1940). Selective localization of Evans blue in subplacental portions of endoderm in the rat. *Proc. Soc. Exp. Biol. Med.* **44**, 64–66.

Bucknall, R. A. and Sutcliffe, J. F. (1965). The nucleic acids and cellular differentiation in the root apex of *Pisum sativum*. II. The nucleic acids and cellular development patterns. *J. Exp. Bot.* **16**, 587–603.

Budd, G. C. (1972). High resolution autoradiography. *In* "Autoradiography for Biologists" (P. B. Gahan, ed.), pp. 95–118. Academic Press, London.

Budd, G. C. and Mills, G. M. (1965). Labelled cytoplasmic organelles in *Allium cepa* var. 'White Lisbon' after administration of tritiated thymidine. *Nature (London)* **205**, 524–525.

Burge, R. E. (1977). Scanning transmission electron microscope at high resolution. *Semin. Ser. Soc. Exp. Biol.* **3**, 171–191.

Buroughs, H. and Bonner, J. (1953). Effects of IAA on metabolic pathways. *Arch. Biochem. Biophys.* **46**, 279–290.

Burstone, M. S. (1956). New histochemical techniques for the demonstration of tissue oxidase (cytochrome oxidase). *J. Histochem. Cytochem.* **7**, 112–122.

Burstone, M. S. (1958). Histochemical demonstration of acid phosphatases with naphthol AS-phosphates. *J. Natl. Cancer Inst.* **21**, 523–540.

Burstone, M. S. (1960). Modification of histochemical techniques for the demonstration of cytochrome oxidase. *J. Histochem. Cytochem.* **9**, 59–65.

Burstone, M. S. (1962). "Enzyme Histochemistry and Its Application to the Study of Neoplasms." Academic Press, New York.

Butcher, R. W. and Sutherland, E. W. (1962). Adenosine 3',5'-phosphate in biological materials. I. Purification and properties of cyclic 3' and 5'-nucleotide phosphodiesterase and the use of this enzyme to characterize adenosine 3',5'-phosphate in human urine. *J. Biol. Chem.* **237**, 1244.

Butcher, R. G., Dawson, A. L., Knaab, S. A. and Gahan, P. B. (1980). Dehydrogenase activity and loss of formazan from tissue sections. *Histochem. J.* **12**, 591–598.

Cain, A. J. (1947). Use of Nile blue in the examination of lipoids. *Q. J. Microsc. Sci.* **88**, 383–392.

Cain, A. J. (1949). A critique of the plasmal reaction, with remarks on recently proposed techniques. *Q. J. Microsc. Sci.* **90**, 411–426.

Cain, A. J. (1950). The histochemistry of lipids in animals. *Biol. Rev. Cambridge Philos. Soc.* **25**, 73–112.

Callow, J. A. (1975). Plant lectins. *Curr. Adv. Plant Sci.* **7**, 181–191.

Cammer, W. and Moore, C. L. (1973). Oxidation of 3,3-diaminobenzidine by rat liver mitochondria. *Biochemistry* **12**, 2502–2509.

Campbell, D. H. (1888). *Unters. Bot. Inst. Tübingen* **2**, 569. (Cited in Baker, 1958.)

Campbell, J. G. (1949). The intracellular localization of β-glucuronidase. *Br. J. Exp. Pathol.* **30**, 548–554.

Campbell, W. G., Bryant, S. A. and Swann, G. (1937). The chlorine-sodium sulphite colour reaction of woody tissues. *Biochem. J.* **31**, 1285–1288.

Caro, L. G. (1964). High resolution autoradiography. *In* "Methods in Cell Physiology" (D. M. Prescott, ed.), Vol. 1, pp. 327–363. Academic Press, New York.

Caro, L. G. and Van Tubergen, R. P. (1962). High resolution autoradiography I—Methods. *J. Cell Biol.* **15**, 173–200.

Carrière, R. and Patterson, D. L. (1962). The counting of mono- and bi-nucleated cells in tissue sections. *Anat. Rec.* **142**, 443–456.

Caspersson, T. (1940). Methods for the determination of the absorption spectra of cell structures. *J. R. Microsc. Soc.* **60**, 8–25.

Caspersson, T. (1950). "Cell Growth and Cell Function." Norton, New York.

Caulfield, J. B. (1957). Effect of varying the vehicle for osmium tetroxide in tissue fixation. *J. Biophys. Biochem. Cytol.* **3**, 827–830.

Cave, C. F. (1971). A histochemical study of chromosomal and nucleolar lipids. Ph.D. Thesis, Univ. of London, England.

Cave, C. F. and Gahan, P. B. (1970). A cytochemical and autoradiographic investigation of nucleolar phospholipids. *Caryologia* **23**, 303–312.

Cawood, A. H., Potter, U. and Dickinson, H. G. (1978). An evaluation of Coomassie blue as a stain for quantitative microdensitometry of protein in section. *J. Histochem. Cytochem.* **26**, 645–650.

Chance, B. (1950). On the reaction of catalase peroxides with acceptors. *J. Biol. Chem.* **182**, 649–658.

Chandler, J. A. (1977a). X-ray microanalysis in the electron microscope. *In* "Practical Methods in Electron Microscopy" (A. M. Glauert, ed.). North-Holland Publ., Amsterdam.

Chandler, J. A. (1977b). Wavelength dispersive X-ray microanalysis in biological research. *Semin. Ser. Soc. Exp. Biol.* **3**, 227–245.

Chandler, D. R., and Williams, J. A. (1978). Intracellular divalent cation release in pancreatic acinar cells during stimulus–secretion coupling. I. Use of chlorotetracycline as a fluorescent probe. *J. Cell Biol.* **76**, 371–385.

Chang, J. P. (1969). Further investigations on the section freeze-substitution technique. *In* "Autoradiography of Diffusible Substances" (L. J. Roth and W. E. Stumpf, eds.), pp. 241–263. Academic Press, New York.

Chayen, J. (1949). Squash preparations of living root tip cells. *Nature (London)* **164**, 930.

Chayen, J. (1952). The structure of root meristem cells of *Vica faba*. *Symp. Soc. Exp. Biol.* **6**, 290–305.

Chayen, J. (1953). Ascorbic acid and its intracellular localization, with special reference to plants. *Int. Rev. Cytol.* **2**, 78–132.

Chayen, J. (1959). The quantitative cytochemistry of DNA and its significance in cell physiology and heredity. *Exp. Cell Res., Suppl.* **6**, 115–131.

Chayen, J. and Denby, E. (1960). The distribution of deoxyribonucleic acid in homogenates of plant roots. *Exp. Cell Res.* **20**, 182–197.

Chayen, J. and Denby, E. (1968). "Biophysical Techniques as Applied to Cell Biology." Methuen, London.

Chayen, J. and Gahan, P. B. (1958). Lipid components in nucleohistone. *Biochem. J.* **69**, 49P.

Chayen, J. and Gahan, P. B. (1959). An improved and rapid embedding method. *Q. J. Microsc. Sci.* **100**, 275–278.

Chayen, J. and Miles, U. J. (1954). Preparing plant root tip cells for microscopical examination. *Stain Technol.* **29**, 33–39.

Chayen, J. and Norris, K. P. (1953). Cytoplasmic localization of nucleic acids in plant cells. *Nature (London)* **171**, 472–473.

Chayen, J., La Cour, L. F. and Gahan, P. B. (1957). Uptake of benzypyrene by a chromosomal phospholipid. *Nature (London)* **180**, 652–653.

Chayen, J., Gahan, P. B. and La Cour, L. F. (1959a). The nature of the chromosomal phospholipid. *Q. J. Microsc. Sci.* **100**, 279–286.

Chayen, J., Gahan, P. B. and La Cour, L. F. (1959b). The masked lipids of nuclei. *Q. J. Microsc. Sci.* **100**, 325–337.

Chayen, J., Cunningham, G. J., Gahan, P. B. and Silcox, A. A. (1960a). Life-like preservation of cytoplasmic detail in plant cells. *Nature (London)* **186**, 1068–1069.

Chayen, J., Cunningham, G. J., Gahan, P. B. and Silcox, A. A. (1960b). Newer methods in cytology. *Bull. Res. Counc. Isr.* **8D**, 273–279.

Chayen, J., Bitensky, L. and Butcher, R. G. (1973). "Practical Histochemistry." Wiley, New York.

Chévremont, M. and Frédéric, J. (1943). Une nouvelle méthode histochimique de mise en evidence des substances à fraction sulphydryl. *Arch. Biol.* **54**, 589–594.

Chiffelle, T. L. and Putt, F. A. (1951). Propylene and ethylene glycol as solvents for Sudan blue and Sudan black B. *Stain Technol.* **26**, 51–56.

Chouinard, L. A. and Leblond, C. P. (1967). Sites of protein synthesis in nucleoli of root merstematic cells of *Allium cepa* as shown by autoradiography with ^{3}H-arginine. *J. Cell Sci.* **2**, 473–480.

Christensen, A. K. (1969). A way to prepare frozen thin sections of fresh tissue for electron microscopy. *In* "Autoradiography of Diffusible Substances" (L. J. Roth and W. E. Stumpf, eds.), pp. 350–362. Academic Press, New York.

Ciaccio, C. (1909). Contributo alla conoscenza dei lipoidi cellulari. *Anat. Anz.* **35**, 17–31.

Clark, J. B., Greenbaum, A. L. and Slater, T. F. (1965). Effects of tetrazolium salts on oxidative phosphorylation in rat-liver mitochondria. *Biochem. J.* **94**, 651–654.

Clarke, J. L. (1851). Researches into the structure of the spinal cord. *Philos. Trans. R. Soc. London* **141**, 607–621.

Cleaver, J. E. (1967). Thymidine metabolism and cell kinetics. *Front. Biol.* **6**, 1–259.

Clowes, F. A. L. (1958). Protein synthesis in root meristems. *J. Exp. Bot.* **9**, 229–238.

Clowes, F. A. L. (1961). "Apical Meristems." Blackwell, Oxford.

Conn, H. J. (1969). "Biological Stains" (R. D. Lillie, ed.), 8th ed. Williams & Wilkins, Baltimore, Maryland.

Considine, J. A. and Knox, R. B. (1979). Development and histochemistry of the cells, cell walls, and cuticle of the dermal system of fruit of the grape, *Vitis vinifera* L. *Protoplasma* **99**, 347–365.

Coons, H. (1958). Fluorescent antibody methods. *In* "General Cytochemical Methods" (J. F. Danielli, ed.), Vol. 1, pp. 400–422. Academic Press, New York.

Coslett, V. E. and Nixon, W. C. (1953). The x-ray shadow microscope. *J. Appl. Phys.* **24**, 616–623.

Couentou. (1825). *Ann. Chim. Phys.* **31** (Cited in Pearse, 1968; Orfila, 1831; also discussed in Thenard, 1818.)

Coulomb, P. J. (1969a). Localisation de l'ésterase thiolacétique dans le méristème radiculaire de la Courge (*Cucurbita pepo* L. Cucurbitacée). *C. R. Acad. Sci.* **268**, 656–659.

Coulomb, P. J. (1969b). Detection de l'aryl-sulfatase dans des particules analogues aux lysosomes des cellules du méristème radiculaire de jeunes courges (*Cucurbita pepo* L. Cucurbitacée). *C. R. Acad. Sci.* **269**, 1400–1403.

Coulomb, P. J. (1969c). Localisation de la désoxyribonucléase acide dans le méristème radiculaire de la courge (*Cucurbita pepo* L. Cucurbitacée) *C. R. Acad. Sci.* **269**, 1514–1516.

Coulomb, P. J., and Coulon, J. (1972). Origine et fonctions des phytolysosomes dans le méristème radiculaire de la courge (*Cucurbita pepo* L. Cucurbitacée). I. Origine des phytolysosomes. Relations reticulum endoplasmique–dictyosomes–phytolysosomes. *J. Microsc.* (*Paris*) **13**, 263–280.

Crewe, A. V. (1971). A high-resolution scanning electron microscope. *Sci. Am.* **224**, 26–35.

Crewe, A. V. and Wall, J. (1970). A scanning microscope with 5 Å resolution. *J. Mol. Biol.* **48**, 375–393.

Croxdale, J. G. (1983). Quantitative measurements of phosphofructokinase in the shoot apical meristem, leaf primordia and leaf tissues of *Dianthus chinensis*, L. *Plant Physiol.* **73**, 66–70.

Culling, C. and Vassar, P. (1961). DNA. A fluorescent histochemical technique. *Arch. Pathol.* **71**, 76–80.

Czaninski, Y. and Catesson, A. M. (1974). Polyphenoloxidases (plants). *In* "Electron Microscopy of Enzymes" (M. A. Hayat, ed.), Vol. 2, pp. 66–78. Van Nostrand-Reinhold, Princeton, New Jersey.

Danielli, J. F. (1953). "Cytochemistry: A Critical Approach." Wiley, New York.

Daoust, R. (1965). Modified procedure for the histochemical localization of RNAse activity by the substrate film method. *J. Histochem. Cytochem.* **14**, 254–259.

Darlington, C. D. (1938). "Recent Advances in Cytology." McGraw-Hill (Blakiston), New York.

Darlington, C. D. and La Cour, L. F. (1976). "The Handling of Chromosomes," 6th ed. Allen & Unwin, London.

Davies, H. G. (1950). Ultra-violet microspectrography of living tissue culture cells. *Discuss. Faraday Soc.* **9**, 442–449.

Davies, H. G., Wilkins, M. F. H., Chayen, J. and La Cour, L. F. (1954). The use of the interference microscope to determine dry mass in living cells as a quantitative cytochemical method. *Q. J. Microsc. Sci.* **95**, 271–304.

Davis, B. J. and Ornstein, L. A. (1959). High resolution enzyme localization with a new diazo reagent "hexazonium pararosaniline." *J. Histochem. Cytochem.* **7**, 297. (Abstr. No. 18.)

De, D. N. (1961). Autoradiographic studies of nucleoprotein metabolism during the division cycle. *Nucleus (Calcutta)* **4**, 1–24.

Deeley, E. M. (1955). An integrating microdensitometer for biological cells. *J. Sci. Instrum.* **32**, 263–267.

Deeley, E. M., Davies, H. G. and Chayen, J. (1957). The DNA content of cells in the root of *Vicia faba*. *Exp. Cell Res.* **12**, 582–591.

Deitch, A. D. (1955). Microspectrophotometric study of the binding of the anionic dye, naphthol yellow S, by tissue sections and by purified proteins. *Lab. Invest.* **4**, 324–351.

Deitch, A. D. (1965). Cytophotometry of nucleic acids. *In* "Introduction to Quantitative Cytochemistry" (G. L. Wied, ed.), Vol. 1, pp. 327. Academic Press, New York.

De Jong, D. W. (1967). An investigation of the role of plant peroxidase in cell wall development by the histochemical method. *J. Histochem. Cytochem.* **15**, 335–346.

Dickens, F. and McIlwain, H. (1938). Phenazine compounds as carriers in the hexose monophosphate system. *Biochem. J.* **32**, 1615–1625.

Dische, Z. (1955). New colour reactions for the determination of sugars in polysaccharides. *Methods Biochem. Anal.* **2**, 313–358.

Dixon, M. and Webb, E. C. (1958). "Enzymes." Academic Press, New York.

Drumm, H., Falk, H., Moller, J. and Mohr, H. (1970). The development of catalase in the mustard seedling. *Cytobiologie* **2**, 335–340.

Duijndam, W. A. L. and Van Duijn, P. (1975a). The influence of chromatin compactness on the stoichiometry of the Feulgen–Schiff procedure studied in model films. I. Theoretical kinetics and experiments with films containing isolated deoxyribonucleic acid. *J. Histochem. Cytochem.* **23**, 882–890.

Duijndam, W. A. L. and Van Duijn, P. (1975b). The influence of chromatin compactness on the stoichiometry of the Feulgen-Schiff procedure studied in model films. II. Investigations on films containing condensed or swollen chicken erythrocyte nuclei. *J. Histochem. Cytochem.* **23**, 891–900.

Du Praw, E. J. (1970). "DNA and Chromosomes." Holt, New York.

Dyson, J. (1949). A unit-magnification optical system for the attainment of long working distances in microscopy. *Proc. Phys. Soc.* **62B**, 565–575.

Dyson, J. (1950). An interference microscope. *Proc. Phys. Soc.* **204A**, 170.

Dyson, J. (1952). An interferometer for opaque objects. *Proc. R. Soc. London, Ser. A* **216**, 493.

Dyson, J. (1953). An interferometer microscope for the accurate measurement of optical thickness. *Nature (London)* **171**, 743–744.

Ekés, M. (1971). The use of diaminobenzidine (DAB) for the histochemical demonstration of cytochrome oxidase activity in unfixed plant tissues. *Histochemie* **27**, 103–108.

Elder, H. Y. (1977). The potential of the scanning transmission electron microscope in biology. *Semin. Ser. Soc. Exp. Biol.* **3**, 159–176.

Elleder, M. and Lojda, Z. (1973). Studies in lipid histochemistry. IX. Lipids in paraffin sections. *Histochemistry* **34**, 143–156.

Engström, A. (1956). Historadiography. *In* "Physical Techniques in Biological Research" (G. Oster and W. A. Pollister, ed.), Vol. 3, pp. 489–544. Academic Press, New York.

Eppig, J. J. (1974). Tyrosinase. *In* "Electron Microscopy of Enzymes" (M. A. Hayat, ed.), Vol. 2, pp. 78–89. Van Nostrand-Reinhold, Princeton, New Jersey.

Erickson, R. O. and Goddard, D. R. (1951). An analysis of root growth in cellular and biochemical terms. *Growth, Suppl.* **15**, 89–116.

Ernst, S. A. (1975). Transport ATPase cytochemistry. Ultrastructural cytochemistry of potassium-dependent and potassium-independent phosphatase in rat kidney cortex. *J. Cell Biol.* **66**, 586–608.

Essner, E. (1973). Phosphatases. *In* "Electron Microscopy of Enzymes" (M. A. Hayat, ed.), Vol. 1, pp. 44–76. Van Nostrand-Reinhold, Princeton, New Jersey.

Ettlinger, M. G. and Kjaer, A. (1968). Sulphur compounds in plants. *Rec. Adv. Phytochem.* **1**, 58–89.

Faberge, A. C. (1945). Snail stomach cytase. A new reagent for plant cytology. *Stain Technol.* **20**, 1–6.

Fahimi, H. D. (1969). Cytochemical localization of peroxidatic activity of catalase in rat hepatic microbodies (peroxisomes). *J. Cell Biol.* **43**, 275–288.

Fahami, H. D. and Amarasingham, C. R. (1963). Histochemical localization of lactic dehydrogenases in the sarcoplasmic reticulum of the striated muscle. *Fed. Proc., Fed. Am. Soc. Exp. Biol.* **23**, 195.

Fahimi, H. D. and Amarasingham, C. R. (1964). Cytochemical localization of lactic dehydrogenase in white skeletal muscle. *J. Cell Biol.* **22**, 29–48.

Fahimi, H. D. (1973). Diffusion artefacts in cytochemistry of catalase. *J. Histochem. Cytochem.* **21**, 999–1009.

Fahn, A. (1974). "Plant Anatomy," 2nd ed. Pergamon, Oxford.

Farber, E., Sternberg, W. H. and Dunlap, C. E. (1956a). Histochemical localization of specific oxidative enzymes I. Tetrazolium stains for diphosphopyridine nucleotide diaphorase and triphosphopyridine nucleotide diaphorase. *J. Histochem. Cytochem.* **4**, 254–265.

Farber, E., Sternberg, W. H. and Dunlap, C. E. (1956b). Histochemical localization of specific oxidases III. Evaluation studies of tetrazolium staining methods for diphosphorpyridine nucleotide diaphorase, triphosphopyridine nucleotide diaphorase and the succinyldehydrogenase system. *J. Histochem. Cytochem.* **4**, 284–294.

Faulkner, G. and Kimmins, W. C. (1976). Staining reactions of the tissue bordering lesions induced by wounding TMV and tobacco necrosis virus in bean *Phytopathology* **65**, 1396–1400.

Feder, N. and Sidman, R. L. (1958). Methods and principles of fixation by freeze-substitution. *J. Biophys. Biochem. Cytol.* **4**, 593–602.

Fernandez-Moran, H. (1960). Low temperature preparation techniques for electron microscopy of biological specimens based on rapid freezing with liquid helium II. *Ann. N. Y. Acad. Sci.* **85**, 689–713.

Feulgen, R. and Rossenbeck, H. (1924). Mikroscopisch-chemischer Nachweis einer Nucleinsaüre vom Typus der Thymonucleinsaüre. *Hoppe-Seyler's Z. Physiol. Chem.* **135**, 203–248.

Feulgen, R. and Voigt, K. (1924). Ueber einen Weitverbreiteten festen Aldehyd seine Entstehung aus Einer Varstufe, sein mikrochemischer Nachweis und die Wege zu seiner preparativen Darstellung. *Pfluegers. Arch. Gesamte Physiol. Menschen Tiere* **206**, 389–396.

Fishman, W. H., Green, S. and Hayashi, M. (1964a). Enzymic hydrolysis of 8-hydroxyquinoline glucuronide in a solid gel β-glucuronidase model system. *J. Histochem. Cytochem.* **12**, 27–28.

Fishman, W. H., Goldman, S. S. and Green, S. (1964b). Several biochemical criteria for evaluating β-glucuronidase localization. *J. Histochem. Cytochem.* **12**, 239–251.

Fishman, W. H., Goldman, S. S. and Delellis, R. A. (1967). Dual localization of β-glucuronidase in endoplasmic reticulum and in lysosomes. *Nature (London)* **213**, 457–460.

Fitzgerald, P. J. (1959). Autoradiography in cytology. *In* "Analytical Cytology" (R. C. Mellors, ed.), 2nd ed., pp. 381–430. McGraw-Hill, New York.

Flax, M. H. and Hines, M. H. (1952). Microscpectrophotometric analysis of metachromatic staining of nucleic acids. *Physiol. Zool.* **25**, 297–311.

Flitney, F. W. (1966). The time course of the fixation of albumin by formaldehyde, glutaraldehyde, acrolein and other higher aldehydes. *J. R. Microsc. Soc.* **85**, 353–364.

Fontana (1781). Cited by De Robertis, E. D. P. and De Robertis, E. M. F. (1980). "Cell and Molecular Biology," p. 359. Saunders College, Philadelphia.

Frederick, S. E. and Newcomb, E. H. (1969). Cytochemical localization of catalase in leaf micro-bodies (peroxisomes). *J. Cell Biol.* **43**, 343–353.

Fukuda, M., Nakawishi, K. and Fujita, S. (1979). Multi-colour fluorescence method in cytofluoro-metry. *Acta Histochem. Cytochem.* **12**, 257–272.

Gadian, G. D. (1982). "Nuclear Magnetic Resonance and Its Applications to Living Systems." Oxford Univ. Press, London and New York.

Gaff, D. F. and Okang'o-Ogola, O. (1971). The use of non-permeating pigments for testing the survival of cells. *J. Exp. Bot.* **22**, 756–758.

Gahan, P. B. (1961). Formalin extraction of lipids from rat-liver nuclei. *Biochem. J.* **81**, 11–12P.

Gahan, P. B. (1965a). Histochemical evidence for the presence of lysosome-like particles in root meristem cells of *Vicia faba*. *J. Exp. Bot.* **16**, 350–355.

Gahan, P. B. (1965b). Histochemical evidence for the presence of lipids on the chromosomes of animal cells. *Exp. Cell Res.* **39**, 136–144.

Gahan, P. B. (1965c). The possible presence of aldehydes and carbohydrates in chromosomes and interphase nuclei. *Histochemie* **5**, 289–296.

Gahan, P. B. (1968). Lysosomes. *In* "Plant Cell Organelles" (J. B. Pridham, ed.), pp. 228–273. Academic Press, New York.

Gahan, P. B. (1972). "Autoradiography for Biologists." Academic Press, London.

Gahan, P. B. (1976). DNA turnover in nuclei of cells from higher plants. *Riv. Istochim. Norm. Patol.* **20**, 108–109.

Gahan, P. B. (1981). An early cytochemical marker of commitment to stelar differentiation in meristems from dicotyledonous plants. *Ann. Bot.* **48**, 769–775.

Gahan, P. B. and Chayen, J. (1965). Cytoplasmic deoxyribonucleic acid. *Int. Rev. Cytol.* **18**, 223–248.

Gahan, P. B. and Dawson, A. L. (1981). Problems encountered with BPST in dehydrogenase histochemistry. *Histochem. J.* **13**, 338.

Gahan, P. B. and Hurst, P. R. (1976). Effects of ageing on the cell cycle of *Zea mays*. *Ann. Bot.* **40**, 887–890.

Gahan, P. B. and Hurst, P. R. (1977). Reduced incorporation of ^{3}H-thymidine into cytoplasmic DNA in ageing cell populations *in vitro*. *Exp. Gerontol.* **12**, 13–15.

Gahan, P. B. and Kalina, M. (1965). The validity of using neotetrazolium for studying labile, NADP-linked dehydrogenases in histological sections; a quantitative study. *Biochem. J.* **96**, 11P.

Gahan, P. B. and Kalina, M. (1968). The use of tetrazolium salts in the histochemical demonstration of succinic dehydrogenase activity in plant tissues. *Histochemie* **14**, 81–88.

Gahan, P. B. and McLean, J. (1967). Acid phosphatases in root tips of *Vicia faba*. *Biochem. J.* **102**, 47–48P.

Gahan, P. B. and McLean, J. (1969). Subcellular localization and possible functions of acid β-glycerophosphatases and naphthol esterases in plant cells. *Planta* **89**, 126–135.

Gahan, P. B. and Maple, A. J. (1966). The behaviour of lysosome-like particles during cell differentiation. *J. Exp. Bot.* **17**, 151–155.

Gahan, P. B. and Rajan, A. K. (1965). Autoradiography of [35]SO$_4$ in plant tissues. *Exp. Cell Res.* **38**, 204–208.

Gahan, P. B. and Rajan, A. K. (1966). The autoradiographic detection of ions in plant tissues. *J. Exp. Bot.* **17**, 34–43.

Gahan, P. B. and Silcox, A. A. (1961). Autoradiographic demonstration of cytoplasmic ^{3}H-thymidine and its implication in the nature of the gene. *Abstr. 1st Int. Biophys. Congr.* p. 232.

Gahan, P. B., Chayen, J. and Silcox, A. A. (1962). Cytoplasmic localization of deoxyribonucleic acid in *Allium cepa*. *Nature (London)* **195**, 1115–1116.

Gahan, P. B., McLean, J., Kalina, M. and Sharma, W. (1967). Freeze sectioning of plant tissues: The technique and its use in histochemistry. *J. Exp. Bot.* **18**, 151–159.

Gahan, P. B., Greenoak, G. C. and James, D. (1970). Preparation of ultra-thin frozen sections of plant tissues for electron microscopy. *Histochemie* **24**, 230–235.

Gahan, P. B., Anker, P. and Stroun, M. (1973). An autoradiographic study of bacterial DNA in *Lycopersicon esculentum. Ann. Bot.* **37**, 681–685.

Gahan, P. B., Perry, J. I., Stroun, M. and Anker, P. (1974). Effect of exogenous DNA on acid deoxyribonuclease activity in intact roots of *Vicia fab Ann. Bot.* **38**, 222–226.

Gahan, P. B., Dawson, A. L. and Fielding, J. (1978). Paranitrophenyl phosphate as a substrate for some acid phosphatases in roots of *Vicia faba Ann. Bot.* **42**, 1413–1420.

Gahan, P. B., Auderset, G. and Greppin, H. (1979). Pentose phosphate pathway activity during floral induction in spinach. *Ann. Bot.* **44**, 121–124.

Gee, M. Reeve, R. M. and McCready, R. M. (1959). Reaction of hydroxylamine with pectinic acids. Chemical studies and histochemical estimation of the degree of esterification of pectic substances in fruit *Agric. Food Chem.* **7**, 34–38.

Gersh, I. (1932). The Altman technique for fixation by drying while freezing. *Anat. Rec.* **53**, 309.

Gersh, I. (1949). Glycoproteins in the thyroid glands of rats. *J. Endocrinol.* **6**, 282–287.

Gersh, I. and Stephenson, J. L. (1954). Freezing and drying of tissues for morphological and histochemical studies. *In* "Biological Applications of Freezing and Drying" (R. J. C. Harris, ed.), pp. 329–385. Academic Press, New York.

Gianinazzi-Pearson, V. and Gianinazzi, S. (1976). Enzymatic studies on the metabolism of vesicular–arbuscular mycorrhiza 1. Effect of mycorrhiza formation and phosphorus nutrition on soluble phosphatase activities in onion roots. *Physiol. Veg.* **14**, 833–841.

Gianinazzi-Pearson, V. and Gianinazzi, S. (1977). Enzymatic studies on the metabolism of vesicular–arbuscular mycorrhiza II. Soluble alkaline phosphatase specific to mycorrhizal infection in onion roots. *Physiol. Plant Pathol.* **12**, 45–53.

Gianinazzi, S., Gianinazzi-Pearson, V. and Dexheimer, J. (1979). Enzymatic studies on the metabolism of vesicular–arbuscular mycorrhiza III. Ultrastructural localization of acid and alkaline phosphatase in onion roots infected by *Glomus mosseae* (Nicol & Gerd). *New Phytol.* **82**, 127–132.

Gibbs, H. D. (1927). Phenol test III. The indophenol test. *J. Biol. Chem.* **72**, 649–664.

Gill, J. E. and Jotz, M. M. (1974). Desoxyribonucleic acid cytochemistry for automated cytology. *J. Histochem. Cytochem.* **22**, 470–477.

Glauert, A. M. (1975). "Fixation, Dehydration and Embedding of Biological Specimens." North Holland Publ., Amsterdam.

Glegg, R. E., Clermont, Y. and Leblond, C. P. (1952). The use of lead tetraacetate, benzidine, *o*-anisidine and a "film test" in investigating the periodic acid–Schiff technique. *Stain Technol.* **27**, 277–305.

Glick, D. and Bloom, D. (1956). Studies in histochemistry. XXXIX. The performance of freeze-drying apparatus for the preparation of embedded tissue and an improved design. *Exp. Cell Res.* **10**, 687–696.

Glick, D. and Malstrom, B. G. (1952). Studies in histochemistry. XXIII. Simple and efficient freeze-drying apparatus for the preparation of embedded tissue. *Exp. Cell Res.* **3**, 125–137.

Glick, D., Swigart, R. H., Nayar, S. N. and Stecklein, H. R. (1955). Flame photometric determination of potassium in microgram quantities of tissue and the distribution of potassium and lipid in the adrenal of the monkey and guinea-pig. Studies in histochemistry. XXXII. *J. Histochem. Cytochem.* **3**, 6–15.

Glimstedt, F. and Hakansson, R. (1951). Measurement of thickness in various parts of histological sections. *Nature (London)* **167**, 397–398.

Goff, C. W. (1973). Localization of nucleoside diphosphatase in the onion root tip. *Protoplasma* **78**, 397–416.

Goff, C. W. and Klohs, W. D. (1974). Nucleoside diphosphatase in the onion root tip I. Effects of fixation and lead on enzyme activity. *J. Histochem. Cytochem.* **22**, 945–951.

Goldfischer, S. (1965). The cytochemical demonstration of lysosomal aryl sulphatase activity by light and electron microscopy. *J. Histochem. Cytochem.* **13**, 520–523.

Goldstein, D. J. (1967). New methods of thickness measurement with the interference microscope. *Nature (London)* **213**, 386–387.

Goldstein, D. J. (1970). Aspects of scanning microdensitometry I. Stray light (glare). *J. Microsc. (Oxford)* **92**, 1–16.

Goldstein, D. J. (1971). Aspects of scanning microdensitometry II. Spot size, focus and resolution. *J. Microsc. (Oxford)* **93**, 14–42.

Goldstein, D. J. (1977a). Integrating microdensitometry. *Semin. Ser. Soc. Exp. Biol.* **3**, 117–136.

Goldstein, D. J. (1977b). Scanning microinterferometry. *Semin. Ser. Soc. Exp. Biol.* **3**, 137–158.

Goldstein, L. and Plaut, W. (1955). Direct evidence for nuclear synthesis of cytoplasmic ribose nucleic acid. *Proc. Natl. Acad. Sci. U.S.A.* **41**, 874.

Golgi, C. (1898). Sur la structure des cellules nerveuses. *Arch. Ital. Biol.* **30**, 60–78.

Gomori, G. (1939). Microtechnical demonstration of phosphatase in tissue section. *Proc. Soc. Exp. Biol. Med.* **42**, 23–26.

Gomori, G. (1945). The microtechnical demonstration of sites of lipase activity. *Proc. Soc. Exp. Biol. Med.* **58**, 362–364.

Gomori, G. (1952). "Microscopic Histochemistry, Principles and Practice." Univ. of Chicago Press, Chicago, Illinois.

Goodspeed, T. H. and Über, F. M. (1934). Application of the Altman freeze-drying techniques to plant cytology. *Proc. Natl. Acad. Sci. U.S.A.* **20**, 495–501.

Gorska-Brylass, A. (1965). Hydrolases in pollen grains and pollen tubes. *Acta Soc. Bot. Pol.* **34**, 589–604.

Gortner, R. A. and Gortner, W. A. (1949). "Outlines of Biochemistry," 3rd ed., p. 750. Wiley, New York.

Gottschalk, A. (1962). The relation between structure and function in some glycoproteins. *Persp. Biol. Med.* **5**, 327–337.

Gräff, S. (1916). Eine Anweisung zur Herstellung von Dauerpräparaten bei Anwendung der Naphtholblau—Oxydasereaktion miteinigen Bemerkungen zur Theorie und Technik der Reaktion. *Zbl. Aug. Pathol.* **26**, 313–318.

Graham, R. C. and Karnovsky, M. J. (1966). The early stages of absorption of injected horseradish peroxidase in the proximal tubules of mouse kidney: Ultrastructural cytochemistry by a new technique. *J. Histochem. Cytochem.* **14**, 291–302.

Gray, P. (1954). "The Microtomists Formulary and Guide." Constable, London.

Greenoak, G. and Maggi, V. (1971). An improved method for the detection of proteolytic activity in tissue sections. *Microscopy* **32**, 10–16.

Guilliermond, A. (1941). "The cytoplasm of the plant cell." (L. R. Atkinson, transl.). Chronica Bot. Co., Waltham, Massachusetts.

Gurney, R. W. and Mott, M. F. (1938). The theory of the photolysis of silver bromide and the photographic latent image. *Proc. R. Soc. London Ser. A* **164**, 151.

Haaijman, J. J. and Van Dalen, J. P. R. (1977). Quantification in immunofluorescence microscopy. A new standard for fluorescein and rhodamine emission measurement. *J. Immunol. Methods* **5**, 359–374.

Hale, A. J. (1957). The histochemistry of polysaccharides. *Int. Rev. Cytol.* **6**, 193–263.

Halkjaer-Kristensen, J. and Ingemann-Hansen, T. (1978). Thickness measurement of skeletal muscle sections using the light microscope. *Histochem. J.* **10**, 497–504.

Hall, J. L. (1969a). Histochemical localization of β-glycerophosphatase activity in young root tips. *Ann. Bot.* **33,** 399–406.

Hall, J. L. (1969b). Localization of cell surface adenosine triphosphatase activity in maize roots. *Planta* **85,** 105–107.

Hall, J. L. (1971). Cytochemical localization of ATPase activity in plant root cells. *J. Microsc. (Oxford)* **93,** 219–226.

Hall, J. L. (1977). Fine structural and cytochemical changes occurring in beet discs in response to washing. *New Phytol.* **79,** 559–566.

Hall, J. L. and Sexton, R. (1972). Cytochemical localization of peroxidase activity in root cells. *Planta* **108,** 103–120.

Hall, T. A., Anderson, H. C. and Appleton, T. C. (1973). The use of thin specimens for X-ray microanalysis in biology. *J. Microsc. (Oxford)* **99,** 177–82.

Hall, J. L., Flowers, T. J. and Roberts, R. M. (1974). "Plant Cell Structure and Metabolism," pp. 177–179 and p. 265. Longman, London.

Hall, J. L., Al-Azzawi, M. J. and Fielding, J. L. (1977). Microscopic cytochemistry in enzyme localization and development. *In* "Regulation of Enzyme Synthesis and Activity in Higher Plants" (H. Smith, ed.), pp. 329–363. Academic Press, London.

Hallén, O. (1956). On the cutting and thickness determination of microtome sections. *Acta Anat.* **26,** Suppl. 25.

Hammar, J. A. (1924). Beitrage zur Konstitu VIII. Methode, die merge des Mark, der Rinde und der Rindenzonen sowie die Menge und verteilung der lipoide der menchlichen Nebenniere zahlen messig festzustellen. *Z. Mikrosk. Anat. Forsch.* **1,** 85–190.

Hanker, J. S., Seaman, A. R., Weiss, L. P., Ueno, H., Bergman, R. A. and Seligman, A. M. (1964). Osmiophilic reagents: New cytochemical principle for light and electron microscopy. *Science* **146,** 1039–1043.

Hanker, J. S., Kosyk, C. J., Clapp, D. H. and Yates, P. E. (1970). Effect of dimethyl sulfoxide (DMSO) on the histochemical demonstration of dehydrogenase. *J. Histochem. Cytochem.* **18,** 673–676.

Hanker, J. S., Yates, P. E., Metz, C. B. and Rustioni, A. (1977). A new specific, sensitive and non-carcinogenic reagent for the demonstration of horseradish peroxidase. *Histochem. J.* **9,** 789–792.

Hapner, S. J. and Hapner, K. D. (1978). Rhodamine immunofluorescence applied to plant tissues. *J. Histochem. Cytochem.* **26,** 478–482.

Hartley, W. G. (1962). "Microscopy." English Universities Press Ltd., London.

Harvey, D. M. R., Flowers, T. J. and Hall, J. L. (1976). Localization of chloride in leaf cells of the halophyte *Suaeda maritima* by silver precipitation. *New Phytol.* **77,** 319–323.

Harvey, D. M. R., Flowers, T. J. and Hall, J. L. (1979). Precipitation procedures for sodium, potassium and chloride localization in leaf cells of the halophyte *Suaeda maritima. J. Microsc. (Oxford)* **116,** 213–226.

Hayashi, M. (1964). Distribution of β-glucuronidase activity in rat tissues employing naphthol AS-BI glucuronide hexazonium pararosanilin. *J. Histochem. Cytochem.* **12,** 659–669.

Hayashi, M., Nakajima, Y. and Fishman, W. H. (1964). The cytological demonstration of β-glucuronidase employing naphthol AS-BI glucuronide and hexazonium pararosaniline: A preliminary report. *J. Histochem. Cytochem.* **12,** 293–297.

Hayat, M. A. (1970). "Principles and Techniques of Electron Microscopy I. Biological Applications." Van Nostrand-Reinhold, Princeton, New Jersey.

Hayat, M. A. (1973). Specimen preparation. *In* "Electron Microscopy of Enzymes, Principles and Methods" (M. A. Hayat, ed.), Vol. 1, pp. 1–24. Van Nostrand–Reinhold, Princeton, New Jersey.

Hayes, E. R. (1949). A rigorous redefinition of the plasmal reaction *Stain Technol.* **24,** 19–23.

Hébant, C. (1970). Étude histochimique, histoenzymologique et infra-structurale de la différencia-
    tion des tissus conducteurs dans la tige feuillé de quelques mousses Polytrichales. *C. R. Acad.*
    Sci. Paris **271**, 1986–1989.
Heilbronn, L. V. (1928). ''The Colloid Chemistry of the Protoplasm.'' Gebrüder Borntraeger,
    Berlin.
Hercik, F. (1939). Die Fluoreszenzmikroskopische Analyse der α-Strahlenwirkung. Protoplasma **32**,
    527–535.
Heslop-Harrison, Y. (1975). Enzyme release in carnivorous plants. *In* ''Lysosomes in Biology and
    Pathology'' (J. T. Dingle and R. T. Dean, eds.), Vol. 4, p. 525. North-Holland Publ.,
    Amsterdam.
Heslop-Harrison, Y. (1977). The pollen–stigma interaction: Pollen-tube penetration in *Crocus. Ann.*
    Bot. **41**, 913–922.
Heslop-Harrison, J. and Heslop-Harrison, Y. (1970). Evaluation of pollen viability by enzymically
    induced fluorescence; Intracellular hydrolysis of fluorescein diacetate. *Stain Technol.* **45**, 115–
    120.
Heyes, J. K. and Brown, R. (1956). *In* ''The Growth of Leaves'' (F. L. Milthorpe, ed.), pp. 31–49.
    Butterworths, London.
Hillary, B. B. (1939). Use of the Feulgen reaction in cytology. I. Effect of fixations on the reaction.
    Bot. Gaz. **101**, 276–300.
Hirai, K. I. (1968). Specific affinity for oxidised amine dye (radical intermediates) for heme en-
    zymes: Study in microscopy and spectrophotometry. *Acta Histochem. Cytochem.* **1**, 43–55.
Hispada, R. and Yagi, T. (1977). 1-methoxy-5-methyl-phenazinium methyl sulfate. A pho-
    tochemically stable electron mediator between NADH and various electron acceptors. *J.*
    Biochem. **82**, 1469–1473.
Holt, S. J. (1952). A new principle for the histochemical localization of hydrolytic enzymes. *Nature*
    (*London*) **169**, 271–273.
Holt, S. J. (1958). Indigogenic staining methods for esterases. *In* ''General Cytochemical Methods''
    (J. F. Danielli, ed.), Vol. 1, pp. 375–399. Academic Press, New York.
Holt, S. J. (1959). Factors governing the validity of staining methods for enzymes, and their bearing
    upon the Gomori acid phosphatase technique. *Exp. Cell Res., Suppl.* **7**, 1–27.
Holt, S. J. and Hicks, R. M. (1965). The localization of acid phosphatase in rat liver cells as revealed
    by combined cytochemical staining and electron microscopy. *J. Biophys. Biochem. Cytol.* **11**,
    47–66.
Holt, S. J. and Hicks, R. M. (1966). The importance of osmiophilia in the production of stable azo–
    indoxyl complexes of high contrast for combined enzyme cytochemistry and electron micro-
    scopy. *J. Cell Biol.* **29**, 361–366.
Holt, S. J., Hobbiger, E. E. and Pawan, G. L. S. (1960). Cytochemical staining purposes. *J.*
    Biophys. Biochem. Cytol. **7**, 383–386.
Hotchkiss, R. D. (1948). A microchemical reaction resulting in the staining of polysaccharide
    structures in fixed tissue preparations. *Arch. Biochem. Biophys.* **16**, 131–141.
Howall, S. L. and Whitfield, M. (1972). Localization of adenyl cyclase in islet cells. *J. Histochem.*
    Cytochem. **20**, 873–879.
Howard, A. and Pelc, S. R. (1951). P^{32} autoradiographs of mouse testis. Preliminary observations of
    the timing of spermatogenic stages. *Br. J. Radiol.* **23**, 634–641.
Howard, A. and Pelc, S. R. (1953). Synthesis of desoxyribonucleic acid in normal and irradiated
    cells and its relationship to chromosome breakage. *Heredity, Suppl.* **6**, 261–273.
Hughes, J. and McCully, M. E. (1975). The use of an optical brightener in the study of plant
    structure. *Stain Technol.* **50**, 319–329.
Hurst, P. R. and Gahan, P. B. (1975). Turnover of DNA in ageing tissues of *Lycopersicon esculen-*
    tum. Ann. Bot. **39**, 71–76.

Hurst, P. R., Gahan, P. B. and Snellen, J. W. (1973). Turnover of labelled DNA in differentiated collenchyma. *Differentiation* **1**, 261–266.

Idelman, S. (1957). Existence d'un complexe lipides-nucléoprotéines à groupements sulfhydridés au niveau du chromosome. *C. R. Acad. Sci.* **244**, 1827–1830.

Idelman, S. (1958a). Localisation du complexe lipides-protéines à groupements sulfhydridés au sein du chromosome. *C. R. Acad. Sci.* **246**, 1098–1102.

Idelman, S. (1958b). Démasquage des lipides du chromosome géant des glandes salivaires de Chironome par digestion enzymatique des protéines. *C. R. Acad. Sci.* **246**, 3282–3286.

Irwin, M. (1927). On the nature of the dye penetrating the vacuole of *Valonia* from solutions of methylene blue. *J. Gen. Physiol.* **19**, 927–947.

Isaac, W. E. and Winch, N. H. (1947). Guiaco–hydrogen peroxide and benzidine–hydrogen peroxide colour reactions in beans *Phaseolus vulgaris* L.) *J. Pomol. Hort. Sci.* **23**, 23–37.

Ishida, M. R. (1961). A cytochemical study of nucleic acids in higher plant cells. VII. Causal analysis of negative Feulgen staining. *Mem. Coll. Sci. Univ. Kyoto, Ser. B* **28**, No. 1.

Iverson, T. H. (1970). Cytochemical localization of myrosinase (β-thioglucosidase) in root tips of *Sinapis alba*. *Protoplasma* **71**, 451–466.

Iverson, T. H. (1973). Myrosinase in cruciferous plants. *In* "Electron Microscopy of Enzymes" (M. A. Hayat, ed.), Vol. 1, pp. 131–149. Van Nostrand-Reinhold, Princeton, New Jersey.

Jacobson, W. and Webb, M. (1952). The two types of nucleoproteins during mitosis. *Exp. Cell Res.* **3**, 163–183.

Jaffe, W. G. (1969). "Toxic Constituents of Plant Foodstuffs." (I. E. Liener, ed.), pp. 69–101. Academic Press, New York.

James, N. T. (1977). Stereology. *Semin. Ser. Soc. Exp. Biol.* **3**, 9–28.

Janigen, D. T. (1965). The effects of aldehyde fixation on acid phosphatase activity in tissue blocks. *J. Histochem. Cytochem.* **13**, 476–483.

Jeanloz, R. W. (1960). The nomenclature of mucopolysaccharides. *Arthritis Rheum.* **3**, 233–237.

Jensen, C. O., Sacks, W. and Baldawski, F. A. (1951). The reduction of triphenyltetrazolium chloride by dehydrogenases of corn embryos. *Science* **113**, 65–66.

Jensen, W. A. (1954a). The application of freeze-dry methods to plant material. *Stain Technol.* **29**, 143–150.

Jensen, W. A. (1954b). A new approach to freezing-drying of tissue. *Exp. Cell Res.* **7**, 572–574.

Jensen, W. A. (1955a). A morphological and biochemical analysis of the early phases of cellular growth in the root tip of *Vicia faba*. *Exp. Cell Res.* **8**, 506–522.

Jensen, W. A. (1955b). The histochemical localization of peroxidase in roots and its induction by indoleacetic acid. *Plant Physiol.* **30**, 426–432.

Jensen, W. A. (1956a). On the distribution of nucleic acids in the root tip of *Vicia faba*. *Exp. Cell Res.* **10**, 222–226.

Jensen, W. A. (1956b). The cytochemical localization of acid phosphatase in root tip cells. *Am. J. Bot.* **43**, 50–54.

Jensen, W. A. (1957). The incorporation of C14-adenine and C14-phenylalanine by developing root tip cells. *Proc. Natl. Acad. Sci. U.S.A.* **43**, 1038–1046.

Jensen, W. A. (1958). The nucleic acid and protein content of root tip cells of *Vicia faba* and *Allium cepa*. *Exp. Cell Res.* **14**, 575–583.

Jensen, W. A. (1960). The composition of the developing primary wall in onion root tip. II. Cytochemical localization. *Am. J. Bot.* **47**, 287–295.

Jensen, W. A. (1962). "Botanical Histochemistry." Freeman, San Francisco, California.

Jensen, W. A. and Ashton, M. (1960). The composition of the developing primary wall in onion root tip cells. I. *Quant. Anal. Plant Physiol.* **35**, 313–323.

Jensen, W. A. and Branton, D. (1962). Recent progress in freeze-drying plant tissue. *Proc. 1st Int. Cong. Histochem.*, p. 76.

Jensen, W. A. and Kavaljian, L. G. (1956). The cytochemical localization of ascorbic acid in root tip cells. *J. Biophys. Biochem. Cytol.* **2**, 87–92.

Jewell, G. G. and Saxton, C. A. (1970). The ultrastructural demonstration of compounds containing 1,2-glycol groups in plant cell walls. *Histochem. J.* **2**, 17–28.

Johansen, D. A. (1958). "Plant Microtechnique." McGraw-Hill, New York.

Johnson, C. B., Holloway, B. R., Smith, H. and Grierson, D. (1973). Isoenzymes of acid phosphatases in germinating peas. *Planta* **115**, 1–10.

Jones, G. R. N. (1964). Quantitative histochemistry. Design and use of a simple microcell for standardized incubation on the slide. *Stain Technol.* **30**, 155–161.

Jones, M. G. K., Outlaw, W. H. and Lowry, O. H. (1977). Enzymic assay of 10^{-7} to 10^{-14} moles of sucrose in plant tissues. *Plant Physiol.* **60**, 379–383.

Kalimo, H. O., Helminsen, H. J., Arstila, A. V. and Hopsu-Havu, K. K. (1968). The loss of enzyme reaction products from ultrathin sections during staining for electron microscopy. *Histochemie* **14**, 123–130.

Kalina, M. and Gahan, P. B. (1965). A quantitative study of the validity of the histochemical demonstration for pyridine nucleotide-linked dehydrogenases. *Histochemie* **5**, 430–436.

Kalina, M. and Gahan, P. B. (1968). A gelatin-film method for improved histochemical localization of dehydrogenases in plant cells. *Stain Technol.* **43**, 51–57.

Kalina, M. and Palmer, J. M. (1968). The reduction of tetrazolium salts by plant mitochondria. *Histochemie* **14**, 366–374.

Kalina, M. and Pease, D. C. (1977). The ultrastructural preservation by tannic acid of saturated phosphatidylcholines; synthetic as well as of type II pneumocytes. *J. Cell Biol.* **74**, 742–746.

Kalina, M., Gahan, P. B. and Jones, G. R. N. (1965). An evaluation of the histochemical demonstration of certain pyridine nucleotide-linked dehydrogenases. *Nature (London)* **207**, 647–649.

Kalina, M., Weavers, B. and Pearse, A. G. E. (1969). Fine structural localization of succinoxidase complex on the mitochondrial cristae. *Nature (London)* **221**, 479–480.

Kalina, M., Paplinger, R. E., Hoshino, Y. and Seligman, A. M. (1972). Nonosmiophilic tetrazolium salts that yield osmiophilic, lipophobic formazans for ultrastructural localization of dehydrogenase activity. *J. Histochem. Cytochem.* **20**, 685–695.

Kasten, F. H. (1958). Additional Schiff-type reagents for use in cytochemistry. *Stain Technol.* **33**, 39–45.

Kasten, F. H. (1959). Schiff-type reagents in cytochemistry I. Theoretical and practical considerations. *Histochemie* **1**, 466–509.

Kasten, F. H. (1961). The chemistry of Schiff's reaction. *Int. Rev. Cytol.* **10**, 1–100.

Kasten, F. H. (1967). Cytochemical studies with acridine orange and the influence of dye contaminants in the staining of nucleic acids. *Int. Rev. Cytol.* **21**, 141–202.

Kaufman, B. P., McDonald, M. R. and Gay, H. (1948). Enzymatic degradation of ribonucleoproteins of chromosomes, nucleoli and cytoplasm. *Nature (London)* **162**, 814–815.

Kawiak, J., Sawicki, W. and Miks, B. (1964). Histochemical reaction of arylsulphatase C activity. *Acta Histochem.* **19**, 184–190.

Kay, D. H. (1965). "Techniques for Electron Microscopy," 2nd ed. Blackwell, Oxford.

Kinzel, H. and Bolay, F. (1961). Über die diagnostische Bedeutung der Entmischungs- und Fällungsformen bei Vitalfärbung von Pflanzenzellen. *Protoplasma* **54**, 177–201.

Kirkpatrick, P. and Pattee, H. H. (1953). Approaches to x-ray microscopy. *Adv. Biol. Med. Phys.* **3**, 247–283.

Kisley, N., Swift, H. and Bogorad, L. (1965). Nucleic acids of chloroplasts and mitochondria in Swiss chard. *J. Cell Biol.* **25**, 327–344.

Kistler, S. S. (1935). Unpublished paper. [Quoted by Salt, R. W. (1934). *Tech. Bull. Minist. Agric. Exp. Stn. No. 116*, pp. 1–41.]

Knox, R. B. (1970). Freeze-sectioning of plant tissues. *Stain Technol.* **45**, 265–272.

Knox, R. B. and Clarke, A. E. (1978). Localization of proteins and glycoproteins by binding to labelled antibodies and lectins. *In* ''Electron Microscopy and Cytochemistry of Plant Cells.'' (J. L. Hall, ed.), pp. 149–186. Elsevier/North-Holland, New York.

Knox, R. B. and Evans, L. T. (1968). Inflorescence initiation in *Lolium temulentum* L. XII. An autoradiographic study of evocation in the shoot apex. *Aust. J. Biol. Sci.* **21**, 1083–1094.

Knox, R. B. and Heslop-Harrison, H. (1970). Pollen-wall proteins: Localization and enzymic activity. *J. Cell Sci.* **6**, 1–27.

Knox, R. B., Vithanage, H. I. M. V. and Howlett, B. J. (1980). Botanical Immunocytochemistry: A review with special reference to pollen antigens and allergens. *Histochem. J.* **12**, 247–272.

Koenig, J. W. (1966). Intracellular localization of individual dehydrogenases in frozen plant tissues by means of specific substrates and coenzymes. *Stain Technol.* **41**, 1–7.

Köhler, A. (1904). Mikrosphotographische Unter-suchungen mit ultraviolettem licht, *Z. Wiss. Mikrosk. Mikrosk. Tech.* **21**, 219–265.

Kolattukudy, P. E. (1975). Biochemistry of cutin, suberin and waxes, the lipid barriers on plants. *Annu. Proc. Phytochem. Soc.* **12**, 203–246.

Kole, R., Sierakowska, H. and Shugar, D. (1976). Novel activity of potato nucleotide pyrophosphatase. *Biochim. Biophys. Acta* **438**, 540–550.

Korn, E. D. (1966a). II. Synthesis of bis(methyl-9,10-dihydroxystearate) osmate from methyl oleate and osmium tetroxide under conditions used for fixation of biological material. *Biochim. Biophys. Acta.* **116**, 317–354.

Korn, E. D. (1966b). III. Modification of oleic acid during fixation of amoebae by osmium tetroxide. *Biochim. Biophys. Acta* **116**, 325–335.

Korn, E. D. (1966c). Structure of biological membranes. *Science* **153**, 1491.

Korn, E. D. (1967). A chromatographic and spectrophotometric study of the products of the reaction of osmium tetroxide with unsaturated lipids. *J. Cell Biol.* **34**, 627–638.

Kupilagi, S., Bryan, A. M. and Stern, H. (1961). Extractability of DNA and its determination in tissues of higher plants. *Plant Physiol.* **36**, 212–215.

Kurnick, N. B. (1955). Histochemistry of nucleic acids. *Int. Rev. Cytol.* **4**, 221–268.

La Cour, L. F. (1963). Ribosenucleic acid and the metaphase chromosome. *Exp. Cell Res.* **29**, 112–118.

La Cour, L. F. and Chayen, J. (1958). A cyclic staining behaviour of the chromosome during mitosis and meiosis. *Exp. Cell Res.* **14**, 462–468.

La Cour, L. F. and Pelc, S. R. (1958). Effect of colchicine on the utilization of labelled thymidine during chromosomal reproduction. *Nature (London)* **182**, 506.

La Cour, L. F. and Pelc, S. R. (1959). Effect of colchicine on the utilization of thymidine labelled with tritium during chromosomal reproduction. *Nature (London)* **183**, 1455–1456.

La Cour, L. F., Deeley, E. M. and Chayen, J. (1956). Variations in the amount of Feulgen stain in nuclei of plants grown at different temperatures. *Nature (London)* **177**, 272–273.

La Cour, L. F., Chayen, J. and Gahan, P. B. (1958). Evidence for lipid material in chromosomes. *Exp. Cell Res.* **14**, 469–485.

Lafontaine, J. G. and Chouinard, L. A. (1963). A correlated light and electron microscope study of the nucleolar material during mitosis in *Vicia faba*. *J. Cell Biol.* **17**, 167–201.

Lake, B. D. and Smith, V. V. (1980). The demonstration of copper and copper-containing proteins. *Int. Congr. Histochem. Cytochem. Brighton VIth,* p. 222 (Abstr.).

Lai, V. and Srivastava, L. M. (1976). Nuclear changes during differentiation of xylem vessel elements. *Cytobiologie* **12**, 220–243.

Lakon, G. (1939). Das Schwinden der Keimfähigkeit der Samen, insbesondere der Getreidefrüchte. *Ber. Dtsch. Bot. Ges.* **57**, 191–203.

Lakon, G. (1942a). Topographischer Nachweis der Keimfähigkeit der Getreidefrüchte durch Tetrazoliumsalze. *Ber. Dtsch. Bot. Ges.* **60**, 299–305.

Lakon, G. (1942b). Topographischer Nachweis der Keimfähigkeit der Mais durch Tetrazoliumsalze. *Ber. Dtsch. Bot. Ges.* **60**, 434–444.

Lance, A. (1957). Recherches cytologiques sur l'evolution de quelques meristémès apicaux et sur ses variations provoquées par des traitements photoperiodiques. *Ann. Sci. Nat. Bot. Biol. Vég.* **18**, 91–421.

Lange, P. W. and Engström, A. (1954). Determination of thickness of microscopic objects. *Lab. Invest.* **3**, 116–131.

Lansink, A. G. W. (1968). Thin layer chromatography and histochemistry of Sudan black B. *Histochemistry* **16**, 68–84.

Laüchli, A. (1966). Cryostat technique for fresh plant tissues and its application in enzyme cytochemistry. *Planta* **70**, 13–25.

Laüchli, A., Stelzer, R., Guggenheim, R. and Henning, L. (1974). Precipitation techniques as a means for intracellular ion localization by use of electron probe analysis. *In* ''Microprobe Analyses as Applied to Cells and Tissues,'' pp. 107–118. (T. Hall, P. Echlin and R. Kaufmann, eds.), Academic Press, London.

Lazarow, A. and Cooperstein, S. J. (1953). Studies on the enzymatic basis for the Janus green B staining reaction. *J. Histochem. Cytochem.* **1**, 234–241.

Le Pecq, J. P. (1973). Ethidium bromide: A fluorescent probe of nucleic acid structure and its potential for *in vivo* studies. *In* ''Fluorescence Techniques in Cell Biology'' (A. A. Thaer and M. Sernetz, eds.), pp. 301–309. Springer-Verlag, Berlin and New York.

Levine, N. D. (1940). The dehydration of methylene blue stained material without loss of dye. *Stain Technol.* **14**, 29.

Lewin, B. (1974). ''Gene Expression II. Eucaryote Chromosomes.'' Wiley, New York.

Lewitsky, G. A. (1931). An essay on cytological analysis of the fixing action of the chromacetic formalin and the chromic formalin. *Bull. Appl. Bot. Genet. Plant Breed.* **27**, 175–185.

Lhotka, J. F. (1953). Histochemical 1,2-glycol cleavage with acetates of manganese. *Stain Technol.* **28**, 245–248.

Lillie, R. D. (1954). ''Histopathologic Technique and Practical Histochemistry.'' McGraw-Hill, New York.

Lillie, R. D. and Ashburn, L. L. (1943). Supersaturated solutions of fat stains in dilute isopropanol for demonstration of acute fatty degeneration not shown by Herxheimer's technic. *Arch. Pathol.* **36**, 432–441.

Linderstrøm-Lang, K. (1952). ''Micromethods in Biological Research, Lane Medical Literature.'' Stanford Univ. Press, Stanford, California.

Linderstrøm-Lang, K. and Engel, C. (1938). Über die Verteiling der Amylase in den äusseren Schichten des Gerstenkornes. *C. R. Trav. Lab. Carlsberg, Sér. Chim.* **21**, 243–258.

Linderstroøm-Lang, K. and Holter, H. (1932). Contributions to the histochemistry of enzymes. II. The distribution of peptidase in the roots and sprouts of malt. *C. R. Trav. Lab. Carlsberg, Sér. Chim.* **19**, 1–39.

Linderstrøm-Lang, K. and Mogensen, K. R. (1938). Studies on enzymatic histochemistry. XXXI. Histological control of histochemical investigations. *C. R. Trav. Lab. Carlsberg, Sér. Chim.* **23**, 27–35.

Linskens, H. F. and Esser, K. (1957). Über eine spezifische Anfärbung der Pollenschläuche in Griffel und die Zahl der Kallosepropfen nach Selbstung und Fremdung. *Naturwissenschaften* **44**, 16.

Lison, L. (1953). ''Histochimie et Cytochimie Animales, Principes et Méthodes,'' 2nd ed. Gauthier-Villars, Paris.

List, A. (1963). Some observations on DNA content and cell and nuclear volume growth in the developing xylem cells of certain higher plants. *Am. J. Bot.* **50**, 320–329.

Livingston, D. C., Coombs, M. M., Franks, L. M., Maggi, V. and Gahan, P. B. (1969). A lead phthalocyanin method for the demonstration of acid hydrolases in plant and animal tissues. *Histochemie* **18**, 48–60.

Long, C., Odavic, R., Bitensky, L. and Chayen, J. (1963). *Annu. Rep. Roy. Coll. Surg.* p. 82.

Longo, G. P., Dragonetti, C. and Ongo, C. P. (1972). Cytochemical localization of catalase in glyoxysomes isolated from maize scutella. *Plant Physiol.* **50**, 463–468.

Lord, B. I. (1963). Autoradiography with tritium labelled cell preparation: Some physical factors affecting image production in two liquid nuclear emulsions, *J. Photogr. Sci.* **11**, 342–346.

Lowry, O. (1953). The quantitative histochemistry of the brain—Histological sampling. *J. Histochem. Cytochem.* **1**, 420–428.

Luft, J. H. (1961). Improvements in epoxy resin embedding methods. *J. Biophys. Biochem. Cytol.* **1**, 409–414.

Luft, J. H. (1966). Improvements in epoxy resin embedding methods. *Fed. Proc., Fed. Am. Soc. Exp. Biol.* **25**, 1776–1784.

Luft, J. H. (1971a). Ruthenium red and violet. I. Chemistry, purification, methods of use for electron microscopy and mechanism of action. *Anat. Rec.* **171**, 347–368.

Luft, J. H. (1971b). Ruthenium red and violet. II. Fine structural localization in animal tissues. *Anat. Rec.* **171**, 369–416.

Lüttge, U. and Weigl, J. (1962). Mikroautoradiographische Untersuchungen der Aufnahme und des Transportes von $^{35}SO_4{}^{2-}$ und $^{45}Ca^{2+}$ in Keimwurzeln von *Zea mays* L. und *Pisum sativum* L. *Planta* **58**, 113–126.

Macallum, A. B. (1905). On the distribution of potassium in animal and vegetable cells. *J. Physiol. (London)* **32**, 95–128.

McAlpine, J. C. (1965). Histochemical survival of diaphorase activity in formalin fixed tissue stored for 18 months in cold gum-sucrose. *J. Histochem. Cytochem.* **13**, 296.

MacDonnell, L. R., Jang, R., Jansen, E. F. and Lineweaver, H. (1950). The specificity of pectinesterases from several sources with some notes on purification of orange pectinesterase. *Arch. Biochem.* **28**, 260–273.

Mace, M. E. (1963). Histochemical localization of phenols in healthy and diseased tomato roots. *Phytopathology* **16**, 915–925.

McLean, J. and Gahan, P. B. (1969). Hydrolase activities in differentiating plant tissues. *Biochem. J.* **111**, 34P.

McLean, J. (1969). A histochemical study of acid hydrolases in dividing and differentiating plant tissues. Ph.D. Thesis, Univ. of London, England.

McLean, J. and Gahan, P. B. (1970). The distribution of acid phosphatases and esterases in differentiating roots of *Vicia faba*. *Histochemie* **24**, 41–49.

McLean, R. C. and Cook, W. R. I. (1941). "Plant Science Formulae." Macmillan, London.

McLeish, J. (1959). Comparative microphotometric studies of DNA and arginine in plant nuclei. *Chromosoma* **10**, 686–697.

McLeish, J. and Sunderland, N. (1961). Measurements of desoxyribose nucleic acid (DNA) in higher plants by Feulgen photometry and chemical methods. *Exp. Cell Res.* **24**, 527–540.

McLeish, J., Bell, L. G. E., La Cour, L. F. and Chayen, J. (1957). The quantitative cytochemical estimation of arginine. *Exp. Cell Res.* **12**, 120–125.

McLeish, J. and Sherratt, H. S. A. (1958). The use of the Sakaguchi reaction for the cytochemical determination of combined arginine. *Exp. Cell Res.* **14**, 625–629.

McManus, J. F. A. (1948). Histological and histochemical uses of periodic acid. *St. Technol.* **23**, 99–108.

Maddy, A. H. (1961a). 1-Fluoro-2:4-dinitrobenzene as a cytochemical reagent. I. Histological application. *Exp. Cell Res.* **22**, 169–180.

Maddy, A. H. (1961b). 1-Fluoro-2:4-dinitrobenzene as a cytochemical reagent. II. The chemical basis of the reaction with cell nuclei. *Exp. Cell Res.* **22**, 181–193.

Maggi, V. (1965). A study of lysosomal acid phosphatase during mitosis in HeLa cells. *J. R. Microsc. Soc.* **85**, 291–295.

Maggi, V. and Carbonell, A. W. (1969). Lysosomes and acid phosphatase during growth and differentiation in mice: A light and electron microscope study. *Histochem. J.* **1**, 383–403.

Marchi, V. (1886). Sulle degenerazioni consecutive all' Estirpazione totale e parziale del cervelletto. *Riv. Sper. Freniat.* **12**, 50–62.

Margoliash, E. and Novogrodsky, A. (1958). A study of the inhibition of catalase by 3-amino-1,2,4-triazole. *Biochem. J.* **68**, 468–475.

Markham, R. (1955). Nucleic acids, their components and related compounds. *In* "Modern Methods of Plant Analysis". (K. Paech and M. V. Tracy, eds.), Vol. 4, pp. 246–304. Springer-Verlag, Berlin and New York.

Marshall, P. N. (1979). Commercially available 'pure' Azure dyes—caveat emptor. *Histochem. J.* **11**, 489–493.

Matile, Ph. (1975). "The Lytic Compartment of Plant Cells." Springer-Verlag, Berlin and New York.

Mattson, A. M., Jensen, C. O. and Dutcher, R. A. (1947). Triphenyl tetrazolium chloride as a dye for vital tissues. *Science* **106**, 294.

Meijer, A. E. F. H. (1967). Histochemical method for the demonstration of the activity of hexokinase and glucokinase. *Acta Histochem.* **28**, 286–290.

Maurer, H. R. (1981). Potential pitfalls of [^{3}H]thymidine techniques to measure cell proliferation. *Cell Tissue Kinet.* **14**, 111–120.

Meek, G. A. (1976). "Practical Electron Microscopy for Biologists," 2nd ed. Wiley, New York.

Meischer, F. (1897). "Die Histochemischen und Physiologischen Arbeiten." Leipzig.

Mendelsohn, M. L. (1966). Absorption cytophotometry: Comparative methodology for heterogeneous objects and the two-wavelength method. *In* "Introduction to Quantitative Cytochemistry" (G. L. Wied, ed.), pp. 202–214. Academic Press, London.

Menten, M. L., Junge, J. and Green, M. H. (1944). A coupling histochemical azo dye test for alkaline phosphatase in kidney. *J. Biol. Chem.* **153**, 471–477.

Meves, F. (1904). Über das Vorkommen von Mitochondrien bezw. Chondromiten in Pflanzenzellen. *Ber. Dtsch. Bot. Ges.* **22**, 284–286.

Michaelis, L. (1950). Reversible polymerization and molecular aggregation. *J. Phys. Coll. Chem.* **54**, 1–17.

Middleton, J. and Gahan, P. B. (1979). A quantitative cytochemical study of acid phosphatases in rat liver. Parenchymal cells of different ploidy values. *Histochem. J.* **11**, 649–659.

Middleton, J., Ryall, M. D., Melas, G., Webb, R., and Gahan, P. B. (1984). Microcomputer control applied to the Vickers M85/86 integrating microdensitometer. *Histochem. J.* **16**, 709–720.

Milch, R. A., Tobie, J. E. and Robinson, R. A. (1961). A microscopic study of tetracycline localization in skeletal neoplasms. *J. Histochem. Cytochem.* **9**, 261–270.

Miller, O. L., Stone, G. E. and Prescott, D. M. (1964). Autoradiography of soluble materials. *J. Cell Biol.* **23**, 654–658.

Millon, A. N. E. (1849). Chimie sur un réactif propre aux composés protéiques. *C. R. Soc. Biol. Paris* **28**, 40–42.

Millot, J. and Giberton, A. (1927). Sur l'utilisation en histologie des piéces conservées dans le formol pour la mise en evidence des graisses. *C. R. Soc. Biol.* **97**, 1674–1675.

Milovidov, P. F. (1949). Physik und Chemie des Zellkernes. *Protoplasma, Monogr.* **20**.

Mitchell, J. P. (1967). DNA synthesis during the early division cycles of Jerusalem artichoke callus cultures. *Ann. Bot.* **31**, 427–435.

Mitchell, J. P. (1968). The pattern of protein accumulation in relation to DNA replication in Jerusalem artichoke callus cultures. *Ann. Bot.* **32**, 315–326.

Mitchell, J. W. (1949). XXIII. The properties of silver halides containing traces of silver sulphide. *Philos. Mag.* **40**, 249–286.

Moses, H. L. and Rosenthal, A. S. (1968). Pitfalls in the use of lead ion for histochemical localization of nucleoside phosphatases. *J. Histochem. Cytochem.* **16**, 530–539.

Mowry, R. W. (1960). Revised method producing improved coloration of acidic polysaccharides with alcian blue 8GX supplied currently. *J. Histochem. Cytochem.* **8**, 323–324.

Nachlas, M. M., Prinn, W. and Seligman, A. M. (1956a). Quantitative estimation of lyo and desmo enzymes in tissue sections with and without fixation. *J. Biophys. Biochem. Cytol.* **2**, 487–502.

Nachlas, M. M., Prinn, W. and Seligman, A. M. (1956b). Quantitative estimation of lyo- and desmo-enzymes in tissue sections with and without fixation. *J. Histochem. Cytochem.* **4**, 414–416.

Nachlas, M. M., Crawford, D. T., Goldstein, T. P. and Seligman, A. M. (1958). The histochemical demonstration of cytochrome oxidase with a new reagent for the NADI reaction. *J. Histochem. Cytochem.* **6**, 445–446.

Nagata, T. (1974). Lipase. *In* "Electron Microscopy of Enzymes" (M. A. Hayat, ed.), Vol. 2, pp. 132–148. Van Nostrand-Reinhold, Princeton, New Jersey.

Nairn, R. C. (1962). "Fluorescent Protein Tracing." Livingstone, Edinburgh.

Nakane, P. K. (1973). Ultrastructural localization of tissue antigens with the peroxidase-labeled antibody method. *In* "Electron Microscopy and Cytochemistry" (E. Wisse, W. Th. Daems, I. Molenaar and P. van Duijn, eds.), pp. 129–143. Elsevier/North-Holland, New York.

Newsholme, E. A. and Crabtree, B. (1979). Theoretical principles in the approaches to control of metabolic pathways and their application to glycolysis in muscle. *J. Mol. Cell Cardiol.* **11**, 839–856.

Newsholme, E. A. and Crabtree, B. (1980). The principles of metabolic regulation. *In* "Placenta: A Neglected Experimental Animal" pp. 7–33. (P. Beaconsfield and C. Villee, eds.).

Nicolet, B. H. and Schinn, L. A. (1941). The determination of serine by the use of periodate. *J. Biol. Chem.* **139**, 687–694.

Northcote, D. H. and Pickett-Heaps, J. D. (1966). A function of the Golgi apparatus in polysaccharide synthesis and transport in root cap cells of wheat. *Biochem. J.* **98**, 159–167.

Nougarède, A. (1967). Experimental cytology of the shoot apical cells during vegetative growth and flowering. *Int. Rev. Cytol.* **21**, 203–351.

Novikoff, A. B. (1967). Enzyme localizations with Wachstein–Meisel procedures. Real or artefact. *J. Histochem. Cytochem.* **15**, 353–355.

Novikoff, A. B. (1970). Their phosphatase controversy: Love's labours lost. *J. Histochem. Cytochem.* **18**, 916–917.

Novikoff, A. B. and Goldfischer, S. (1969). Visualization of peroxisomes (microbodies) and mitochondria with diaminobenzidine. *J. Histochem. Cytochem.* **17**, 675–680.

Novikoff, A. B. and Masek, B. (1958). Survival of lactic dehydrogenase and DPNH-diaphorase activities after formal-calcium fixation. *J. Histochem. Cytochem.* **6**, 217a.

Nowell, P. C. (1960). Phytohaemagglutinin: An initiator of mitosis in cultures of normal human leucocytes. *Cancer Res.* **20**, 462–466.

O'Brien, T. P., Feder, N. and McCully, M. E. (1964). Polychromatic staining of plant cell walls by toluidine blue O. *Protoplasma* **59**, 367–373.

Odartchenko, N., Cottier, H., Feinedegen, L. E. and Bond, V. P. (1964). Mitotic delay in more mature erythrocytes of the dog, induced *in vivo* by sublethal doses of x-rays. *Radiat. Res.* **21**, 413–422.

Ogawa, K., Saito, T. and Mayahara, H. (1968). The site of ferricyanide reduction by reductases within mitochondria as studied by electron microscopy. *J. Histochem. Cytochem.* **16**, 49–57.

Ogur, M. and Rosen, G. (1950). The nucleic acids of plant tissues. I. The extraction and estimation of desoxypentose nucleic acid. *Arch. Biochem.* **25**, 262–276.

Oliver, P. T. P. (1974). Localization of free sulphydryl groups by ferricyanide reduction in developing conidiophores by *Aspergillus nidulans*. *Histochem. J.* **6**, 319–326.

Opik, H. (1975). The reaction of mitochondria in the coleoptiles of rice (*Oryza sativa* L.) with diaminobenzidine. *J. Cell Sci.* **17**, 43–55.

Orfila, M. (1831). "Eléménts de Chimie Appliqué à la Medicine et aux Arts," 5th ed., Vol. 2, pp. 36–45. Librairie de Crochard, Paris.

Ornstein, L., Mautner, W., Davis, B. J. and Tamura, R. (1957). New horizons in fluorescence microscopy. *J. Mt. Sinai Hosp. (N.Y.)* **24**, 1066–1078.

Oster, G. (1956). Birefringence and dichroism. *In* "Physical Techniques in Biological Research" (G. Oster and W. A. Pollister, eds.), Vol. 1, pp. 439–460. Academic Press, New York.

Osumi, M. and Sato, M. (1978). Further studies on the localization of catalase in yeast microbodies by ultra-thin frozen sections. *J. Electron Microsc.* **27**, 127–136.

Olszewska, M. J. and Gabara, B. (1964). Recherches cytochimiques sur la présence de certaines hydrolases au cours de la cytocinèse chez les plantes supérieurs. *Protoplasma* **59**, 163–180.

Olszewska, M. J., Gabara, B. and Steplewski, Z. (1966). Recherches cytochimiques sur la succession d'enzymes hydrolytiques, sur la présence de la thiamine pyrophosphatase et des polysaccharides au cours du développement de la plaque cellulaire. *Protoplasma* **61**, 60–80.

Palevitz, B. A. and Newcombe, E. H. (1970). A study of sieve element starch using sequential enzymatic digestion and electron microscopy. *J. Cell Biol.* **45**, 383–398.

Pallaghy, C. K. (1973). Electron probe microanalysis of potassium and chlorine in freeze-substituted leaf sections of *Zea mays*. *Aust. J. Biol. Sci.* **26**, 1015–1021.

Palmer, J. M. (1976). Structures associated with catabolism. *In* "Plant Structure, Function and Adaptation" (M. A. Hall, ed.), pp. 91–124. Macmillan, London.

Papadimitriou, J. M., Van Duijn, P., Brederoo, P. and Streefkerk, J. G. (1976). A new method for the cytochemical demonstration of peroxidase for light, fluorescence and electron microscopy. *J. Histochem. Cytochem.* **24**, 82–90.

Parups, E. V. and Moinar, J. M. (1972). Histochemical study of xylem blockage in cut roses. *J. Am. Soc. Hortic. Sci.* **97**, 532–534.

Patau, K. and Swift, H. (1953). The DNA content (Feulgen) of nuclei during mitosis in a root tip of onion. *Chromosoma* **6**, 149–160.

Pearse, A. G. E. (1968). "Histochemistry: Theoretical and Applied," 3rd ed. Vol. I. Churchill, London.

Pearse, A. G. E. (1972). "Histochemistry: Theoretical and Applied," 3rd ed. Vol. II. Churchill, London.

Pearse, A. G. E. (1980). "Histochemistry: Theoretical and Applied," 4th ed., Vol. I. Churchill, London.

Pearse, A. G. E. and Bancroft, J. D. (1966). Controlled temperature cold microtomy (the thermoelectric cryostat). *J. R. Microsc. Soc.* **85**, 385–389.

Pearse, A. G. E. and Marks, R. (1976). Further studies on section thickness measurement. *Histochem. J.* **8**, 383–386.

Pelc, S. R. (1947). Autoradiograph technique. *Nature (London)* **160**, 749–750.

Pelc, S. R. (1958). Autoradiography as a cytochemical method, with special reference to C^{14} and S^{35}. *In* "General Cytochemical Methods" (J. F. Danielli, ed.), pp. 279–316. Academic Press, New York.

Pelc, S. R. (1972). Metabolic DNA in ciliated protozoa, salivary gland chromosomes and mammalian cells. *Int. Rev. Cytol.* **32**, 327–355.

Pelc, S. R. and La Cour, L. F. (1959). H^3-Thymidine in newly differentiated nuclei of roots of *Vicia faba*. *Experientia* **15**, 131–133.

Pelc, S. R., Coombes, J. D. and Budd, G. C. (1961). On the adaptation of autoradiographic techniques for use with the electron microscope. *Exp. Cell Res.* **24**, 192–207.

Pelc, S. R., Appleton, T. C. and Welton, M. G. E. (1965). *In* "The Use of Radioautography in Investigating Protein Synthesis" (C. P. Leblond and K. B. Warren, eds.), Academic Press, New York.

Perkins, H. J., Nelson, C. D. and Gorham, P. R. (1959). A tissue autoradiographic study of the translocation of ^{14}C-labelled sugars in stems of young soybean plants. *Can. J. Bot.* **37**, 871–877.

Pette, D. and Hofer, H. W. (1980). The constant proportion enzyme group concept in the selection of reference enzymes in metabolism. *CIBA Found. Symp.* No. 73, pp. 231–244.

Pfeffer, W. (1886). Cited in Baker (1948).

Pickett-Heaps, J. D. (1967). Preliminary attempts at ultrastructural polysaccharide localization in root tip cells. *J. Histochem. Cytochem.* **15**, 442–455.

Pickett-Heaps, J. D. (1968). Further ultrastructural observations on polysaccharide localization in plant cells. *J. Cell Sci.* **3**, 55–64.

Pitt, D. (1975). "Lysosomes and Cell Function." Longman, London.

Planchon, L. and Hugounen, Q. L. (1884). "Le Microscope: Theorie, Applications, Traité Pratique." Rothschild, Paris.

Ploem, J. S. (1971). A study of filters and light sources in immunofluorescence microscopy. *Ann. N. Y. Acad. Sci.* **177**, 414–429.

Ploem, J. S. (1975). General introduction. *Ann. N. Y. Acad. Sci.* **254**, 4–20.

Ploem, J. S. (1977). Quantitative fluorescence microscopy. *Semin. Ser. Soc. Exp. Biol.* **3**, 55–89.

Ploem, J. S. (1980). Appropriate technology for the quantitative assessment of the final reaction product of histochemical techniques. *In* "Trends in Enzyme Histochemistry and Cytochemistry," CIBA Foundation Symposium 73, pp. 275–303. Excerpta Medica, Amsterdam.

Polya, G. M. and Ashton, A. R. (1973). Inhibition of wheat seedlings 5'(3')-ribonucleotide phosphohydrolase by adenine 3',5'-cyclic monophosphate. *Plant Sci. Lett.* **1**, 349–357.

Popper, H. (1944). Distribution of vitamin A in tissue as visualized by fluorescence microscopy. *Physiol. Rev.* **24**, 205–224.

Porter, K. R. and Kallman, F. (1953). The properties and effects of osmium tetroxide as a tissue fixative with special reference to its use for electron microscopy. *Exp. Cell Res.* **4**, 127–141.

Poux, N. (1963). Localisation de la phosphatase acide dans les cellules méristèmatiques de blé (*Triticum vulgare* Vill.) *J. Microsc. (Paris)* **2**, 485–489.

Poux, N. (1967). Localisation d'activités enzymatiques dans les cellules du méristème radiculaire de *Cucumis sativus.* L. *J. Microsc. (Paris)* **6**, 1043–1058.

Pratt, L. H. and Coleman, R. A. (1974). Phytochrome distribution in etiolated grass seedlings as assayed by an indirect antibody labelling method. *Am. J. Bot.* **61**, 195–202.

Prenna, G. (1969). Use of a fluorescent Schiff-Type reagent in qualitative and quantitative histochemical studies. *Tsitolgiya* **11**, 2, 4–8.

Raap, A. K. (1983). Studies on phenazine methosulphate-tetrazolium salt capture reaction in NAD(P)$^+$-dependent dehydrogenase cytochemistry III. The role of superoxide in tetrazolium reduction. *Histochem. J.* **15**, 977–986.

Raap, A. K. and Van Duijn, P. (1983). Studies on the phenazine methosulphate-tetrazolium capture reaction in NAD(P)$^+$-dependent dehydrogenase cytochemistry. II. A novel hypothesis for the mode of action of PMS and a study of the properties of reduced PMS. *Histochem. J.* **15**, 881–894.

Raap, A. K., Van Hoof, G. R. M. and Van Duijn, P. (1983). Studies on the phenazine methosulphate-tetrazolium salt capture reaction in NAD(P)$^+$-dependent dehydrogenase cytochemistry. I. Localization artefacts caused by the escape of reduced co-enzyme during cytochemical reactions for NAD(P)$^+$-dependent dehydrogenases. *Histochem. J.* **15**, 861–880.

Rabinowitch, M., Junquiera, L. C. and Fajer, A. (1949). A chemical and histochemical study of the technic for acid phosphatase. *Stain Technol.* **24**, 147–156.

Rambourg, A. (1968). Detection des glycoprotéines en microscopie electronique par l'acide phosphotungstique à bas pH. *Electron Microsc. (Rome)* **2**, 57.

Rappaport, B. Z. (1955). A semiquantitative DOPA reaction for use of frozen dried skin. *Arch. Pathol.* **60**, 444–450.

Rasch, E. and Swift, H. (1960). Microphotometric analysis of the cytochemical Millon reaction. *J. Histochem. Cytochem.* **8**, 4–17.

Raspail, F.-V. (1825a). Developpement de la fécule dans les organes de la fructification des céréales et analyse microscopique de la fécule, suivie d'expériences propres à enexpliquer la conversion engomme. *Ann. Sci. Nat.* **6**, 224–239.

Raspail, F.-V. (1825b). "Mémoires sur la fammile des Graminées." Paris.

Raspail, F.-V. (1830). "Essai de chimie microscopique appliquée a la physiologie, ou l'Art de transporter le laboratoire sur le porte-objet dans l'étude des crops organisés." Meilhac, Paris.

Raspail, F.-V. (1833). "Nouveau système de chimie organique fondé sur des méthodes nouvelles d'observation." J.-B. Baillière, Paris.

Recheigl, M. and Evans, W. H. (1963). Role of catalase and peroxidase in the metabolism of leucocytes. *Nature (London)* **199**, 1001–1002.

Reeve, R. M. (1950). Histochemical tests for polyphenols in plant tissues. *St. Technol.* **26**, 91–96.

Reeve, R. M. (1959). A specific hydroxylamine–ferric chloride reaction for histochemical localization of pectin. *St. Technol.* **34**, 209–211.

Reichard, P. and Estborn, B. (1951). Utilization of desoxyribosides in the synthesis of polynucleotides. *J. Biol. Chem.* **188**, 839–846.

Reiss, J. (1971). Dimethyl sulfoxide as carrier in enzyme cytochemistry. *Histochemie* **26**, 93–94.

Richards, B. M. and Bajer, A. (1961). Mitosis in endosperm: Changes in nuclear and chromosome mass during mitosis. *Exp. Cell Res.* **22**, 503–508.

Richterich, R. (1951). Die Qualitative und Quantitative verteilung der Esterasen im Magen und Duodenum des Schweines. (*Sus scrofa*, L.). *Enzymologia* **15**, 40–43.

Rickard, J. E. (1982). Investigation into post-harvest behaviour of *Cassava* roots and their response to wounding. Ph.D. Thesis, Univ. of London, England.

Rigler, R. (1966). Microfluorometric characterization of intracellular nucleic acids and nucleoproteins by acridine orange. *Acta Physiol. Scand., Suppl.* **267**, 1–122.

Roberts, L. W., Baba, S. and Urban, K. (1966). On the use of phenazine methosulphate in the histochemistry of succinic dehydrogenase in frozen plant tissues. *Plant Cell Physiol.* **7**, 177–181.

Robertson, W. M., Storey, B. and Griffiths, B. S. (1983). An interference technique for measuring the thickness of semi-thin and thick sections. *J. Microsc.*, **133**, 121–124.

Robinson, A. L. (1982). High resolution imaging with soft x-rays. *Science* **215**, 150–152.

Robinson, E. and Brown, R. (1952). The development of the enzyme complement in growing root cells. *J. Exp. Bot.* **3**, 356–374.

Roelofson, P. A. and Huette, I. (1951). Chitin in the cell walls of yeasts. *Antonie van Leeuwenhoek* **17**, 297–313.

Roels, H. (1967). "Metabolic DNA": A cytochemical study. *Int. Rev. Cytol.* **19**, 1–34.

Rogers, A. W. (1979). "Techniques of Autoradiography," 3rd ed. Elsevier, Amsterdam.

Rogers, G. E. (1959). Electron microscopy of wool. *J. Ultrastruct. Res.* **2**, 309–330.

Roland, J. C. (1978a). General preparation and staining of thin sections. *In* "Electron Microscopy and Cytochemistry of Plant Cells" (J. L. Hall, ed.), pp. 1–62. Elsevier/North-Holland, New York.

Roland, J. C. (1978b). Early differences between radial walls and tangential walls of actively growing cambial zone. *I.A.W.A. Bull.* **1**, 7–10.

Roland, J. C., Vian, B. and Reis, D. (1975). Observations with cytochemistry and ultracryotomy on the fine structure of the expanding walls in actively elongating plant cells. *J. Cell Sci.* **19**, 239–259.

Roomans, G. M. and Seveus, L. A. (1976). Subcellular localization of diffusible ions in the yeast *Saccharomyces cerevisiae:* Quantitative microprobe analysis of thin freeze-dried sections. *J. Cell Sci.* **21**, 119–127.

Roozemonde, R. C. (1971). The staining and chromium binding of rat brain tissue and of lipids in model systems subjected to Baker's acid haematein technique. *J. Histochem. Cytochem.* **19**, 244–251.

Rosenthal, A. S., Moses, H. L., Beaver, D. L. and Schuffman, S. S. (1966). Lead ion and phosphatase histochemistry. I. Nonenzymatic hydrolysis of nucleoside phosphates by lead ion. *J. Histochem. Cytochem.* **14**, 698–701.

Ross, K. F. A. (1967). "Phase Contrast and Interference Microscopy for Cell Biologists. Arnold, London.

Roy, A. B. (1962). The histochemical detection of aryl sulphatases. *J. Histochem. Cytochem.* **10**, 106–107.

Ruch, F. (1956). Birefrigence and dichroism of cells and tissues. *In* "Physical Techniques in Biological Research" (G. Oster and W. A. Pollister, eds.), Vol. 3, pp. 149–176. Academic Press, New York.

Rutenburg, A. M., Cohen, R. B. and Seligman, A. M. (1952). Histochemical demonstration of aryl sulphatase. *Science* **116**, 539–543.

Rutenburg, A. M., Rutenburg, S. H., Monis, B., Teague, R. and Seligman, A. M. (1958a). Histochemical demonstration of β-D-galactosidase in the rat. *J. Histochem. Cytochem.* **6**, 122–129.

Rutenburg, A. M., Lang, R., Golberg, J. A. and Rutenburg, S. H. (1958b). A new method for the histochemical demonstration of α-glucosidase. *J. Histochem. Cytochem.* **6**, 396.

Rutenburg, A. M., Goldberg, J. A., Rutenburg, S. H. and Lang, R. I. (1960). The histochemical demonstration of α-D-glucosidase in mammalian tissue. *J. Histochem. Cytochem.* **8**, 268–272.

Sabatini, D. D., Bensch, K. and Barrnett, R. J. (1963). Cytochemistry and electron microscopy. The preservation of ultrastructure and enzymatic activity by aldehyde fixation. *J. Cell Biol.* **17**, 19–58.

Sagan, L., Ben Shaul, Y., Schiff, J. A. and Epstein, H. T. (1964). Radiographic localization of DNA in the chloroplasts of *Euglena*. *J. Cell Biol.* **23**, 81A.

Sakaguchi, S. (1925). Über eine neue Farbenreaktion von Protein und Arginin. *J. Biochem. (Tokyo)* **5**, 25–31.

Sakai, Y., Yamamoto, N. and Yasuda, K. (1979). Localization of acrosomal proteinase in sheep testis. *Acta Histochem. Cytochem.* **12**, 151–156.

Salpeter, M. N. and Bachman, L. (1964). Autoradiography with the electron microscope. A procedure for improving resolution, sensitivity and contrast. *J. Cell Biol.* **22**, 469–479.

Salpeter, M. M., Bachmann, L. and Salpeter, E. E. (1969). Resolution in electron microscope radiography. *J. Cell Biol.* **41**, 1–20.

Sampson, M. and Davies, D. D. (1963). Metabolically labile DNA in mitotic and non-mitotic cells of *Zea mays*. *Life Sci.* **5**, 1239–1247.

Sanger, R. (1945). The free amino groups of insulin. *Biochem. J.* **39**, 507–515.

Sato, S. (1953). The histochemical detection of succinic dehydrogenase with 2,3,5-triphenyltetrazolium chloride. *Bot. Mag.* **66**, 277–285.

Sato, S. and Sato, K. (1965). Mode of action of triphenyltetrazolium chloride on mitochondrial respiration. *J. Biochem.* **58**, 470–479.

Sawhney, B. L. and Zelitch, I. (1969). Direct determination of potassium ion accumulation in guard cells in relation to stomatal opening in light. *Plant Physiol.* **44**, 1350–1354.

Schleiden, M. J. (1838). Beiträge zur Phytogenesis. *Arch. Anat. Physiol., Wiss. Med.* p. 137.

Schulman, R. G., Brown, T. R., Ugurbil, K., Ogawa, S., Cohen, S. M. and Den Hollander, J. A. (1979). Cellular application of ^{31}P and ^{13}C nuclear magnetic resonance. *Science* **205**, 160–161.

Schultze, B. (1969). Autoradiography at the cellular level. "Physical Techniques in Biological Research" (A. W. Pollister, ed.), 2nd ed., Vol. 3B, Academic Press, New York.

Schwabe, U., Puchstein, C., Hannermann, H. and Söchtig, E. (1979). Activation of adenylate cyclase by vanadate. *Nature (London)*, **277**, 143–145.

Schwann, T. (1838a). Ueber die Analogie in der Structur und dem wachsthume der Thiere und Pflanzen. *Neue Not. Geb. Nat. Heilk. (Froriep)* **1–5**, No. 91, columns 33–38.

Schwann, T. (1838b). Fortsetzung der Untersuchungen über die Uebereinstimmuren in der structur der Thiere und Pflanzen. *Neue Not. Geb. Nat. Heitk. (Froriep)* **1–5**, No. 103, columns 225–229.

Scott, G. H. (1933). A critical study and review of the method of microincineration. *Protoplasma* **20**, 113–121.

Scott, G. H. (1937). The microincineration method of demonstrating mineral elements in tissues. "Microscopical Techniques" (C. E. McClung, ed.), 2nd ed., pp. 643–665. Hoebert, New York.

Scott, J. E. (1967). On the mechanism of the methyl green–pyronin stain for nucleic acids. *Histochemie* **9**, 30–47.

Scott, J. F. and Harbinson, R. J. (1971). The Schiff reaction of polyaldehydes. *Proc. Roy. Microsc. Soc.* **6**, 22.

Seifriz, W. (1936). "Protoplasm." McGraw-Hill, New York.

Seligman, A. M., Nachlas, M. M., Manheimer, L. H., Friedman, O. M. and Wolf, G. (1949). Development of new methods for the histochemical demonstration of hydrolytic intracellular enzymes in a program of cancer. *Ann. Surg.* **130**, 333–341.

Seligman, A. M., Hanker, J. S., Wasserkrug, H., Dmochowski, H. and Katzoff, L. (1965). Histochemical demonstration of some oxidized macromolecules with thiocarbohydrazide (TCH) or thiosemicarbohydrazide (TSC) and osmium tetroxide. *J. Histochem. Cytochem.* **13**, 629–639.

Seligman, A. M., Ueno, H., Morizoni, Y., Wasserkrug, H. L., Katzoff, L. and Hanker, J. S. (1967). Electron microscopic demonstration of dehydrogenase activity with a new osmiophilic ditetrazolium salt (TC-NBT). *J. Histochem. Cytochem.* **15**, 1–13.

Seligman, A. M., Karnovsky, M. J., Wasserkrug, H. L. and Hanker, J. S. (1968). Non-droplet ultrastructural demonstration of cytochrome oxidase activity with a polymerizing osmiophilic reagent, diaminobenzidine (DAB). *J. Cell Biol.* **38**, 1–14.

Seligman, A. M., Shannon, W. A., Hoshino, Y. and Paplinger, R. E. (1973). Some important principles in 3,3'-diaminobenzidine ultrastructural cytochemistry. *J. Histochem. Cytochem.* **21**, 756–758.

Serra, J. A. (1946). Histochemical tests for proteins and amino acids: The characterization of basic proteins. *Stain Technol.* **21**, 5–18.

Serra, J. A. (1958). A method for the cytochemical detection of masked lipids. *Rev. Port. Zool. Biol. Gen.* **1**, 109–129.

Serra, J. A. and Seixas, M. P. (1962). Demonstration of lipids in nucleoli and nucleolar regions of the chromosomes by a specific test. *Rev. Port. Zool. Biol. Gen.* **3**, 255–262.

Sexton, R. and Hall, J. L. (1978). Enzyme cytochemistry. *In* "Electron Microscopy and Cytochemistry of Plant Cells" (J. L. Hall, ed.), Elsevier/North-Holland, New York.

Sexton, R., Cronshaw, J. and Hall, J. L. (1971). A study of the biochemistry and cytochemical localization of β-glycerophosphatase in root tips of maize and pea. *Protoplasma* **73**, 417–442.

Sheikh, K. L. M. and Gahan, P. B. (1976). Soluble proteins and hydrolases during crown gall induction in the tomato, *Lycopersicon esculentum*. *Histochem. J.* **8**, 87–92.

Sierakowska, H., Gahan, P. B. and Dawson, A. L. (1978). The cytochemical localization of nucleotide pyrophosphatase activity in plant tissues using naphthyl esters of thymidine 5'-phosphate. *Histochem. J.* **10**, 679–693.

Sievert, R. M. (1936). Two methods of Roentgen microphotography. *Acta Radiol.* **17**, 299–309.

Smith, M. M. and McCully, M. E. (1978). A critical evaluation of the specificity of aniline blue induced fluorescence. *Protoplasma* **95**, 229–254.

Smith, R. E. and Fishman, W. H. (1968). p-(Acetoxymercuric)aniline diazotate: A reagent for vizualizing the naphthol AS-BI product of acid hydrolase action at the level of the light and electron microscope. J. Histochem. Cytochem. 17, 1–22.

Smith, R. E. and Van Frank, R. M. (1975). The use of amino acid derivatives of 4-methoxy-β-naphthylamine for the assay and subcellular localization of tissue proteinases. Front. Biol. 43, 193–249.

So, L. L. and Goldstein, I. J. (1968). Protein–carbohydrate interaction XII. The interaction of concanavalin A with δ-mannans from a variety of microorganisms. J. Biol. Chem. 243, 2003–2007.

Sorokin, H. P. (1955). Mitochondria and spherosomes in the living epidermal cell. Am. J. Bot. 42, 225–231.

Sorokin, H. P. and Sorokin, S. (1966). The spherosomes of Campanula persicifolia L. A light and electron microscope study. Protoplasma 62, 216–236.

Sterling, C. (1970). Crystal structure of ruthenium red and stereochemistry of its pectic stain. Am. J. Bot. 57, 172–175.

Stone, G. E. and Miller, O. L. (1965). A stable mitochondrial DNA in Tetrahymena pyriformis. J. Exp. Zool. 159, 33–37.

Steward, P. J. (1967). Studies in fluorescence histochemistry. J. R. Microsc. Soc. 87, 237–246.

Stowell, R. E. (1951). A modified freeze drying apparatus for tissues. St. Technol. 26, 105–108.

Strasburger, E. (1930). "Test-Book of Botany." [Re-written by H. Fritting, H. Sierp., R. Harder and G. Karsten, 17th ed. (6th Engl. ed., Frans. Witt. Lang]. Macmillan, London.

Strügger, S. (1937). Die vitalfärbung als gewebsanalytische untersuchungsmethode. Arch. Exp. Zellforsch. 19, 199–208.

Strügger, S. (1938). Die Vitalfärbung des Protoplasms mit Rhodamine B und 6G. Protoplasma 30, 85–100.

Sutherland, E. W. and Rall. T. W. (1958). Fractionation and characterization of a cyclic adenine ribonucleotide formed by tissue particles. J. Biol. Chem. 232, 279.

Surrey, K. (1957). Azo-coupling reactions of protein-bound amino groups in plant tissue by oxidative deamination method. J. Histochem. Cytochem. 5, 606–610.

Surrey, K. (1958). Detection of protein-bound amino groups in plant tissue by Schiff base formation and azo coupling. Stain Technol. 33, 109–114.

Surrey, K. and van Fleet, D. S. (1955). Localization of non-specific sulfatases by 8-hydroxy-quinoline sulfate. (Cited in van Fleet, 1957.)

Sutcliffe, J. F. and Sexton, R. (1968). Cell differentiation in the root in relation to physiological function. In "Root Growth" (W. J. Whittington, ed.), pp. 80–102. Butterworths, London.

Suyama, Y. and Bonner, W. D. (1965). DNA from plant mitochondria. Plant Physiol. 41, 183–188.

Svendsen, A. B. (1951). Paper chromatography in polychemical analyses II. Occurence of chlorogenic and caffeic acids in the Umbelliferae. Pharm. Acta Helv. 26, 253–258.

Swift, H. (1950). The constancy of desoxyribose nucleic acid in plant nuclei. Proc. Natl. Acad. Sci. U.S.A. 36, 643–654.

Swift, H. and Rasch, E. (1956). Microphotometry with visible light. In "Physical Techniques in Biological Research" (G. Oster and W. A. Pollister, eds.), Vol. 3, pp. 353–400. Academic Press, New York.

Sylvén, B. (1954). Metachromatic dye–substrate interaction. Q. J. Microsc. Sci. 95, 327–358.

Takamatsu, H. (1939). Histologische und biochemische Studien über die Phosphatase. Histochemische Untersuchungsmethodik der Phosphatase und deren Verteilung in verschiedenen Organen und Geweben. Trans. Soc. Pathol. Jpn. 29, 492–498.

Tampion, J., McKendrick, M. E. and Holt, G. (1973). Use of fluorescent brighteners to visualize the sites of cellulose synthesis in root hairs of species of Peperomia. Physiol. Plant. 29, 440–441.

Tas, J. (1977a). The alcian blue and combined alcian blue–safranin O staining of glycosaminoglycans studied in a model system and in mast cells. Histochem. J. 9, 205–230.

Tas, J. (1977b). Polyacrilamide films as a tool for investigating qualitative and quantitative aspects of the staining of glycosaminoglycans with basic dyes. *Histochem. J.* **9**, 267–276.

Tas, J., Oud, P. and James, J. (1974). The naphthol yellow S stain for proteins tested in a model system of polyacrilamide films and evaluated for practical use in histochemistry. *Histochemistry* **40**, 231–240.

Taylor, C. E. D., Heimer, G. V. and Lidwell, O. M. (1971). Use of a fibre optic probe for quantitative immunofluorescence studies. *Lancet* **ii**, 785–786.

Taylor, J. H. (1957). The tissue and mode of duplication of chromosomes. *Am. Nat.* **91**, 209–222.

Taylor, J. H. (1963). Replication and organization of DNA in chromosomes. *In* "Molecular Genetics," Vol. I. (J. H. Taylor, ed.), pp. 65–113. Academic Press, New York.

Terner, J. Y., Schnur, J. and Gurland, J. (1963). Stable sudenophilia: Contributions to the histochemistry of Sudan dyes. *Lab. Invest.* **12**, 405–411.

Thaine, R. (1962). Freeze-drying of plant tissues. *Nature (London)*, **195**, 1014–1016.

Thaine, R. and Bullas, D. O. (1965). The preservation of plant cells, particularly sieve tubes, by vacuum freeze-drying. *J. Exp. Bot.* **16**, 192–196.

Thenard, L. J. (1818). "Traité de Chimié Elémentaire, Théorique et Pratique." 2ᵉ ed, Vol. III, pp. 180–192. Crochard, Paris.

Thiéry, J. P. (1967). Mise en évidence des polysaccharides sur coupes fines en microscopie électronique. *J. Microsc.* **6**, 987–989.

Thornberg, W. and Mengers, P. E. (1957). An analysis of frozen section techniques I. Staining of fresh-frozen tissue. *J. Histochem. Cytochem.* **5**, 47–52.

Tice, L. W. (1969). Lead–adenosine triphosphate complexes in adenosine triphosphate histochemistry. *J. Histochem. Cytochem.* **17**, 85–94.

Tranzer, J.-P. (1965). Coupes ultrafines de tissues non inclus après fixation et séchage à l'air. *J. Microsc.* **4**, 319–336.

Trembley, A. (1774). Mémoires, pour servir a l'histoire d'un genre de polypes d'eau douce, à bras en forme de cornes." Leide (Verbeek).

Tsou, K. C., Goodwin, C. W., Seamond, B. and Lynn, D. (1968). Intracristal localization of succinic dehydrogenase activity with a new osmium-containing tetra-tetrazolium salt. *J. Histochem. Cytochem.* **16**, 487–493.

Über, F. M. (1940). Microincineration and ash analysis. *Bot. Rev.* **6**, 204–226.

Van den Born, W. H. (1963). Histochemical studies of enzyme distribution in the shoot-tips of white spruce. *Can. J. Bot.* **41**, 1569–1572.

van Fleet, D. S. (1952). Histochemical localization of enzymes in vascular plants. *Bot. Rev.* **18**, 354–398.

van Fleet, D. S. (1957). Histochemistry of enzymes in plant tissues. *Handb. Histochem.* **7**, 1–38.

van Fleet, D. S. (1959). Analysis of the histochemical localization of peroxidase related to the differentiation of plant tissue. *Can. J. Bot.* **37**, 449–458.

Van Iren, F. and Van der Spiegel, A. (1974). Subcellular localization of inorganic ions in plant cells by *in vivo* precipitation. *Science* **187**, 1210–1211.

Van Noorden, C. J. F. and Tas, J. Advantages of 1-methoxy PMS as an electron carrier in dehydrogenase cytochemistry studied *in vitro* and with a model system of polyacrilamide films. J. Histochem. Cytochem. *30,* 12–20

Van Steveninck, R. F. M. (1979). The verification of cytochemical tests for ATPase activity in plant cells using x-ray microanalysis. *Protoplasma* **99**, 211–220.

Van Steveninck, R. F. M. and Van Steveninck, M. E. (1978). Ion localization. *In* "Electron Microscopy and Cytochemistry of Plant Cells." (J. L. Hall, ed.), pp. 187–234. Elsevier/North-Holland, Amsterdam.

Van Steveninck, M. E., Van Steveninck, R. F. M., Peters, P. D. and Hall, T. A. (1978). X-ray microanalysis of antimonate precipitates in barley roots. *Protoplasma* **90**, 47–52.

Van't Hof, J. (1963). DNA, RNA and protein synthesis in the mitotic cycle of pea root meristems. *Cytologia* **28**, 30–35.

Vendreley, R. and Vendreley, C. (1953). Arginine and deoxyribonucleic acid content of erythrocyte nuclei and sperms of some species of fish. *Nature (London)*, **172**, 29–30.

Vendreley, C., Knoblach, A. and Vendreley, R. (1956). Contribution à l'étude biochimique comparée de divers désoxyribonucléoprotéines d'origine animale. *Biochim. Biophys. Acta* **19**, 472–479.

Vian, B. (1979). Ultracryotomy: Its use for the study of cell wall components and organization. *Proc. R. Microsc. Soc.* **14**, 226–227.

Vigil, E. L. (1970). Cytochemical and developmental changes in microbodies (glyoxysomes) and related organelles of castor bean endosperms. *J. Cell Biol.* **46**, 435–454.

Vinassa, E. (1891). Beiträge zur pharmakognostischen Mikroskopie. *Z. Wiss. Mikrosk. Mikrosk. Tech.* **8**, 34–50.

Viola-Magni, M. P., Gahan, P. B., and Pacy, J. (1984). Biochemical and phytochemical study of phospholipids in chromatin. *Cell Biochem. Function,* in press.

Vithanage, H. I. M. and Knox, R. B. (1976). Pollen-wall proteins: Quantitative cytochemistry of the origins of intine and exine enzymes in *Brassica oleracea. J. Cell Sci.* **21**, 423–435.

Vithanage, H. I. M. and Knox, R. B. (1977). Development and cytochemistry of stigma surface and response to self and foreign pollenation in *Helianthus annuus. Phytomorphology* **27**, 168–179.

Vogel, A. I. (1951). "A Textbook of Quantitative Inorganic Analysis: Theory and Practice," 2nd ed. Longmans, Green, London.

Von Ardenne, M. (1939). Zur heistungsfähigkeit des Electronen–Schattenmikroskopes und über ein Röntgenstrahlen–Schattenmikroskop. *Naturwissenschaften* **27**, 485–486.

von Pechmann, H. and Runge, P. (1894a). Oxydation der Formazylverbindungen I. *Ber Dtsch. Chem. Ges.* **27**, 323–324.

von Pechmann, H. and Runge, P. (1894b). Oxydation der Formazylverbidungen II. *Ber. Dtsch. Chem. Ges.* **28**, 1688–1695.

Vorbrodt, A. (1961). Histochemical studies on the intracellular localization of acid deoxyribonuclease. *J. Histochem. Cytochem.* **9**, 647–655.

Vorsatz, F. (1942). Über eine kolorimetrische Methode der Gerhstoffbestimmung. *Collegium No. 872,* pp. 421–427.

Wachstein, M. and Meisel, E. (1957). Histochemistry of hepatic phosphatases at a physiological pH with special reference to the demonstration of bile canaliculi. *Am. J. Clin. Pathol.* **27**, 13–20.

Wachstein, M. and Meisel, E. (1960). Histochemistry of "thiolacetic acid esterase" in relation to de Duve's lysosomes. *J. Histochem. Cytochem.* **8**, 317–318.

Wagner, R. C. and Bitensky, M. W. (1974). Adenylate cyclase. *In* "Electron Microscopy of Enzymes" (M. A. Hayat, ed.), vol. 2, pp. 110–131. Van Nostrand-Reinhold, Princeton, New Jersey.

Walek-Czernecka, A. (1962). Mise en évidence de la phosphatase acide (monophosphoesterase II) dans les sphérosomes des cellules épidermiques des écailles bulbaires d'*Allium cepa. Acta Soc. Bot. Pol.* **31**, 539–543.

Walek-Czernecka, A. (1963). Note sur la détection d'une ésterase non spécifique dans les sphérosomes. *Acta. Soc. Bot. Pol.* **32**, 405–406.

Walek-Czernecka, A. (1965). Histochemical demonstration of some hydrolytic enzymes in the spherosomes of plant cells. *Acta Soc. Bot. Pol.* **34**, 573–588.

Walker, P. M. B. (1956). Ultraviolet absorption techniques. *In* "Physical Techniques in Biological Research" (G. Oster and A. W. Pollister, eds.), vol. 3, pp. 402–487. Academic Press, New York.

Walker, P. M. B. and Yates, H. B. (1952). Nuclear components of dividing cells. *Proc. R. Soc. London, Ser. B* **140**, 274–299.

Walton, K. W. and Ricketts, C. R. (1954). Investigation of the histochemical basis of meta-chromasia. *Br. J. Exp. Pathol.* **35,** 227–240.

Wardrop, A. B. (1971). Lignins in the plant kingdom. Occurrence and formation in plants. *In* "Lignins; Occurrence, Formation, Structure and Reactions" (K. V. Sarkanen and C. H. Ludwig, eds.), pp. 19–41. Wiley, New York.

Wardrop, A. B. and Bland, D. E. (1959). The process of lignification in woody plants. *4th Int. Congr. Biochem.* **2,** 92–116.

Washitani, I. and Sato, S. (1976). On the reliability of the lead salt precipitation method of acid phosphatase localization in plant cells. *Protoplasma* **89,** 157–170.

Weaver, G. M. and Layne, R. E. C. (1965). Cryostat sectioning of woody plant material. *Can. J. Bot.* **43,** 478–481.

Webb, J. L. (1963). "Enzyme and Metabolic Inhibitions," Vol. 1, Academic Press, New York.

Weil, A. (1929). The influence of formalin fixation on the lipids of the central nervous system. *J. Biol. Chem.* **83,** 601–609.

Welford, W. T. (1972). On the relationship between the modes of image formation in scanning microscopy and conventional microscopy. *J. Microsc. (Oxford)* **96,** 105–107.

Whaley, W. G., Mericle, L. W. and Heimsch, C. (1952). The wall of the meristematic cell. *Am. J. Bot.* **39,** 20–26.

Widholm, J. M. (1972). The use of fluorescein diacetate and phenosafranin for determining viability of cultured cells. *Stain Technol.* **47,** 189–194.

Wigglesworth, V. B. (1957). The use of osmium in the fixation and staining of tissues. *Proc. R. Soc. London, Ser. B* **147,** 185–199.

Wilkins, M. F. H. (1953). The performance of spherical mirror reflecting objectives when used for ultra-violet photomicrography. *J. R. Micrsc. Soc.* **73,** 77–81.

Wilkins, M. F. H. (1956). Physical studies of the molecular structure of deoxyribose nucleic acid and nucleoprotein. *Cold Spring Harbor Symp. Quant. Biol.* **21,** 75–90.

Williams, J. W. and Green, L. (1935). Effect of dyes on colonies of certain pathogenic fungi. *Proc. Soc. Exp. Biol. Med.* **32,** 625–628.

Williams, M. A. (1969). *Adv. Opt. Electron Microsc.* **3,** 219–272.

Williamson, B. (1973). Acid phosphatase and esterase activity in orchid mycorrhyza. *Planta* **112,** 149–158.

Williamson, B., Mitchell, C. P. and Millar, C. S. (1976). Histochemistry of corsican pine needles infected by *Lophodermella sulcigena* (Rostr.) v. Hohn. *Ann. Bot. (London)* **40,** 281–288.

Williamson, D. H., and Moustacchi, E. (1971). The synthesis of mitochondrial DNA during the cell cycle in the yeast *Saccharomyces cerevissiae*. *Biochem. Biophys. Res. Commun.* **42,** 195–201.

Willmer, C. M. and Pallas, J. E. (1973). A survey of stomatal movements and associated potassium fluxes in the plant kingdom. *Can. J. Bot.* **51,** 37–42.

Wilson, C. L., Jumper, G. A. and Mason, D. L. (1978). Acridine orange as a lysosomal marker in fungal spores. *Phytopathology* **68,** 1564–1567.

Wimber, D. E. (1961). Asynchronous replication of DNA in root tip chromosomes of *Tradescantia paludosa*. *Exp. Cell Res.* **23,** 402–407.

Wimber, D. E. (1966). Duration of the nuclear cycle in *Tradescantia* root tips at three temperatures as measured with ^{3}H-thymidine. *Am. J. Bot.* **53,** 21–24.

Wolman, M. (1955). Problems of fixation in cytology, histology and histochemistry. *Int. Rev. Cytol.* **4,** 79–99.

Wolman, M. (1957). Histochemical study of changes occurring during the degeneration of myelin. *J. Neurochem.* **1,** 370.

Wolman, M. and Weiner, H. (1965). Structure of the myelin sheath as a function of concentration of ions. *Biochim. Biophys. Acta* **102,** 269–272.

Wooding, F. B. P. (1968). Radioautographic and chemical studies of incorporation into sycamore vascular tissue walls. *J. Cell Sci.* **3**, 71–80.

Woods, P. S. (1962). Autoradiographic studies of RNA metabolism with tritium-labelled cytidine. *In* "Tritium in the Physical & Biological Sciences," Proc. Symp. Int. Atomic Energy Agency, Vienna, pp. 335–346. International Publications Ltd., New York.

Woods, P. S. and Taylor, J. H. (1959). Studies of ribonucleic acid metabolism with ^{3}H-labelled cytidine. *Lab. Invest.* **8**, 309–318.

Woodward, J. Rasch, E. and Swift, H. (1961). Nucleic acid and protein metabolism during the meiotic cell cycle in *Vicia faba. J. Biophys. Biochem. Cytol.* **9**, 445–462.

Wyllie, R. G. (1965). Fixation in enzyme histochemistry. *Nature (London)* **207**, 93–94.

Yamada, K. (1978). Concanavalin A–peroxidase–diaminobenzidine–periodic acid–*m*-aminophenol–fast black salt K: A method for the dual staining of neutral complex carbohydrates. *Histochem. J.* **10**, 573–584.

Yamada, M. (1957). Studies on fat metabolism in germinating castor beans III. Lipase in decotylated embryo tissue. *Biol. Inst. Coll. Gess. Edn. (Univ. Tokyo)* **7**, 97–104.

Yeoman, M. M., Kilpatrick, D. C. and Jeffree, C. E. (1979). Tissue and subcellular distribution of the lectin from *Datura stramonium. Proc. R. Microsc. Soc.* **14**, 242.

Zalokar, M. (1959). Nuclear origin of ribonucleic acid. *Nature (London)* **183**, 1330.

Zalokar, M. (1960a). Cytochemistry of centrifuged hyphae of *Neurospora. Exp. Cell Res.* **19**, 114–132.

Zalokar, M. (1960b). Sites of protein and ribonucleic acid synthesis in the cell. *Exp. Cell Res.* **19**, 559–576.

Zeiss, F. C. (1941). "Phasenkontrast" Einrichtung, Jena.

Zernicke, F. (1934). Diffraction theory of the knife edge test and its improved form of the phase contrast method. *Physica* **1**, 689–704.

Zernicke, F. (1935). Das Phasenkontrast verfahren bei der mikroskopischen Beobachtung. *Phys. Z.* **36**, 848–851.

Zernicke, F. (1942). Phase-contrast, a new method for microscopic observation of transparent objects. *Physica* **9**, 686–698, 974–986.

Zernicke, F. (1946). Phase-contrast, a new method for microscopic observation of transparent objects. *In* "Achievements in Optics," p. 116. Elsevier, Amsterdam.

Zirkle, C. (1928a). Nucleolus in root tip mitosis in *Zea mays. Bot. Gaz.* **86**, 402–418.

Zirkle, C. (1928b). The effect of hydrogen-ion concentration upon the fixation image of various salts of chromium. *Protoplasma* **4**, 201–227.

Index

EXPERIMENTAL BOTANY

An International Series of Monographs

CONSULTING EDITORS

J. F. Sutcliffe† and J. Cronshaw